A-Level

Mathematics

for AQA
Decision Maths 1

The Complete Course for AQA D1

Contents

Chapter 4

Travelling Salesperson Problem

Chapter 5

Linear Programming

Chapter 6

Matchings

Reference

About this book

In this book you'll find...

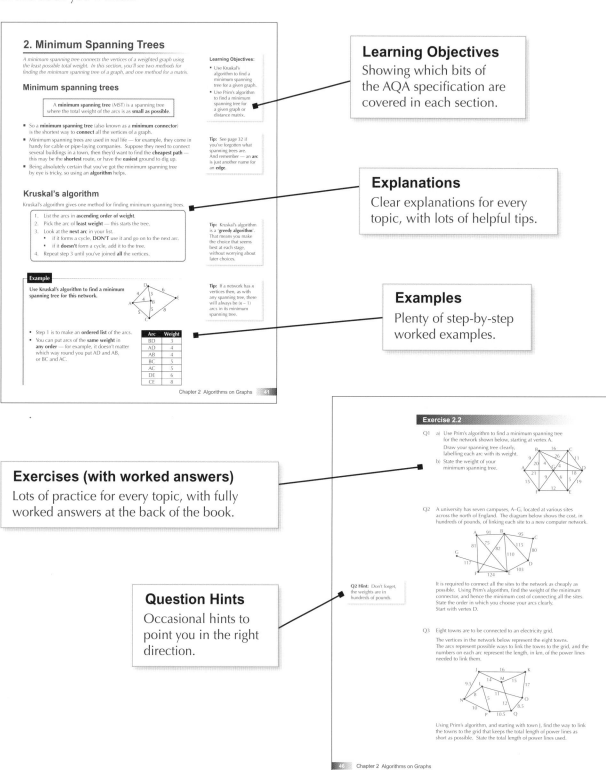

Learning Objectives

Showing which bits of the AQA specification are covered in each section.

Explanations

Clear explanations for every topic, with lots of helpful tips.

Examples

Plenty of step-by-step worked examples.

Exercises (with worked answers)

Lots of practice for every topic, with fully worked answers at the back of the book.

Question Hints

Occasional hints to point you in the right direction.

Review Exercise — Chapter 2

Q1 Explain what the following are: a) network b) digraph c) tree d) spanning tree

Q2 Graph G is shown on the left.
a) Draw a spanning tree of Graph G.
b) Which vertex would you have to remove to make G a Hamiltonian graph?
c) Which edges would you have to remove to make G a simple graph?

Q3 Padmaja is a town planner. She has prepared a scheme for a town centre road system that's entirely one-way. The one-way system connects five points, A, B, C, D and E. Padmaja's scheme has direct one-way streets from A to B, D to A, B to D, C to D, D to C, and E to A.
a) Draw a digraph to represent Padmaja's scheme.
b) How would you get from C to A?
c) Suggest a flaw in Padmaja's plan.

Q4 Doris and Harry are friends, Beryl and Harry are friends, Beryl and Melvyn are friends, Norman and Harry are friends, and Norman and Melvyn are friends.
a) Draw a bipartite graph to represent this information.
b) Which of the five friends is most popular within the group?

Q4 Hint: You'll need to draw each link twice here.

Q5 Graph G is shown on the right.
a) Draw two subgraphs of G.
b) How many arcs do you need to add to G to make it into a complete graph?
c) Describe a possible path in G.
d) Describe a possible cycle in G.
e) Graph G is currently connected. Delete some edges so that it isn't connected any more.
f) List the degree of each vertex of G. Explain the link between the number of edges and the sum of the degrees.

Graph G

Q6
	P	Q	R	S	T	U
P	0	1	0	1	0	0
Q	1	0	1	0	0	1
R	0	1	0	1	2	0
S	1	0	1	2	0	0
T	0	0	2	0	2	0
U	0	1	0	0	0	0

This is the adjacency matrix for a graph. Without drawing the graph, find:
a) a path from P to T
b) a cycle starting from Q
c) the degree of vertex R
d) the number of edges in the graph

Q7 The arcs in the network shown on the right represent possible ways to lay pipes in a planned sewerage system. The numbers on each arc represent the cost, in hundreds of pounds, for laying the pipe. The vertices represent houses which must be connected to the sewerage system.

Using Kruskal's algorithm, plan the most cost-effective way to join all the houses to the sewerage system. State the cost of connecting the pipes in the way you have planned.

Review Exercises
Mixed questions covering the whole chapter, with fully worked answers.

Exam-Style Questions — Chapter 2

1 **Figure 1** shows the potential connections for a sprinkler system between greenhouses at a plant nursery. The numbers on each arc represent the cost in pounds of each connection.

Figure 1

a) Use Kruskal's algorithm to find a minimum spanning tree for the network in **Figure 1**. List the edges in the order that you consider them and state whether you are adding them to your minimum spanning tree.
(3 marks)

b) State the minimum cost of connecting the sprinkler system.
(1 mark)

c) Draw the minimum spanning tree obtained in a).
(2 marks)

d) If Prim's algorithm had been used to find the minimum spanning tree, starting from E, find which edge would have been the final edge added. Show your working.
(2 marks)

e) State two advantages of Prim's algorithm over Kruskal's algorithm for finding a minimum spanning tree.
(2 marks)

2 The table shows the lengths, in miles, of the roads between five towns.

a) Use Prim's algorithm, starting from A, to find a minimum spanning tree for this table. Write down the arcs in the order that they are selected.
(3 marks)

b) Draw your tree and state its total weight.
(2 marks)

c) State the number of other spanning trees that are the same length as your answer in part (b).
(1 mark)

	A	B	C	D	E
A	–	14	22	21	18
B	14	–	19	21	20
C	22	19	–	21	15
D	21	21	21	–	24
E	18	20	15	24	–

Exam-Style Questions
Questions in the same style as the ones you'll get in the exam, with worked solutions and mark schemes.

Glossary
All the definitions you need to know for the exam, plus other useful words.

Practice Exam Papers (on CD-ROM)
Two printable exam papers, with fully worked answers and mark schemes.

Published by CGP

Editors:
Paul Jordin, Sharon Keeley-Holden, Simon Little, Kirstie McHale, Matteo Orsini Jones, Caley Simpson.

Contributors:
Peter Clegg, Claire Creasor, Paul Freeman, Charlotte O'Brien, Andy Pierson, Rosemary Rogers.

ISBN: 978 1 84762 797 1

With thanks to Helen Greaves for the proofreading.

Groovy website: www.cgpbooks.co.uk

Printed by Elanders Ltd, Newcastle upon Tyne.
Jolly bits of clipart from CorelDRAW®

1. Algorithms

Algorithms are sets of instructions that turn inputs into outputs, or end results. There are loads of different types of algorithms and they can be presented in a number of different ways — in words, graphically, mathematically, and so on.

Algorithms in words

An **algorithm** is just a fancy mathematical name for a **set of instructions** for solving a problem. You come across lots of algorithms in everyday life — **recipes**, **directions** and **assembly instructions** are all examples of algorithms.

- Algorithms start with an **input** (e.g. in a recipe, the inputs are the raw ingredients). You carry out the algorithm on the input, following the instructions **in order**.

- Algorithms have an **end result** — something that you **achieve** by carrying out the algorithm (e.g. a cake).

- This means that algorithms will **stop** when you've reached a **solution**, or produced your **finished product**. They'll often have a **stopping condition** — an **instruction** that tells you to stop when you've reached a certain point.

- Algorithms are often written so that **computers** could follow the instructions. **Computer programming** is an important use of decision maths.

Learning Objectives:

- Be able to follow algorithms in words to turn given inputs into an end result.
- Be able to follow algorithms in pseudo-code to turn inputs into a printed end result.
- Be able to understand and use flow charts to follow algorithms through and produce an end result.

Tip: Anybody should be able to follow an algorithm — not just the person who wrote it.

Example

Here's an example of an algorithm for making a soft-boiled egg:

- Fill a small pan with enough water to cover your egg by roughly 1 cm.

- Place the pan over heat and bring it to the boil.

- Adjust the heat so that the water is simmering at a steady rate.

- Gently lower the egg into the pan and leave it to simmer with the lid off for 1 minute.

- Remove the pan from the heat and cover it with a lid.

- Leave the pan for 6 minutes.

- Remove the now soft-boiled egg, and enjoy.

Tip: Here the inputs are water, egg, (fuel for the stove).

Tip: The end result is a soft-boiled egg.

Algorithms can be used to solve **mathematical problems** too, where the **end result** is the **solution** to the problem.

- The **input** in a mathematical algorithm is the **number** (or numbers) you start with. Your **end result** is the **final number** you end up with — this'll be the **solution** to the original problem.

- Any number you put in will have a **unique** output — you won't get different solutions for the same input.

- It's a good idea to **write down** the numbers each instruction produces in a **table** — sometimes the algorithm will **tell you** when to do this. This table is called a **trace table**.

Tip: Most mathematical algorithms are general — they work for a range of inputs (e.g. any number bigger than 0) not just one specific input (like the example on the previous page, which only works if you input water, an egg and some fuel).

Tip: 'Input' and 'output' just mean 'write down' so you can keep track of what you're doing.

Examples

An algorithm for finding out whether a number divides by 3 goes like this:

> 1 Input starting number a.
>
> 2 Add together all of the digits of a to form number b. Output b.
>
> 3 If b has 1 digit, go to step 4. Otherwise, let $a = b$ and go back to step 2.
>
> 4 If b is 3, 6, or 9, your starting number a is divisible by 3. If b is any other number, then a is not divisible by 3.

a) Use the algorithm to find if 976 836 is divisible by 3.

- Set up a trace table to record the steps of your algorithm, then just go through the algorithm and follow the instructions.

Input a	Working out	Output b
976 836	$9 + 7 + 6 + 8 + 3 + 6$	39
39	$3 + 9$	12
12	$1 + 2$	3

- The 1-digit number you end up with is 3, so 976 836 is divisible by 3.

b) Use the algorithm to find if 3 924 326 is divisible by 3.

- Just go through the steps of the algorithm exactly the same way as before.

Input a	Working out	Output b
3 924 326	$3 + 9 + 2 + 4 + 3 + 2 + 6$	29
29	$2 + 9$	11
11	$1 + 1$	2

- This time you end up with a 1-digit number that's not 3, 6 or 9, so 3 924 326 is not divisible by 3.

Tip: There are no real rules for how your trace table should look. As long as it's easy to understand what's going on, and it helps you keep track of what you're doing, it's probably fine.

The Russian Peasant Algorithm

The Russian Peasant Algorithm is a well-known algorithm that **multiplies** two numbers together.

> **1** Write down the two numbers that you're multiplying in a table. Call them x and y.
>
> **2** Divide x by 2 and write down the result underneath x, ignoring any halves. For example if $x = 11$, when you divide it by 2 you write down 5, not 5.5.
>
> **3** Multiply y by 2 and write down the result underneath y.
>
> **4** Repeat steps **2 - 3** for the numbers in the new row. Keep going until the number in the x-column is 1.
>
> **5** Work down your table and cross out every row that has an even value for x.
>
> **6** Add up the remaining numbers in the y-column (i.e. the ones that haven't been crossed out). This is the solution $x \times y$.

Tip: Step 4 gives you an example of a stopping condition — you stop when the number in the x-column reaches 1.

Tip: Step 5 includes the very first row — so if you started with an even number, cross out the top row.

Examples

a) Use the Russian Peasant Algorithm to multiply 37 and 43.

$37 \div 2 = 18.5$, so write down 18.

x	y
37	43
~~18~~	~~86~~
9	172
~~4~~	~~344~~
~~2~~	~~688~~
1	1376
Total	1591

The x-values in these rows are even, so cross them out.

The x-value is 1, so stop here.

Add together the numbers left in the y-column.

This is the end result.

$37 \times 43 = 1591$

b) Use the Russian Peasant Algorithm to multiply 21 and 52.

x	y
21	52
~~10~~	~~104~~
5	208
~~2~~	~~416~~
1	832
Total	1092

Just set up the trace table as before and go through the steps of the algorithm.

This is the end result.

$21 \times 52 = 1092$

Q1 Identify the input and output for the following algorithms:
  a) Growing radishes
  b) Knitting a scarf
  c) Making a cake
  d) Preparing a company's accounts

Q2 Here's an algorithm that lets you convert from °C to °F:
  Step 1: Input temperature in °C.
  Step 2: Multiply by 9.
  Step 3: Divide by 5.
  Step 4: Add 32.
  Output: Temperature in °F.

  Use this algorithm to convert these temperatures from °C to °F.
  a) 0 °C
  b) 20 °C
  c) 100 °C
  d) –35 °C

Q3 Here's an algorithm for working out an electricity bill:
  Step 1: Input units used
  Step 2: Input price per unit
  Step 3: Input standing charge
  Step 4: Multiply units used by price per unit
  Step 5: Add standing charge
  Step 6: Multiply by 1.2
  Output: Electricity bill in £

  Use this algorithm to work out the electricity bill when:
  a) Units used = 300, price per unit = £0.12, standing charge = £15.
  b) Units used = 460, price per unit = £0.09, standing charge = £42.
  c) Units used = 320, price per unit = £0.23, standing charge = £22.
  d) Explain how you would amend the algorithm if the tax rate changed from 20% to 15%.

Q4 Hint: A good trace table to use for this question would record the variables a and b each time you go through the algorithm.

Q4 Work through the following algorithm for parts a) to d).
  Step 1: Input n
  Step 2: Input $a = 1$
  Step 3: Calculate $b = a \times n$
  Step 4: Output b
  Step 5: If $b \geq 1000$, stop
  Step 6: Otherwise, let $a = b$ and go back to step 3

  a) $n = 5$ b) $n = 10$ c) $n = 3$ d) $n = 8$
  e) What is the algorithm in this question doing?

Q5 Use the algorithm on page 2 to find if these numbers will divide by 3:
  a) 18   b) 239   c) 928 741   d) 298 218 744

Q6 Use the Russian Peasant Algorithm (page 3) to find the solution to:
  a) 29 × 41   b) 102 × 87   c) 57 × 67

Pseudo-code and flow charts

Pseudo-code

Algorithms can be written in lots of different ways — a set of **written instructions** like the algorithms you've covered so far, a **flow chart** (see p.7), computer **programming language** or **pseudo-code**.

Pseudo-code is a bit like computer **programming language**, but less formal. It's meant for a **person** to read but it's written with the kind of **logic** a computer uses — it's often used to describe how a computer program works in a way that's **easier to read** and understand than programming language. It won't be written in full sentences though — just a set of **brief instructions**.

You need to be able to **follow** an algorithm written in pseudo-code, but you don't need to be able to write one yourself.

Tip: Don't worry if the stuff about programming is a bit baffling — all you need to be able to do for the exam is follow through an algorithm in pseudo-code and write down your working.

- Pseudo-code algorithms are often written in **numbered lines** — each line gives you an instruction and once you've done it you move on to the next line.
- There are **particular words** that crop up in pseudo-code — some words you'd normally use in an algorithm but others are a bit more like **computer code**.
- You might have conditions like **if** and **then** — you only have to carry out the **then** part if the **if** part is **true**.

Here's the pseudo-code for an algorithm that outputs the first 10 triangle numbers:

Tip: The nth triangle is the sum of all the whole numbers from 1 to n. So the 3rd triangle number is $1 + 2 + 3 = 6$. They can be shown as a pattern of dots arranged in a triangle like this:

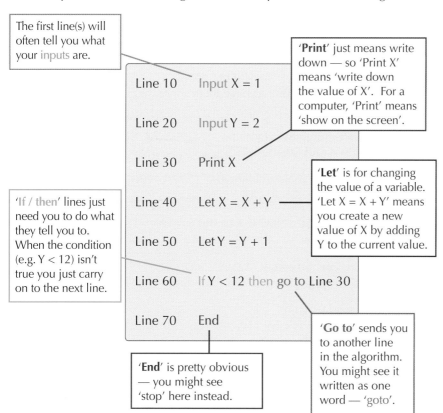

The first line(s) will often tell you what your inputs are.

Line 10	Input X = 1
Line 20	Input Y = 2
Line 30	Print X
Line 40	Let X = X + Y
Line 50	Let Y = Y + 1
Line 60	If Y < 12 then go to Line 30
Line 70	End

'Print' just means write down — so 'Print X' means 'write down the value of X'. For a computer, 'Print' means 'show on the screen'.

'Let' is for changing the value of a variable. 'Let X = X + Y' means you create a new value of X by adding Y to the current value.

'If / then' lines just need you to do what they tell you to. When the condition (e.g. Y < 12) isn't true you just carry on to the next line.

'End' is pretty obvious — you might see 'stop' here instead.

'Go to' sends you to another line in the algorithm. You might see it written as one word — 'goto'.

Tip: You might see a line that says something like: Print X, "is the answer" — this just means write down the value of X, then the words 'is the answer'.

Tip: The lines are numbered in tens so that you can add extra lines later if you need to.

Following this algorithm gives **1, 3, 6, 10, 15, 21, 28, 36, 45, 55**.

Following through a pseudo-code algorithm like the one on the previous page and recording the values as you go is known as **tracing** the algorithm.

You can write the values down however you like (as long as it's laid out **clearly**), but putting them in a **trace table** is probably your best bet — have a look back at page 2 for a reminder about how to set up a trace table.

Example

The algorithm below is for finding the lowest common multiple of two numbers A and B. Trace the algorithm for A = 12 and B = 8.

Line 10	Input A
Line 20	Input B
Line 30	Let C = A
Line 40	Let D = B
Line 50	If C = D then go to Line 110
Line 60	If C > D then go to line 90
Line 70	Let C = C + A
Line 80	Go to line 50
Line 90	Let D = D + B
Line 100	Go to Line 50
Line 110	Print C, "is the LCM"
Line 120	End

- Write down A and B — they're not going to change but it's helpful to have them written down.

- Then work through the algorithm. First let C = A and D = B.

- C ≠ D and C > D so go to Line 90. Now D = D + B = 8 + 8 = 16.

- Go back to Line 50. Now C ≠ D, but C < D so carry on to Line 70. C = 12 + 12 = 24.

- Go back to Line 50 again. Again C ≠ D, but C > D so go to Line 90. D = 16 + 8 = 24.

- Back to Line 50 again. Now C = D so go to Line 110, write down C and stop.

A	B	C	D
12	8		
		12	
			8
			16
		24	
			24

24 is the LCM

Tip: You don't have to lay the numbers out exactly like this, (you don't even have to draw a table if you don't want to) — as long as you can follow the working and it's clear which numbers are which you should be fine.

Flow charts

Instead of giving instructions in **words** (like in the Russian Peasant example on page 3), or **pseudo-code** (like the examples on pages 5-6) some algorithms are written as **flow charts**. In these cases the algorithms are carried out by working through the flow chart from start to finish.

There are three different types of boxes used in flow charts:

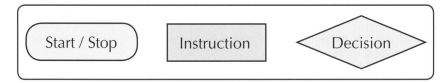

The boxes are connected with **arrows** to guide you through the flow chart. 'Decision' boxes will ask a question, and for each one you have a **choice** of arrows — one arrow for '**yes**' and one for '**no**', which will take you to another box.

Sometimes flow charts will include a loop which takes you back to an earlier stage in the chart. Loops are a way of **repeating steps** until the algorithm is **finished**.

Example

Here's the Russian Peasant Algorithm shown as a flow chart.

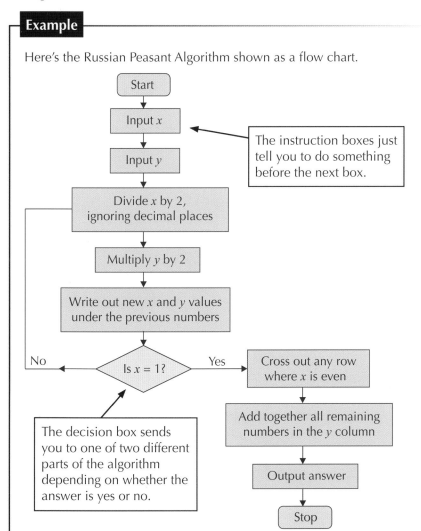

Tip: As you can see, the flow chart says the same thing as the wordy algorithm, but shows it in a way that's easier to follow. You just work your way through following the arrows and doing what each box tells you to.

It can sometimes be a bit tricky keeping track of the **results** of a flow chart, especially if you have to go round a **loop** lots of times. It's a good idea to put your results into a **trace table** — it's much easier to see the **solutions** that way.

To set up your trace table, look at the flow chart and think about what you would need to keep track of with every stage of the algorithm.

- Any input that **changes** with each loop will need its own column.

- If there are any **outputs** before the end of a loop, there should be a column to keep track of those.

- If a **decision box** affects where you go with the next loop (for example, if a 'yes' causes you to stop), then it's a good idea to give that a column too.

Tip: You can use a column for the inputs that don't change too, so you don't have to keep referring back to the question.

Tip: Some flow charts won't actually tell you what the algorithm does — you'll have to work it out yourself by looking for a pattern in the results. This is another reason trace tables can be useful when carrying out algorithms.

Examples

The flow chart shows an algorithm for finding the factors of a number *a*. Use it to find all of the factors of 10.

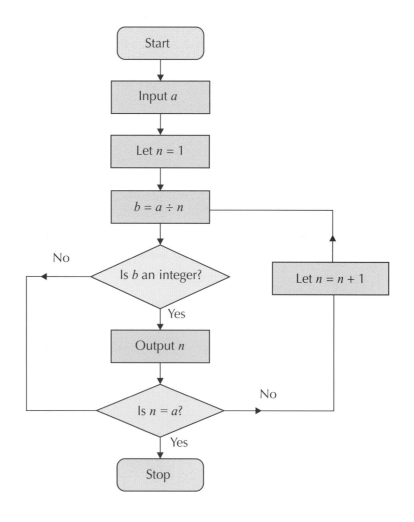

- Start by setting up a trace table for the flow chart. To do this, look down the chart and think about what you need to keep track of.

- Here the input a is constant, so leave that.

- n and b, on the other hand, change with each pass, so give those a column.

- Every time you calculate b, there's a chance of outputting n before the end, so make a column for the output.

- Finally, you'll need a column to check if you can stop (when $n = a$).

- Once your trace table is set up, just make your way through the flow chart and fill in each row with the correct numbers until you reach the stop box.

$a = 10$

n	b	Output	$n = a?$
1	10	1	No
2	5	2	No
3	$3\frac{1}{3}$		No
4	$2\frac{1}{2}$		No
5	2	5	No
6	$1\frac{2}{3}$		No
7	$1\frac{3}{7}$		No
8	$1\frac{1}{4}$		No
9	$1\frac{1}{9}$		No
10	1	10	Yes

Tip: You've reached the stopping condition, so you can stop there and output the answer(s).

- All the factors of 10 will then be shown in the output column, so the factors of 10 are 1, 2, 5 and 10.

Use the flow chart to find all of the factors of 7.

- Just set up your trace table as before and work your way through the flow chart, starting with $a = 7$.

$a = 7$

n	b	Output	$n = a?$
1	7	1	No
2	$3\frac{1}{2}$		No
3	$2\frac{1}{3}$		No
4	$1\frac{3}{4}$		No
5	$1\frac{2}{5}$		No
6	$1\frac{1}{6}$		No
7	1	7	Yes

- So the factors of 7 are 1 and 7.

Q1 a) Follow the flow chart on the right
       with the following inputs:
         (i) $a = 10$, $b = -3$
         (ii) $a = 30$, $b = -7$

    b) What does the algorithm do?

Q1 Hint: Remember, setting up a trace table will make your life a lot easier. In this case, b stays the same but a changes, so you'll need a column for that. You'll also need a column for the changing output variable c and another to check if c is below 0.

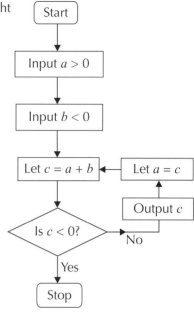

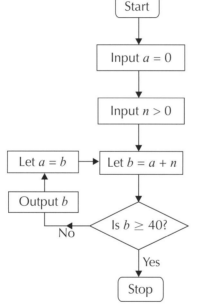

Q2 a) Follow the flow chart on the left
       with the following inputs:
         (i) $n = 6$
         (ii) $n = 13$

    b) What does the algorithm do?

Q3 The algorithm for finding the factors of a number from page 8
    is shown below as a pseudo-code algorithm. Use it to find all
    the factors of these numbers:

      a) $a = 15$ b) $a = 12$

          Line 10   Input a
          Line 20   Let $n = 1$
          Line 30   Let $b = a \div n$
          Line 40   If b is an integer then Print n
          Line 50   If $n = a$ then go to line 80
          Line 60   Let $n = n + 1$
          Line 70   Go to line 30
          Line 80   End

Q4 A charity provides funding for amateur theatre productions.
The flow chart below shows an algorithm to calculate the maximum grant a group can apply for, where C is the capacity of the venue being used and P is the number of performances that will take place.

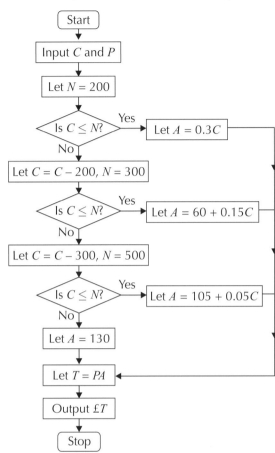

a) Complete the trace table when the flow chart is applied with $C = 800$, $P = 7$.

C	P	N	$C \leq N$?	A	T
800	7	200	no		

What is the maximum grant available in this case?

b) A group is preparing a show and will use funding from the charity to help hire the venue. They have two options: Venue A has a capacity of 350 seats and is available for 6 nights. Venue B holds 600 people but is only available for 4 nights. Calculate the maximum grant available for each venue.

Q5 Show the algorithm for finding whether a number is divisible by 3 on page 2 in the form of a flow chart.

Q6 Use the pseudo-code algorithm on page 6 to find the lowest common multiple of:

a) 6 and 8   b) 4 and 11

Q5 Hint: You probably won't be asked to produce a flow chart in an exam, but it might help you to understand them better if you think about how they're made.

2. Sorting Algorithms

Sorting things into numerical or alphabetical order might seem a bit easy for A-level maths, but you need to be able to do it using algorithms. Sorting this way is useful in computer programming.

Bubble sort

The bubble sort is an **algorithm** that **sorts** numbers or letters into order. It's pretty easy to do, but can get a bit fiddly, so take care when using it.

It's called the bubble sort because the **highest** numbers **rise** to the end of the list like bubbles. It works like this:

1) Look at the **first two numbers** in your list. If they're in the right order, you don't have to do anything with them. If they're the wrong way round, **swap** them.

2) Move on to the **next** pair of numbers (the first will be one of the two you've just compared) and **repeat step 1**. Keep going through the list until you've compared the **last two numbers**. This set of comparisons is called a **pass**.

3) When you've finished the first pass, go back to the beginning of the list and **start again**. You won't have to compare the **last pair** of numbers, as the last number is now **in place**. Each pass has **one fewer comparison** than the one before it. When there are **no swaps** in a pass, the list is **in order** (this is a **stopping condition**).

Tip: You might find it helpful to make note of which numbers you swap each time.

Example 1

Use bubble sort to write the list 14, 10, 6, 15, 9, 21, 17 in ascending order.

First pass:

14, 10, 6, 15, 9, 21, 17	14 and 10 compared and swapped
10, 14, 6, 15, 9, 21, 17	14 and 6 compared and swapped
10, 6, 14, 15, 9, 21, 17	14 and 15 compared, no swap
10, 6, 14, 15, 9, 21, 17	15 and 9 compared and swapped
10, 6, 14, 9, 15, 21, 17	15 and 21 compared, no swap
10, 6, 14, 9, 15, 21, 17	21 and 17 compared and swapped
10, 6, 14, 9, 15, 17, 21	End of first pass

Tip: 14 and 15 are already in ascending order, so leave them as they are.

Tip: After the first pass you know 21 is in the right place now, so you can 'lock' it in place — you don't need to compare it in future passes.

At the end of the second pass the list is: 6, 10, 9, 14, 15, 17, 21.

At the end of the third pass the list is: 6, 9, 10, 14, 15, 17, 21.

On the fourth pass there are **no swaps**, so the numbers are in **ascending order**. Even though the numbers were in order after the **third** pass, you have to carry out the fourth pass to check that there are no more swaps.

You can also use the algorithm to put the numbers in **descending** order
— on each comparison, just put the **higher** number **first** instead.

Example 2

**Use bubble sort to write the list 14, 10, 6, 15, 9, 21, 17
in descending order.**

First pass:

<u>14, 10</u>, 6, 15, 9, 21, 17	14 and 10 compared, no swap
14, <u>10, 6</u>, 15, 9, 21, 17	10 and 6 compared, no swap
14, 10, <u>6, 15</u>, 9, 21, 17	6 and 15 compared and swapped
14, 10, 15, <u>6, 9</u>, 21, 17	6 and 9 compared and swapped
14, 10, 15, 9, <u>6, 21</u>, 17	6 and 21 compared and swapped
14, 10, 15, 9, 21, <u>6, 17</u>	6 and 17 compared and swapped
14, 10, 15, 9, 21, 17, 6	End of first pass

At the end of the second pass the list is: 14, 15, 10, 21, 17, 9, 6

At the end of the third pass the list is: 15, 14, 21, 17, 10, 9, 6

At the end of the fourth pass the list is: 15, 21, 17, 14, 10, 9, 6

At the end of the fifth pass the list is: 21, 17, 15, 14, 10, 9, 6

On the sixth pass there are **no swaps**, so the numbers are
in **descending order**.

Tip: Even though it's the same list as the previous example, it takes 2 more passes to organise in descending order.

Some lists need **more comparisons** and **swaps** to put them in order. If your list
is in **reverse** order to start with, you're going to need to make the **maximum**
number of **passes** and **swaps** to put it in order.

- If there are n numbers in the list, the **maximum** number of **passes** you
  might have to make is n, including the **final pass** where **no swaps** are
  made. On each pass, you'd only get **one** number in the right place, up to
  the $(n - 1)^{th}$ **pass**, which swaps the **last two** numbers into the right places.

- On the **first** pass, you have to make $n - 1$ comparisons, with a **maximum**
  of $n - 1$ swaps. On the **second** pass, you have to make $n - 2$ comparisons,
  as one number is in place from the first pass. On the **third** pass, there'll be
  $n - 3$ comparisons, etc.

So for a bubble sort with **7 numbers**, the maximum number of
comparisons (or swaps) is $6 + 5 + 4 + 3 + 2 + 1 = 21$.

Or for a bubble sort with **50 numbers**, the maximum number of
comparisons (or swaps) is $\frac{1}{2} \times 49 \times 50 = 1225$.

Tip: For big lists, use the formula $S_k = \frac{1}{2}k(k + 1)$ for the sum of the first k whole numbers. Careful though — if $n = 50$, you want to put $k = 49$ into the formula.

Q1 a) Use a bubble sort to sort these numbers into ascending order: 5, 2, 7, 6, 3, 5.

b) How many swaps were there on the first pass?

c) How many passes were needed?

Q1 Hint: If two numbers are the same there's no need to swap them.

Q2 a) Use a bubble sort to sort these numbers into descending order: 3, 11, 5, 0, 7, 6, 4.

b) How many swaps were there on the first pass?

c) How many passes were needed?

Q3 a) Use a bubble sort to sort these letters into alphabetical order: Z, W, T, S, M, L, K.

b) What do you notice about the number of passes needed?

Q4 Use a bubble sort to sort these letters into reverse alphabetical order: A, F, B, J, M, B, C.

Q5 Hint: The formulas for working these out are on page 13.

Q5 A list of 5 numbers is sorted using a bubble sort.

a) What is the maximum number of passes you would need to make?

b) What is the maximum number of comparisons you would need to make?

Q6 A list of 8 numbers is sorted using a bubble sort.

a) What is the maximum number of passes you would need to make?

b) What is the maximum number of swaps you would need to make?

Q7 Use a bubble sort to sort these numbers into ascending order: 6, 7, 9, 4, 5, 6, 2.

Q8 Use a bubble sort to sort these numbers into descending order: 59, 39, 89, 79, 69, 29, 39.

Q9 Use a bubble sort to sort these letters into alphabetical order: E, L, E, P, H, A, N, T.

Q10 a) Use a bubble sort to sort these numbers into ascending order: 1, 5, 2, 3, 11, 10, 9, 3, 4, 7

b) Use this key to form two words from the list in part a) once the numbers are in order:

Number	1	5	2	3	11	10	9	4	7
Letter	B	E	U	B	T	R	O	L	S

Shuttle sort

The **shuttle sort** algorithm is an **improved** version of the **bubble sort** algorithm.

The main problem with the bubble sort is that you have to make a lot of **comparisons**. The shuttle sort is a bit **more efficient**, as it **reduces** the overall number of comparisons needed.

To do a shuttle sort:

1) Look at the **first two numbers** in your list. If they're in the right order, leave them as they are. If they're the wrong way round, **swap them**. This is your **first pass**.

2) Move on to the **next pair** of numbers (the first will be one of the two you've just compared), and **swap** them if they're the wrong way round.

3) If you made a swap on the second comparison, **compare** the number you've just swapped to the **first number** in the list. If they're the wrong way round, swap them. This is your **second pass**.

4) Now move on to the **next pair** of numbers (the third and fourth in the list) and **compare** them. If you make a swap, **compare** the number you've just swapped to the number before it, and **swap** if you need to. Keep working **backwards** until either you get to a number it **can't** be swapped with or you reach the **beginning** of the list. This is **another pass** completed.

5) Continue through the list, **repeating step 4** until you get to the last number in the list. Each time, **compare backwards** until you can't swap the number anymore.

Tip: A pass in a shuttle sort is different from a pass in a bubble sort. In a bubble sort, a pass moves through the whole list, but in a shuttle sort a pass takes you only as far as the number you're comparing will go.

Though the shuttle sort usually needs **fewer comparisons** than the bubble sort (which is why it's quicker) you'll still have to make the **same** number of **swaps**.

After the **first** pass of the shuttle sort the first **two** numbers will be in the right order. After the **second** pass, the first **three** numbers will be in the right order and so on. So for a list of n **numbers**, you'll always need to make $n - 1$ **passes** to get the list in order, though you might not make a swap on every pass.

Example 1

Use a shuttle sort to write the numbers 14, 10, 6, 15, 9, 21, 17 in ascending order.

First pass: <u>14, 10</u>, 6, 15, 9, 21, 17   14 and 10 compared and swapped

Second pass: 10, <u>14, 6</u>, 15, 9, 21, 17   14 and 6 compared and swapped
             <u>10, 6</u>, 14, 15, 9, 21, 17   10 and 6 compared and swapped

Third pass: 6, 10, <u>14, 15</u>, 9, 21, 17   14 and 15 compared, no swap

Fourth pass:	6, 10, 14, <u>15, 9</u>, 21, 17	15 and 9 compared and swapped
	6, 10, <u>14, 9</u>, 15, 21, 17	14 and 9 compared and swapped
	6, <u>10, 9</u>, 14, 15, 21, 17	10 and 9 compared and swapped
	<u>6, 9</u>, 10, 14, 15, 21, 17	6 and 9 compared, no swap

| Fifth pass: | 6, 9, 10, 14, <u>15, 21</u>, 17 | 15 and 21 compared, no swap |

Sixth pass:	6, 9, 10, 14, 15, <u>21, 17</u>	21 and 17 compared and swapped
	6, 9, 10, 14, <u>15, 17</u>, 21	15 and 17 compared, no swap
	6, 9, 10, 14, 15, 17, 21	End of shuttle sort.

So the numbers in order are: 6, 9, 10, 14, 15, 17, 21

There are **7 numbers**, so you have to make **7 – 1 = 6 passes**.

Tip: The list in Example 1 is the same list as on page 12 — you only needed 11 comparisons here, whereas for the bubble sort you needed 18 comparisons.

As with the bubble sort you can also use a shuttle sort to put numbers in **descending order** (or letters in reverse alphabetical order) — you just move **higher** numbers (or letters closer to Z) towards the start of the list.

Example 2

Use a shuttle sort to write the letters T, O, P, I, A, R, Y in reverse alphabetical order.

| First pass: | <u>T, O</u>, P, I, A, R, Y | T and O compared, no swap |

| Second pass: | T, <u>O, P</u>, I, A, R, Y | O and P compared and swapped |
| | <u>T, P</u>, O, I, A, R, Y | T and P compared, no swap |

| Third pass: | T, P, <u>O, I</u>, A, R, Y | O and I compared, no swap |

| Fourth pass: | T, P, O, <u>I, A</u>, R, Y | I and A compared, no swap |

Fifth pass:	T, P, O, I, <u>A, R</u>, Y	A and R compared and swapped
	T, P, O, <u>I, R</u>, A, Y	I and R compared and swapped
	T, P, <u>O, R</u>, I, A, Y	O and R compared and swapped
	T, <u>P, R</u>, O, I, A, Y	P and R compared and swapped
	<u>T, R</u>, P, O, I, A, Y	T and R compared, no swap

Sixth pass:	T, R, P, O, I, <u>A, Y</u>	A and Y compared and swapped
	T, R, P, O, <u>I, Y</u>, A	I and Y compared and swapped
	T, R, P, <u>O, Y</u>, I, A	O and Y compared and swapped
	T, R, <u>P, Y</u>, O, I, A	P and Y compared and swapped
	T, <u>R, Y</u>, P, O, I, A	R and Y compared and swapped
	<u>T, Y</u>, R, P, O, I, A	T and Y compared and swapped
	Y, T, R, P, O, I, A	End of shuttle sort.

Tip: In a bubble sort, the number of comparisons you have to make gets smaller with each pass, but in a shuttle sort that's not always the case.

So the letters in reverse alphabetical order are: Y, T, R, P, O, I, A

Exercise 2.2

Q1   Use a shuttle sort to sort these numbers into ascending order.
a) 12, 6, 7, 3, 11   b)   22, 54, 76, 43, 66, 19
c) 16, 1, 7, 8, 3, 17, 12, 15

Q2   Ishmael asked his colleagues how long (to the nearest hour) they
spent on the internet per day. His results were: 2, 3, 1, 4, 8, 5, 7, 6.
a) Sort his results into descending order using a shuttle sort.
b) How many comparisons and swaps did you make?

Q3   The marks of 7 students in a campanology exam were:
85%, 66%, 40%, 75%, 56%, 58%, 81%
Sort these marks into descending order using a shuttle sort.

Q4   The ages of the first 5 people through the door of a leisure centre
one Saturday were: 23, 56, 4, 17, 60.
a) Sort these ages into ascending order using a shuttle sort.
b) How many comparisons and swaps were made on the first pass?

Q5   Maeve recorded the heights of the six geranium plants she was
studying for her genetics project. Their heights were:
17.0 cm, 16.8 cm, 17.4 cm, 15.9 cm, 16.5 cm, 18.0 cm
a) Sort these heights into ascending order using a shuttle sort.
b) Write down how many comparisons were needed in total.

Q6   Write down how many passes are needed to put the list 1, 5, 12, 8,
6, 9, 14, 11, 7, 2, 15, 3 into ascending order using a shuttle sort.

Q6 Hint: You don't
need to sort the list.

Q7   A pack of moderately annoyed commuters recorded how late the
7.05 train left Welshtown station every day for one working week.
This is what they recorded: 13 min, 20 min, 5 min, 7 min, 25 min.
a) Sort these times into descending order using a shuttle sort.
b) How many exchanges did you make on each pass?

Q7 b) Hint: Exchanges
just means swaps.

Q8   a) Use a shuttle sort to write the letters
M, S, A, T, O, L in alphabetical order.
b) Write down how many comparisons and swaps
you made on each of the first three passes.

Q9   A group of competitive wheelbarrow racers are training. Their times
for the 30 m race are: 12.1 s, 11.7 s , 12.8 s, 11.3 s, 12.5 s, 13.0 s,
12.6 s. Sort these times into ascending order using a shuttle sort.

Q10 Hint: If you get
every item on the list in
the same unit (£ or p)
you won't have to write
the units out all the way
through, but make sure
you put them back in at
the end.

Q10 Tubbs surveyed 10 local shops to find the price of a 450 g
can of Broiled Beans. Her results were:
£1.10, 85p, 90p, 99p, £1.30, 78p, 88p, 87p, 95p, £1.05.
a) Sort her results into ascending order using a shuttle sort.
b) Write down how many swaps were needed on each pass.

Shell sort

- To do a **Shell sort** you have to **break the list down** into smaller lists called **subsets**.

- Each of the subsets is **sorted separately**, then the list is put back **together**.

- The Shell sort is **faster** than the bubble or shuttle sorts. Dividing the list into subsets gets it **nearly in order** really **quickly** — then you can **finish** off with a **shuttle sort**, which won't take long on the 'nearly ordered' list.

- The Shell sort works particularly well for **big sets** of numbers — making **one swap** in a subset can move a number **several places** in the list, so you don't have to spend ages moving a number from one end to the other.

To do a Shell sort:

> 1) Share the n numbers in your list between $n/2$ subsets (if n is odd ignore the remainder, so for $n = 5$ there would be 2 subsets). Put the **first number** in the **first subset**, the **second number** in the **second subset** etc. Write the first subset on one line, the next one underneath it and so on.
>
> 2) **Sort** each subset into order.
>
> 3) Put the subsets back **together**, working **down** your sets (so take the first number from the first subset, then the first number from the second subset etc.). This is **one pass**.
>
> 4) **Share** your **new list** between subsets — this time, you want **half** the number of subsets you had before (again, ignore the remainder if you need to), and **sort** each subset. Put your list back **together** like you did in step 3.
>
> 5) Repeat step 4 until you only have **one subset** — sort this subset using a **shuttle sort** (see p.15).

A **computer** would use the **shuttle sort** on **every step** to sort the subsets — you're only expected to use it on the **last step** when you sort the whole list, as you can most likely sort the smaller subsets **by eye**. So the **last pass** of the Shell sort is just a final **shuttle sort**.

It's important to get the **layout** right when you work through a Shell sort — if you have your subsets **lined up** in the wrong way it's easy to make a mistake when you're putting the list **back together**. You might find writing them out **diagonally** (like in the example on the next page) makes them easier to read.

Tip: The Shell sort is named after the computer scientist Donald Shell who came up with it in 1959.

Tip: A shell suit is a highly flammable 1980s tracksuit. This probably won't be on the exam.

Tip: Each pass of the Shell sort involves splitting the list into subsets, sorting these subsets, then putting the list back together again.

Tip: You don't include the passes in the final shuttle sort when you're counting the passes of the Shell sort.

Example

Use a Shell sort to write the numbers 12, 32, 24, 11, 17, 5, 19, 13, 22 in ascending order.

- For the **first pass** divide the list into **4 subsets** ($n = 9$ so $n/2 = 9/2 = 4.5$).

  Put the **1st item** into the **1st subset**, the **2nd item** into the **2nd subset**, the **3rd item** into the **3rd subset** and the **4th item** into the **4th subset**.

  Then put the **5th item** into the **1st subset**, the **6th item** into the **2nd subset** and so on, until finally putting the **9th item** into the **1st subset**.

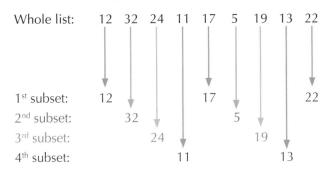

Whole list:	12	32	24	11	17	5	19	13	22
1st subset:	12				17				22
2nd subset:		32				5			
3rd subset:			24				19		
4th subset:				11				13	

- Next you **sort** each subset — after sorting, the subsets are:

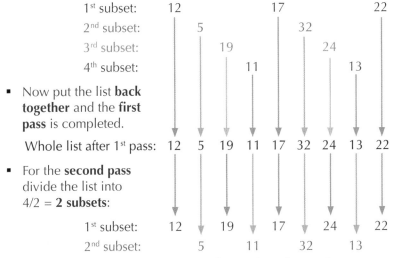

1st subset:	12				17				22
2nd subset:		5				32			
3rd subset:			19				24		
4th subset:				11				13	

Tip: The Shell sort is fast because it lets you move numbers a long way in one go — e.g. here 32 moves 4 places to the right with one swap because it's swapped while it's in a subset.

- Now put the list **back together** and the **first pass** is completed.

  Whole list after 1st pass: 12 5 19 11 17 32 24 13 22

- For the **second pass** divide the list into $4/2 = $ **2 subsets**:

1st subset:	12		19		17		24		22
2nd subset:		5		11		32		13	

- Again, **sort** each subset into ascending order. The results are:

1st subset:	12		17		19		22		24
2nd subset:		5		11		13		32	

- Put the list **back together**, and that's the second pass **done**.

  Whole list after 2nd pass: 12 5 17 11 19 13 22 32 24

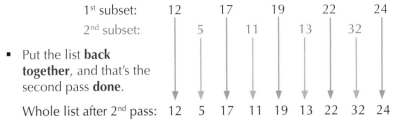

- $2/2 = 1$ so on the **third pass** you only need **1 subset** — in other words, you're now working with the **whole list**. Sort it using a **shuttle sort** and you're finished — the final list is:

> 5, 11, 12, 13, 17, 19, 22, 24, 32

Tip: Remember, the whole shuttle sort (p.15) is included in the last pass of the Shell sort, no matter how many passes it takes you.

Q1   Put each set of numbers below into ascending order using a Shell sort.
a) 14, 3, 7, 15, 8, 5   b) 3.5, 3.8, 3.6, 3.5, 3.9, 3.0, 3.7, 3.7
c) 22, 45, 74, 21, 56, 18, 46, 34, 24, 60, 43

Q2   The times taken for a group of teachers to complete a crossword were:
6 min, 3.5 min, 8 min, 2.5 min, 4.5 min, 7.5 min, 5.5 min, 5 min.
Sort these times into ascending order using a Shell sort.

Q3 Hint: Make sure you read the question carefully — you're asked for descending order here.

Q3   The ages of the first ten dogs in a race, to the nearest year, were:
3 years, 6 years, 7 years, 1 year, 10 years,
12 years, 2 years, 8 years, 13 years, 4 years.
Sort these ages into descending order using a Shell sort.

Q4   Petra asked her friends how many cups of coffee they drink each day. Their answers were:
10 cups, 4 cups, 0 cups, 2 cups, 8 cups, 3 cups, 5 cups, 4 cups.
a) Sort this list into ascending order using a Shell sort.
b) How many comparisons did you make on the first pass?
c) How many swaps did you make on the first pass?

Q5   Use a Shell sort to put 'N, P, E, S, B, M, T, O' into alphabetical order.

Q6   Vincent is training for a marathon. These are the distances of his training runs last week (he ran twice on Monday and Saturday):
10 km, 8 km, 12 km, 12 km, 20 km, 15 km, 7 km, 10 km, 18 km
Use a Shell sort to put these distances into descending order.

Q7   The lengths of the tracks on Alain's new CD, in minutes, are:
8.39, 6.02, 4.27, 4.24, 4.04, 4.12, 4.41, 5.03, 2.50, 3.48
Sort these times into ascending order using a Shell sort.

Q8   Phoebe is researching how much a booklet on evil twins costs on some websites. The prices she finds are:
£1.45, £1.25, £1.30, £1.10, £1.05, £1.50, £1.35.
a) Sort these prices into ascending order using a Shell sort.
b) How many comparisons did you make on the second pass?

Q9   a) A set of 32 randomly generated numbers is to be sorted into ascending order using a Shell sort.
(i)   How many subsets will be needed for the first pass?
(ii)   How many passes will be needed to complete the Shell sort?
b) 2, 7, 5, 9, 2, 5, 9, 1, 3, 1, 6, 9, 5, 6, 4, 2, 8, 0
This set of randomly-generated numbers is to be sorted into ascending order using a Shell sort.
(i)   How many subsets will be needed for the first pass?
(ii)   Complete the first two passes.

Quick sort

The **quick sort algorithm** works by choosing a **pivot** (see below) which **breaks down** the list into two **smaller lists**, which are then broken down in the same way until the numbers are in order. To use it, follow these steps:

1) Choose the first number in the list as the **pivot**.
   Move any numbers that are **less** than the pivot to a new list on the **left** of it and the numbers that are **greater** to a new list on the **right**. Don't change the **order** of the numbers though.

2) **Repeat the first step** for each of the smaller lists you've just made. You'll need a **new pivot** for each of the new lists.

3) When **every number** has been chosen as a pivot you can **stop**, as the list is in order.

Tip: Sometimes the smaller lists either side of the pivot will only have one number in them — you don't need to do anything with these as they're already in order.

- Although the pivot can be **any item** in the list, it's easiest to choose the **first number** in the list (that's what you'll be expected to do in the exam).

- It's a good idea to **circle** or **underline** the pivots you're using at each step of the quick sort — it helps you keep track of where you're up to.

- In the next example, the numbers are written in orange when they're in the correct place.

Example

Sort the numbers 54, 36, 29, 56, 45, 39, 32, 27 into ascending order using a quick sort.

- The **pivot** is the first number in the list: **54**.

- Go through the numbers **one by one** and place each number that's **lower** than 54 to the **left** of the pivot. Then add all the numbers **higher** than 54 to the **right** of the pivot:

$$36 \quad 29 \quad 45 \quad 39 \quad 32 \quad 27 \quad \underline{54} \quad 56$$
$$\underbrace{\hspace{5cm}}_{l_1} \qquad \underbrace{\hspace{1cm}}_{l_2}$$

Tip: Don't reorder the numbers, just write them down in the order they appear in the original list, but on the correct side of the pivot.

- Now 54 is in the **correct place** (because it's been chosen as a pivot), and the list has been divided into **smaller lists**: l_1 and l_2.
  The new pivot in l_1 is the first number — **36**.
  There's only **1 item** in l_2, so you don't have to do anything with it, that means 56 is in the **correct place**.
  Rearranging l_1 around the new pivot gives:

$$\underline{36} \quad 29 \quad 45 \quad 39 \quad 32 \quad 27 \quad 54 \quad 56$$

$$29 \quad 32 \quad 27 \quad \underline{36} \quad 45 \quad 39 \quad 54 \quad 56$$
$$\underbrace{\hspace{3cm}}_{l_3} \qquad \underbrace{\hspace{2cm}}_{l_4}$$

- Now 36 is in the **correct place** and you've got two lists with multiple items in, so you need a new pivot for each list.
  The pivot for list l_3 is **29** and the pivot for list l_4 is **45**.
  Rearranging l_3 and l_4 using the new pivots gives:

$$27 \quad 29 \quad 32 \quad 36 \quad 39 \quad 45 \quad 54 \quad 56$$
$$\underbrace{}_{l_5} \qquad \underbrace{}_{l_6} \qquad \underbrace{}_{l_7}$$

- As there's only **one item** left in each of the final lists, the list is now in the **right order**:

$$27, 29, 32, 36, 39, 45, 54, 56$$

Exercise 2.4

Q1 a) Use a quick sort to sort these numbers into ascending order:
7, 8, 3, 4, 6, 2, 9
    b) List the pivots you used.

Q2 a) Use a quick sort to sort these letters into alphabetical order:
M, N, A, F, G, H, Q
    b) List the pivots you used.

Q3 The marks achieved in an exam were: 101, 96, 103, 94, 107, 98
    a) Use a quick sort to sort the marks into descending order.
    b) List the pivots you used.

Q4 The weights of some apples, in ounces, were:
4.4, 3.9. 3.3, 3.7, 4.1, 3.2, 4.2, 3.8
    a) Use a quick sort to sort the weights into ascending order.
    b) List the pivots you used.

Q5 Use a quick sort to sort these letters into reverse alphabetical order, listing the pivots you used: S, O, R, T, I, N, G

Q6 Times for a race are recorded as:
13.1 s, 11.0 s, 11.3 s, 12.3 s, 11.7 s, 12.9 s, 12.8 s
    a) Use a quick sort to list the times in ascending order.
    b) List the pivots you used.

Q7 Some husky dogs were weighed and their weights in kg were found to be:
14.4, 7.6, 18.0, 10.6, 15.4, 23.0
    a) Use a quick sort to list the weights in descending order.
    b) List the pivots you used.

Q8 The names of students in a class are recorded as:
Ben, Jane, Mary, Pete, Rob, Ian, Freda, Lorna, Kim, Babatunde
    a) Use a quick sort to list the names in alphabetical order.
    b) List the pivots you used.

Review Exercise — Chapter 1

Q1 For each of the following sets of instructions, identify the input and output.

    a) a recipe for vegetable soup

    b) directions from Leicester Square to the Albert Hall

    c) flat-pack instructions for building a TV cabinet

Q2 Use the Russian Peasant Algorithm on page 3 to multiply 17 and 56.

Q3 Use the flow chart on page 8 to work out the factors of 16.

Q4 Use a bubble sort to write the numbers 72, 57, 64, 54, 68, 71 in ascending order. How many passes do you need to make?

Q5 If you had to put a list of 12 numbers in order using a bubble sort, what is the maximum number of comparisons you'd need to make?

Q6 Use a shuttle sort to write the numbers 21, 11, 23, 19, 28, 26 in ascending order.

Q7 Sort the numbers 101, 98, 79, 113, 87, 108, 84 into ascending order using a Shell sort.

Q8 Ten students took part in an egg and spoon race. Their times, in seconds, were recorded as:

    23   29   17   23   24   30   19   252

    a) Use a shuttle sort to put the times in descending order.

    b) If you used a bubble sort to sort the list you obtained in part a) into ascending order, how many comparisons would you have to make? (Don't actually carry out a bubble sort.)

Q9 Sort the numbers 0.8, 1.2, 0.7, 0.5, 0.4, 1.0, 0.1 into ascending order using a Shell sort.

Q10 Use a quick sort to list these vegetables in alphabetical order:

    onion, carrot, parsnip, swede, turnip, leek, endive

> **Q10 Hint:** You don't need to know this, but endive is a leafy vegetable similar to chicory.

1   77   83   96   105   78   89   112   80   98   94

(a) Use a quick sort to arrange the list of numbers above into ascending order.
You must clearly show the pivots you use at each stage.

(4 marks)

(b) A list of six numbers is to be sorted into ascending order using a bubble sort.

    (i) Which number(s) will definitely be in the correct position after
the first pass?

(1 mark)

    (ii) After how many passes will the list definitely be in ascending order?

(1 mark)

    (iii) Write down the maximum number of swaps needed to
sort a list of six numbers into ascending order.

(1 mark)

2 (a) Rearrange the following set of numbers into ascending order using a shuttle sort.
     1.3   0.8   1.8   0.5   1.2   0.2   0.9
State how many passes you made.

(5 marks)

(b) How many comparisons and swaps were made on the first pass?

(1 mark)

3   Mark   Adam   Dan   James   Stella   Helen   Robert

Use a quick sort to list the above names in alphabetical order.
Show clearly the pivots you use.

(4 marks)

4   Consider the following algorithm:

   Line 10:   Input A, B with $A < B$

   Line 20:   Input $N = 1$

   Line 30:   Calculate $C = A \div N$

   Line 40:   Calculate $D = B \div N$

   Line 50:   If both C and D are integers then print N

   Line 60:   If $N \neq A$ then let $N = N + 1$ and go to Line 30

   Line 70:   Stop

   (a)   Carry out the algorithm with $A = 8$ and $B = 12$. Record your results.

   (3 marks)

   (b)   (i)   What does this algorithm produce?

   (1 mark)

         (ii)   Using your answer to part (i) or otherwise, write down the output that
                would be produced if you applied the algorithm to $A = 19$ and $B = 25$, and
                explain your answer. You do not need to carry out the algorithm again.

   (2 marks)

   (c)   Explain what will happen if $A = 0$.

   (1 mark)

5   The numbers 54, 71, 63, 72, 68, 59, 60, 55 are to be sorted into ascending order
   using a Shell sort.
   After the first pass, the order of the numbers is 54, 59, 60, 55, 68, 71, 63, 72

   (a)   State the number of comparisons and the number of swaps made
         in the first pass.

   (2 marks)

   (b)   Complete the Shell sort, stating the new order after each pass.
         Use a shuttle sort on your final pass.

   (5 marks)

1. Graphs

The graphs you find in Decision Maths look quite different to the ones you'll know from other parts of maths. Here they're all about showing how different people, places or things are connected.

Graphs

> A **graph** is made up of points (called **vertices** or **nodes**) joined by lines (called **edges** or **arcs**).

Graphs can be used to **model** or **solve** real-life problems.

- In this graph, the **vertices** represent towns and the **edges** represent roads.
- The graph **doesn't** show where the towns are in relation to each other — just how they are **linked** by roads.

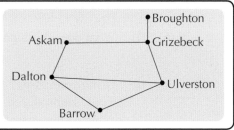

Bipartite graphs

Bipartite graphs have two sets of vertices.
The edges only join vertices in **one set** to vertices in the **opposite set**.

- This bipartite graph shows the jobs a group of students would prefer to do at the end-of-term barbecue.

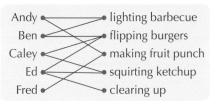

- The edges can only join students to jobs. So you could never join Andy and Caley, or "lighting barbecue" and "flipping burgers".

- In this bipartite graph, both groups have the same members. The graph shows how the members of a quiz team voted to choose a captain.

- The column on the left shows who voted, and the one on the right shows who they voted for.

- You can see that each team member voted twice, and Gurjit got the most votes.

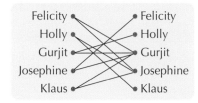

Paths and cycles

A **path** is a route in a graph — a **sequence of edges** that are all **connected end to end**. A path can't go through any vertex more than once.

Graphs like graph G, shown on the right, contain lots of paths.

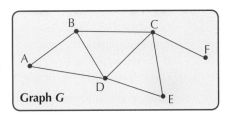

Graph G

One path in graph G is ABDECF.   Another is CBAD.

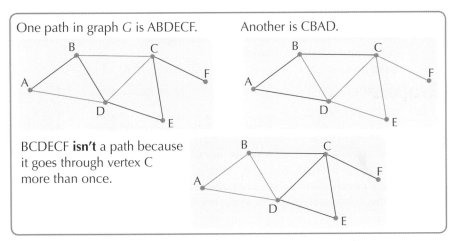

BCDECF **isn't** a path because it goes through vertex C more than once.

A **cycle** (or **circuit**) is a **closed path** — a path that brings you back to your **starting point**. The end vertex is the **same** as the start vertex.

So on graph G, ABDA is a cycle.   CEDBC is also a cycle.

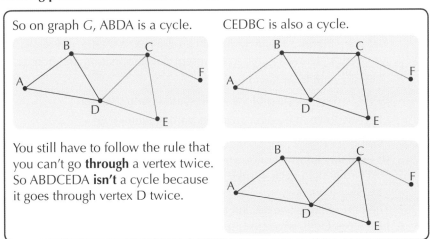

You still have to follow the rule that you can't go **through** a vertex twice. So ABDCEDA **isn't** a cycle because it goes through vertex D twice.

- A **Hamiltonian cycle** is a cycle which goes through **every** vertex of the graph.
- Like all cycles, it brings you back to the **start vertex**.
- Not all graphs contain Hamiltonian cycles — those that do are called **Hamiltonian graphs**.

Tip: There's more about Hamiltonian cycles in Chapter 4.

Graph G above **isn't** a Hamiltonian graph because there are **no cycles** that contain all of the vertices (if you try to make a cycle through F you always go through C twice).

If you **remove** vertex F you get a Hamiltonian graph that contains the Hamiltonian cycle ABCEDA.

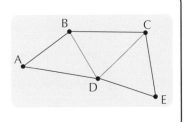

Tip: For a Hamiltonian graph with n vertices, each Hamiltonian cycle has n edges.

Exercise 1.1

Q1 An electrical circuit has six components, A, B, C, D, E and F.

A is connected to D and E.   D is connected to A, B, C and E.
B is connected to C, D and F.   E is connected to A and D.
C is connected to B, D and F.   F is connected to B and C.

Draw a graph to represent the circuit.

Q2 Identify whether the following are paths on the graph on the right. If they are not paths, explain why.

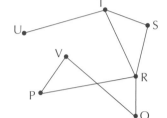

a) TURP

b) SRPVQ

c) TRQVPRS

Q3 Five friends answered a survey about which sports they like to play. Akio likes football and tennis; Betty likes tennis and hockey; Clare likes netball; Daisy likes football and hockey; Emma likes tennis. Draw a bipartite graph to represent this information.

Q4 For a Hamiltonian graph with n vertices, state the number of edges in each Hamiltonian cycle when:

a) $n = 7$ b) $n = 11$ c) $n = 67$.

Q5 Liang and Sue are friends. Weizhe and Sue are friends. Liang and Nelly are friends. Kevin and Nelly are friends. Weizhe and Nelly are friends. Draw a graph to represent this information and hence:

a) Find a path from Kevin to Sue.

b) Write down, if possible, a cycle starting with Weizhe.

c) Write down, if possible, a cycle starting with Kevin.

Ava makes friends with Kevin and Liang.

d) Add this information to your graph and find a Hamiltonian cycle for the new graph.

Q5 Hint: Remember — a cycle can't go through a vertex more than once.

Q6 The Borer family live far apart and keep in touch by letter. Last week Dolly wrote to Cheryl, Cheryl wrote to Flora and Nellie, Flora wrote to Cheryl, and Zelda wrote to Flora. Draw a bipartite graph to represent this information.

Q7 Find all the Hamiltonian cycles for the graph on the right which start from A.

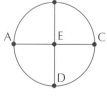

Q8

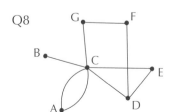

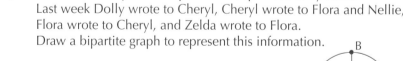

In this graph:

a) How many cycles start from A?

b) How many cycles start from C?

c) Which vertex cannot be part of any cycle?

Networks and digraphs

Networks

In a **weighted graph**, or **network**, each edge has a number associated with it. This number is called the **weight** of the edge.

- Weights often give you **lengths**. This network shows points in a nature reserve and the footpaths joining them. The weights represent the lengths of the footpaths.

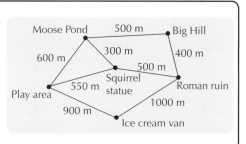

- Weights can also be used to show things like **costs** or **times**.

Tip: Typical costs shown on a network include the cost of travelling between two points, or the cost of connecting two points in some way, e.g. by installing wiring or piping, or by building roads or paths.

Digraphs

Sometimes edges have **directions**, e.g. to show one-way streets. If they do, they're called **directed edges** and the graph is a **digraph**.

- The edges on this digraph show the bus routes between the towns.

- There's a direct bus from Dalton to Askam, but not from Askam to Dalton.

- There's no direction on the edge connecting Broughton and Grizebeck, so buses run between them in **both directions**.

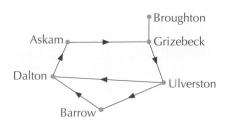

- This is a **weighted digraph**.

- There are two edges between A and B and two edges between A and E. For each of those pairs, you can travel between them in either direction but the weights are different depending on which direction you go.

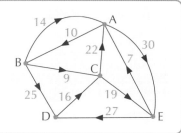

Subgraphs

A **subgraph** of graph G is a graph where all the vertices and edges are in G.

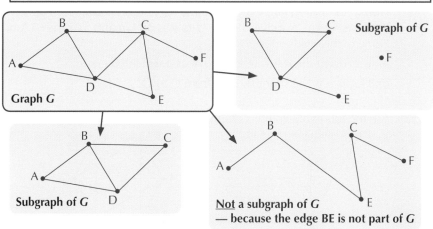

Tip: One way to think of a subgraph is that if you take a graph, then rub a few bits out, what you're left with is a **subgraph** of the original graph.

Complete graphs

In a **complete graph**, all the vertices are **directly connected** to each other.

Tip: A complete graph with n vertices has $\frac{n(n-1)}{2}$ edges.

Each vertex is connected to $n-1$ other vertices. Counting all these connections gives $n(n-1)$ — this is **twice** the number of edges, because it's a total of the number of **edge ends** at each vertex. (But this isn't true for complete bipartite graphs.)

For each vertex in a **complete graph**, there will be an edge joining it **directly** to every other vertex.

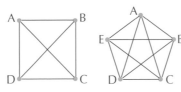

The notation K_n is used for a **complete graph** with n **vertices**, so these graphs are K_4 and K_5.

In a **complete bipartite graph**, each vertex in one set is joined directly to every vertex in the **other set**.

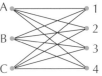

The notation $K_{m,n}$ is used for complete bipartite graphs. m is the number of **vertices** in one set, n the number of vertices in the other, so the graph above is $K_{3,4}$.
There are $m \times n$ **edges** altogether.

This graph is **not complete** — there's no direct link between R and T.

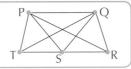

Simple graphs

Graphs can have **more than one** edge between a **pair** of vertices. There can also be **loops** connecting vertices to themselves.

Graphs **without** any loops or multiple edges between vertices are called **simple graphs** (like the nature reserve and bus route examples on page 29).

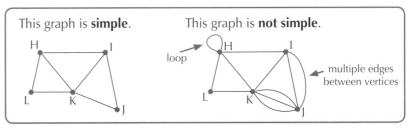

This graph is **simple**.

This graph is **not simple**.

loop

multiple edges between vertices

Exercise 1.2

Q1 The following roads connect six towns, P, Q, R, S, T and U:
From P to Q is 60 km, P to T is 50 km, Q to R is 70 km, U to T is 40 km, R to S is 35 km, U to R is 30 km and S to T is 65 km. None of the roads intersect.

Q1 Hint: 'None of the roads intersect' means the edges of your graph shouldn't cross.

a) Represent the roads listed above as a weighted graph.

b) How far is the shortest route from U to Q?

Q2 Are the following graphs complete? Give reasons for each answer.

a)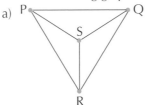

b)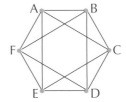

Q3   Draw a complete graph with: a)   3 vertices,   b)   7 vertices.

Q4   Without trying to draw one, calculate how many edges there are on a complete graph with 40 vertices.

Q4 Hint: Look back at page 30 if you're stuck on this one.

Q5   This is Graph G:

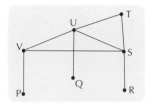

a)   State which of the following is not a subgraph of G, giving a reason for your answer.

(i)

(ii)

(iii)

b)   Draw a subgraph of G with 5 vertices and 5 edges.

Q6   State whether or not each of the following graphs is simple.

a)

b)
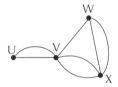

c)
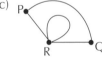

d)
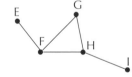

Trees and spanning trees

Two **vertices** are **connected** if there's a **path** between them — it doesn't have to be direct.

A **graph** is **connected** if all its vertices are connected.

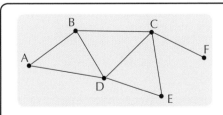

Graph G is connected.

This subgraph of G is **not** connected — you can't get from some vertices to others. E.g. there's no path between B and C, or between E and A.

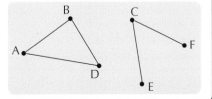

Tip: You can show that G is connected because you can join two of its vertices by a path which visits every vertex.
E.g. you can get from A to F by the path ABDECF — and because this path visits every vertex, you can connect any two vertices of G using part of the path.

A connected graph which contains no cycles is called a **tree**.

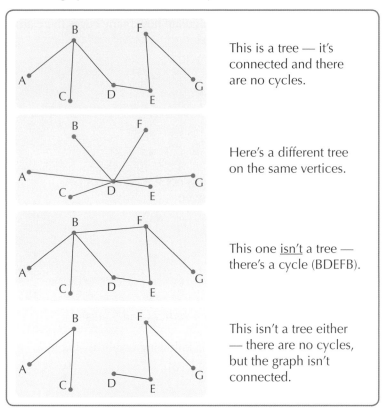

This is a tree — it's connected and there are no cycles.

Here's a different tree on the same vertices.

This one <u>isn't</u> a tree — there's a cycle (BDEFB).

This isn't a tree either — there are no cycles, but the graph isn't connected.

Tip: You could make this last example into a tree by adding an edge joining any of A, B or C to any of D, E, F or G.

Spanning trees are **subgraphs** that are also **trees, and** that include **all** the vertices of the original graph.

So if you're asked to draw a spanning tree of a graph, you can **only** delete **edges** from the original graph.

Tip: Look back at p.29 if you can't remember what a subgraph is.

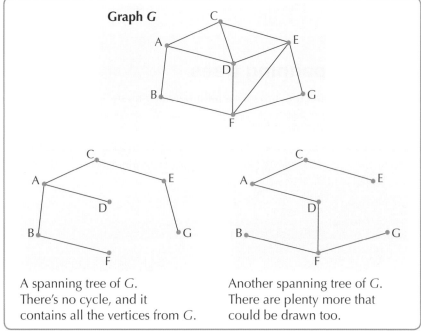

Graph *G*

Tip: Make sure you're really happy with what spanning trees are — you'll need them later in the chapter.

A spanning tree of *G*. There's no cycle, and it contains all the vertices from *G*.

Another spanning tree of *G*. There are plenty more that could be drawn too.

Both the spanning trees above have seven vertices and six edges. In fact, the number of edges in any tree is **always** one less than the number of vertices.

Q1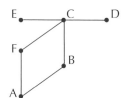

a) Is E connected to F?

b) Write down all the paths from:
  (i) E to D   (ii) B to D

Q2 State whether each of the following graphs are trees.
For each one that is not a tree, give a reason.

a)  b) 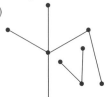 c)

d) 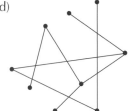 e)

Q3 State whether each of these graphs is connected or not connected.

a)   b)   c)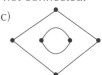

Q4 Draw ten different spanning trees for the graph shown on the right.

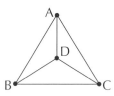

Q5 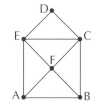 Draw a spanning tree for this graph.

Degree of a vertex

> The **degree** or **valency** of a vertex is the number of edges connected to it.

The sum of the degrees is always **double** the number of edges — it's a count of how many **edge ends** there are. So the sum of degrees is **always even**.

Example

Calculate the degree of each vertex in this graph.

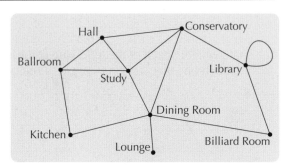

- Just count the number of edges that end at each vertex. Record them in a table.
- Loops, like the one at the library count twice at the same vertex, because they have two ends at that vertex. So the degree of the library is 4, not 3.

Tip: Here, there are 14 edges and the sum of the degrees is 28 (2 × 14).

Vertex	Degree
Ballroom	3
Billiard Room	2
Conservatory	4
Dining Room	5
Hall	3
Kitchen	2
Library	4
Lounge	1
Study	4

A vertex with an odd degree is **odd**, and one with an even degree is **even**. So in the example above, the Billiard Room, Conservatory, Kitchen, Library and Study are all even, and the rest are odd.

Exercise 1.4

Q1 Hint: Check each answer by confirming (sum of degrees) = (twice number of edges).

Q1 Find the degree of each vertex in the following graphs.

a)

b)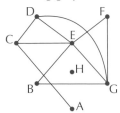

c)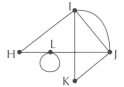

d)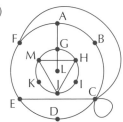

Q2 Aroon made this table for a graph with five vertices, P, Q, R, S, T.

Vertex	P	Q	R	S	T
Degree	2	3	1	4	1

Explain how you can tell that Aroon has made a mistake.

Q3 A tree has 15 vertices.
State: a) the number of edges in the tree,
              b) the sum of the degrees of the tree's vertices.

Q4 Copy the following graphs and add edges to each one to make all the vertices even.

a)   b)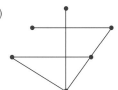

c)   d)

Q5 Ibrahim made this table for a graph with four vertices, P, Q, R and S.

Vertex	P	Q	R	S
Degree	3	5	6	2

How many edges does his graph have?

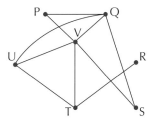

Q6 By deleting the least possible number of edges, draw a subgraph of the graph on the right where every vertex is even.

Q6-7 Hint: A vertex with a degree of zero counts as an even vertex — and don't forget that a loop adds 2 to the degree of a vertex.

Q7 Draw a graph with:
a) four vertices, of degrees 2, 3, 2 and 1
b) five vertices, of degrees 2, 5, 4, 4 and 1
c) three vertices, of degrees 4, 1 and 1
d) four vertices, of degrees 1, 5, 2 and 6

Q8 Sara made this table for a connected graph with vertices A, B, C and D.

Vertex	A	B	C	D
Degree	3	4	5	2

Q8 Hint: Think about how many edges there are in a spanning tree.

a) How can you tell from the table that Sara's graph isn't a tree?
b) How many edges should be deleted to get a spanning tree?

Adjacency matrices and distance matrices

Adjacency matrices

Adjacency matrices show the number of links between each pair of vertices.

To **draw** an adjacency matrix from a **graph**, go through each space in the matrix and count the number of **direct connections** from the vertex at the left of the row to the vertex at the top of the column.

Tip: A matrix is just a set of numbers arranged into rows and columns. You can think of the matrices you get in D1 as just being a type of table — you might even come across questions that call them tables instead of matrices.

Example 1

Represent this graph with an adjacency matrix.

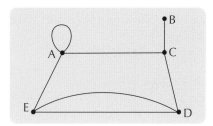

- The graph has five vertices, so we need a matrix with five rows and five columns.
- Label the rows and columns with the names of the vertices.

$$\begin{array}{c@{\quad}ccccc} & A & B & C & D & E \\ A & \\ B & \\ C & \\ D & \\ E & \end{array}$$

- The first row shows the number of links to each vertex from A.

- There's a loop from A to A. You can go in either direction, so it counts as 2 links.

- There's no direct link from A to B, so put a zero here...

$$\begin{array}{c@{\quad}cccc} & A & B & C & D & E \\ A & 2 & 0 & 1 & \end{array}$$

- ... and there's one direct link from A to C, so that goes in the next space.

- Fill in the rest of the matrix in the same way.

- Notice that the completed matrix is symmetrical along the diagonal from top left to bottom right.

$$\begin{array}{c@{\quad}ccccc} & A & B & C & D & E \\ A & 2 & 0 & 1 & 0 & 1 \\ B & 0 & 0 & 1 & 0 & 0 \\ C & 1 & 1 & 0 & 1 & 0 \\ D & 0 & 0 & 1 & 0 & 2 \\ E & 1 & 0 & 0 & 2 & 0 \end{array}$$

Tip: The sum of all the numbers in the adjacency matrix for an undirected graph is always even. That's because each edge is counted twice, as you can travel along it in either direction.

You might have to **draw a graph** using the corresponding adjacency matrix.

Example 2

Draw the graph represented by this adjacency matrix.

$$\begin{array}{c c c c c c} & J & K & L & M & N \\ J & 0 & 1 & 1 & 1 & 0 \\ K & 1 & 0 & 1 & 0 & 2 \\ L & 1 & 1 & 0 & 0 & 1 \\ M & 1 & 0 & 0 & 2 & 0 \\ N & 0 & 2 & 1 & 0 & 0 \end{array}$$

Tip: If it helps you to remember which way round is which, add 'from' and 'to' labels at the side and top of your matrices.

- Start by drawing the vertices.

- Use the first row to draw the edges from J — there's one to each of K, L and M.

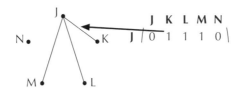

- Use the second row to draw the edges from K. There's already an edge between K and J, so we don't need to draw another one.

$$\begin{array}{c c c c c c} & J & K & L & M & N \\ J & 0 & 1 & 1 & 1 & 0 \\ K & 1 & 0 & 1 & 0 & 2 \end{array}$$

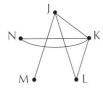

- Add one edge from K to L and two from K to N.

- Use the other rows to add the remaining edges. Remember, two links from M to M means a loop.

Distance matrices

Distance matrices show the **weights** between vertices.
To draw a distance matrix from a **weighted graph**, go through each space in the matrix and write down the weight between the two vertices.

As with adjacency matrices, you only include **direct links** — don't start adding weights together.

Be really careful with **directed edges**. A weight on a directed edge only goes in **one** space of the matrix.

Tip: There's more about weighted graphs and directed edges on p.29.

Example 1

Represent this graph with a distance matrix.

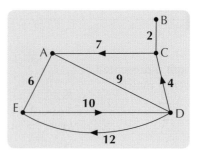

$$\begin{array}{c c} & \begin{array}{c c c c c} A & B & C & D & E \end{array} \\ \begin{array}{c} A \\ B \\ C \\ D \\ E \end{array} & \left(\begin{array}{c c c c c} - & - & - & 9 & 6 \\ & & & & \\ & & & & \\ & & & & \\ & & & & \end{array}\right) \end{array}$$

- As for an adjacency matrix, the labels down the side of a distance matrix are the 'from' vertices and the labels across the top are the 'to' vertices.
- So the entries in the first row here are the distances from A to A, from A to B, A to C, and so on.
- Put a dash, not a zero, if there's no edge.

Tip: A zero in a distance matrix means there is an edge, but its weight is zero.

- Remember to watch out for directed edges. There's no edge **from** A **to** C, so we need a dash here...
- ...but there's an edge of weight 7 **from** C **to** A, so we need a 7 here.
- Weights for undirected edges like the one between A and D appear twice, because you can go along those edges in either direction.

$$\begin{array}{c c} & \begin{array}{c c c c c} A & B & C & D & E \end{array} \\ \begin{array}{c} A \\ B \\ C \\ D \\ E \end{array} & \left(\begin{array}{c c c c c} - & - & - & 9 & 6 \\ - & - & 2 & - & - \\ 7 & 2 & - & - & - \\ 9 & & & & \\ & & & & \end{array}\right) \end{array}$$

$$\begin{array}{c c} & \begin{array}{c c c c c} A & B & C & D & E \end{array} \\ \begin{array}{c} A \\ B \\ C \\ D \\ E \end{array} & \left(\begin{array}{c c c c c} - & - & - & 9 & 6 \\ - & - & 2 & - & - \\ 7 & 2 & - & - & - \\ 9 & - & 4 & - & 12 \\ 6 & - & - & 10 & - \end{array}\right) \end{array}$$

- The completed matrix for a graph with directed edges **won't** be symmetrical.
- There's an edge of weight 12 from D to E, but only one of weight 10 from E to D. (Look at the arrows on the graph.)

Example 2

Draw the graph represented by this distance matrix.

- Start by drawing the vertices.

$$\begin{array}{c c} & \begin{array}{c c c c c} V & W & X & Y & Z \end{array} \\ \begin{array}{c} V \\ W \\ X \\ Y \\ Z \end{array} & \left(\begin{array}{c c c c c} - & 8 & - & 12 & - \\ 8 & - & - & - & 9 \\ 5 & - & - & 2 & 1 \\ 7 & - & - & - & - \\ - & - & 1 & - & - \end{array}\right) \end{array}$$

- Look for **repeated weights** to find any **undirected edges**. Here there are two — the weights are the same in both directions between V and W, and between X and Z.

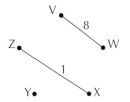

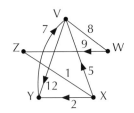

- The other numbers in the matrix represent **directed edges**. Remember, the labels down the **side** of the matrix are the 'from' vertices, and across the **top** are the 'to' vertices.

Tip: It's up to you how you arrange the vertices when you're drawing a graph like this. Try to lay them out so that you can draw a straight edge from any vertex to any other vertex if you need to.

Exercise 1.5

Q1 Represent each of these graphs with an adjacency matrix.

a)
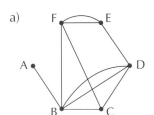

b)
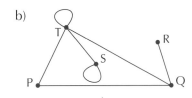

Q1 Hint: Remember, a loop counts for 2 connections in an adjacency matrix.

c)
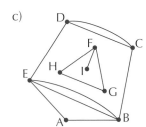

d)
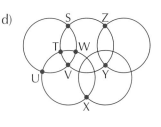

Q2 Construct a graph from each of these adjacency matrices.

a)

	P	Q	R	S	T	U
P	0	1	0	0	0	0
Q	1	0	1	0	0	1
R	0	1	0	1	0	0
S	0	0	1	0	1	1
T	0	0	0	1	0	1
U	0	1	0	1	1	0

b)

	A	B	C	D	E	F
A	0	0	0	1	0	0
B	0	0	0	1	0	1
C	0	0	0	2	1	0
D	1	1	2	0	2	0
E	0	0	1	2	0	1
F	0	1	0	0	1	0

c)

	A	B	C	D	E	F
A	0	0	0	0	0	1
B	0	0	1	0	1	0
C	0	1	0	1	1	0
D	0	0	1	2	1	0
E	0	1	1	1	2	0
F	1	0	0	0	0	0

d)

	U	V	W	X
U	0	2	0	1
V	2	0	1	1
W	0	1	0	0
X	1	1	0	4

Q3 Hint: See page 30 for the definition of a complete graph.

Q3 A complete graph has four vertices, W, X, Y and Z. Without drawing the graph, write out the adjacency matrix.

Q4 Represent each of the following graphs using a distance matrix.

a)

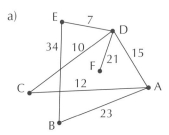

b)

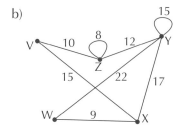

Q4 c), d) Hint: Be careful with the direction of the arrows.

c)

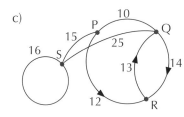

d)

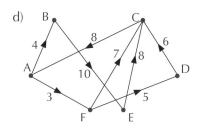

Q5 Construct a graph from each of these distance matrices.

a)

	A	B	C	D	E	F
A	–	–	–	–	20	–
B	–	–	10	–	–	30
C	–	10	–	–	15	–
D	–	–	–	–	25	40
E	20	–	15	25	–	–
F	–	30	–	40	–	–

b)

	A	B	C	D	E	F
A	10	12	–	–	–	–
B	12	–	14	–	18	–
C	–	14	–	–	16	–
D	–	–	–	–	–	20
E	–	18	16	–	–	–
F	–	–	–	20	–	–

c)

	P	Q	R	S	T	U
P	–	–	–	–	–	25
Q	32	–	–	–	–	–
R	–	40	–	–	–	20
S	–	–	30	–	–	–
T	–	–	–	19	–	–
U	–	–	24	–	41	–

d)

	T	U	V	W	X	Y	Z
T	22	26	25	–	–	–	21
U	–	–	33	–	–	–	–
V	20	–	–	–	–	15	–
W	–	–	–	–	14	–	–
X	–	–	–	14	–	13	–
Y	–	–	–	–	13	–	8
Z	–	–	–	–	–	8	–

e) The matrix in part d) represents a road system.
   (i)   Explain why the system is not viable.
   (ii) Describe how you could make the system viable by changing the direction of one edge.

2. Minimum Spanning Trees

A minimum spanning tree connects the vertices of a weighted graph using the least possible total weight. In this section, you'll see two methods for finding the minimum spanning tree of a graph, and one method for a matrix.

Minimum spanning trees

> A **minimum spanning tree** (MST) is a spanning tree where the total weight of the arcs is as **small as possible**.

- So a **minimum spanning tree** (also known as a **minimum connector**) is the shortest way to **connect** all the vertices of a graph.
- Minimum spanning trees are used in real life — for example, they come in handy for cable or pipe-laying companies. Suppose they need to connect several buildings in a town, then they'd want to find the **cheapest path** — this may be the **shortest** route, or have the **easiest** ground to dig up.
- Being absolutely certain that you've got the minimum spanning tree by eye is tricky, so using an **algorithm** helps.

Tip: See page 32 if you've forgotten what spanning trees are. And remember — an **arc** is just another name for an **edge**.

Kruskal's algorithm

Kruskal's algorithm gives one method for finding minimum spanning trees.

> 1. List the arcs in **ascending order of weight**.
> 2. Pick the arc of **least weight** — this starts the tree.
> 3. Look at the **next arc** in your list.
>   - if it forms a cycle, **DON'T** use it and go on to the next arc.
>   - if it **doesn't** form a cycle, add it to the tree.
> 4. Repeat step 3 until you've joined **all** the vertices.

Tip: Kruskal's algorithm is a '**greedy algorithm**'. That means you make the choice that seems best at each stage, without worrying about later choices.

Example

Use Kruskal's algorithm to find a minimum spanning tree for this network.

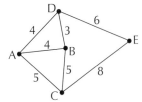

Tip: If a network has n vertices then, as with any spanning tree, there will always be $(n - 1)$ arcs in its minimum spanning tree.

- Step 1 is to make an **ordered list** of the arcs.
- You can put arcs of the **same weight** in **any order** — for example, it doesn't matter which way round you put AD and AB, or BC and AC.

Arc	Weight
BD	3
AD	4
AB	4
BC	5
AC	5
DE	6
CE	8

- The **shortest arc** is **BD**, so that starts the tree, and you can mark the edge as 'used' in the table.

Arc	Weight	Used?
BD	3	✓

- The next arc, AD, **doesn't** form a cycle, so it can be added on.

AD	4	✓

- AB would form a cycle, so it's **rejected**.

AB	4	✗

Tip: You'll often be asked to find the weight of your MST. This is easy — just add all the weights up. So the weight of the MST in this example is $3 + 4 + 5 + 6 = 18$.

- Continue down the list like this until **all** vertices are connected, meaning the MST is **complete**.

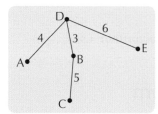

Arc	Weight	Used?
BD	3	✓
AD	4	✓
AB	4	✗
BC	5	✓
AC	5	✗
DE	6	✓
CE	8	✗

- There are often **a few different** minimum spanning trees that can be found for a network — and you might be asked to find them all.
- In the example above, **AB** could have been used instead of AD, or **AC** instead of BC.
- All the different combinations of these arcs give **three more MSTs**:

Tip: These minimum spanning trees all have the same weight.

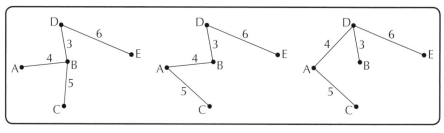

Exercise 2.1

Q1 Hint: Don't worry if parts of your MST aren't connected to start with. Keep going and you should find that it all connects up in the end.

Q1 a) List the arcs of the network below in ascending order of weight.
   b) Use Kruskal's algorithm to find a minimum spanning tree for the network. Draw your spanning tree clearly, labelling each arc with its weight.
   c) State the weight of your minimum spanning tree.

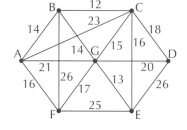

Q2 A graph has *n* vertices. State the number of edges in its MST when:
a) *n* = 14   b) *n* = 32   c) *n* = 98

Q3 The matrix below represents the distances, in km, between six towns.

	A	B	C	D	E	F
A	–	17	24	–	25	19
B	17	–	21	–	19	–
C	24	21	–	18	19	22
D	–	–	18	–	23	22
E	25	19	19	23	–	17
F	19	–	22	22	17	–

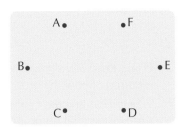

Q3 Hint: Have a look at pages 38-39 for a reminder of how to draw a graph from a distance matrix.

a) Draw a weighted network to represent the information given in the table. Copy the vertices shown next to the matrix and use them to plan your diagram.

b) Using your weighted network, and Kruskal's algorithm, find a minimum spanning tree for this network and state its weight. List the arcs and the order in which you chose them.

Q4 The matrix on the right represents the distances, in metres, between computer terminals in an office. The computers need to be linked using electronic cables.

By drawing a weighted network diagram, use Kruskal's algorithm to find the most efficient way to link the computers. State the total amount of cabling needed. Show your method clearly.

	P	Q	R	S	T	U
P	–	7.5	–	3.8	1.9	2.7
Q	7.5	–	3.5	1.6	1.9	–
R	–	3.5	–	4.1	2.6	2.2
S	3.8	1.6	4.1	–	–	–
T	1.9	1.9	2.6	–	–	3.3
U	2.7	–	2.2	–	3.3	–

Q5 A park warden has identified nine attractions in a park, and is planning to lay a number of pathways so that visitors can visit each attraction. He wishes to use the minimum amount of materials possible when laying the pathways and so plans to join the nine attractions to form a minimum spanning tree. The cost of laying the pathways is £175 per metre.

The diagram below shows the distances between the attractions in metres, and all the possible routes on which pathways can be laid.

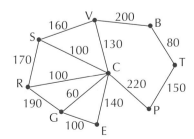

V = view point
B = bird table
T = T. rex paddock
P = pond
E = entrance
G = garden centre
R = rockery
S = swings and slides
C = cafe

Q5 Hint: Remember, a minimum connector is just another name for a minimum spanning tree.

By using Kruskal's algorithm to find a minimum connector, state the total cost of the pathway needed to join all nine attractions. List the arcs carefully in the order in which they are chosen.

Q6   The diagram on the right represents the distances, in metres, between six till points in a department store. The tills need to be linked using cabling.

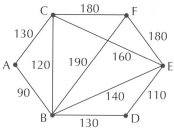

a) Using Kruskal's algorithm, find the minimum amount of cabling required. Show the order in which the arcs are selected.

Q6 b) Hint: The modified spanning tree will no longer be a minimum spanning tree.

b) When installing the cabling, the computer engineer instructs the store owner that till points B and F must be directly linked in order for the system to operate correctly. Modify your tree from part (a) to find the new minimum amount of cabling that will be required.

Q7   The graphs below shows the paths between the ten most popular rides in a theme park, and the distances between them in metres.

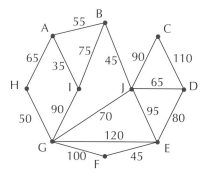

A sudden snowfall blocks all the pathways in the theme park and the park maintenance team only has enough equipment to unblock one path at a time. Use Kruskal's algorithm to work out which paths should be cleared first in order to make all ten rides accessible as quickly as possible. What is the minimum total length of path the team will need to clear?

Prim's algorithm on graphs

Prim's algorithm is another method for finding minimum spanning trees. It does the same job as Kruskal's algorithm, but in a slightly different way. You need to know both algorithms, so make sure you learn these three steps:

Tip: When you're using Prim's algorithm, you don't have to check for cycles like you did with Kruskal's algorithm. Connecting to a vertex outside the tree will never make a cycle.

1. Start the tree by picking **any vertex**.
2. Look at each arc that joins a vertex **already in** the tree to one **not yet in** the tree. Add the one with the **least weight** to the tree. (If more than one arc could be chosen, pick one at random.)
3. Repeat step 2 until you've joined **all** the vertices.

Use Prim's algorithm to find a minimum spanning tree for the network on the right.

Find the weight of the minimum spanning tree.

- Pick a vertex to start the tree.
  I've randomly chosen to start with E.
- There are **two arcs** that join E to vertices not yet in the tree, EA and EF. They're both the same weight (3), so choose one at random — I've picked **EA**.

Tip: In this example, the dashed grey lines represent the edges you could have added at each stage, but rejected.

- There are three arcs that join a vertex **in** the tree (A or E) to a vertex **outside** the tree: AB (2), AF (4) and EF (3).
- **AB** has the **least weight**, so that's the one to add.

- Now the choice is from arcs AF (4), EF (3) or BC (6) — they each join a vertex in the tree (A, B or E) to one not yet in the tree.
- **EF** has the **least weight**, so it's added next.

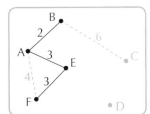

- Nearly there now — the next choice is from BC (6), FC (7) or FD (4).
- **FD** has **least weight**, so that's the one to add.

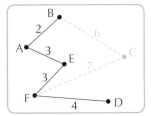

- Finally, C could be joined by BC (6), FC (7) or DC (5).
- **DC** has the **least weight**, so that's the final arc.

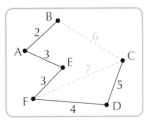

Tip: You might be asked to comment on how appropriate your solution is. For example, if the edges are bus routes of different lengths and you're considering cancelling some, even though the towns are still all connected in the MST, the people who live at B and work at C are likely to be a bit cross.

- The **weight** of the completed minimum spanning tree is

  $2 + 3 + 3 + 4 + 5 = 17$

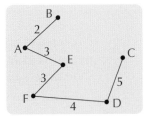

Q1 a) Use Prim's algorithm to find a minimum spanning tree for the network shown below, starting at vertex A.

Draw your spanning tree clearly, labelling each arc with its weight.

b) State the weight of your minimum spanning tree.

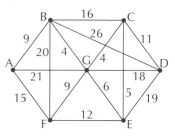

Q2 A university has seven campuses, A–G, located at various sites across the north of England. The diagram below shows the cost, in hundreds of pounds, of linking each site to a new computer network.

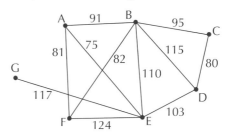

Q2 Hint: Don't forget, the weights are in hundreds of pounds.

It is required to connect all the sites to the network as cheaply as possible. Using Prim's algorithm, find the weight of the minimum connector, and hence the minimum cost of connecting all the sites. State the order in which you choose your arcs clearly.
Start with vertex D.

Q3 Eight towns are to be connected to an electricity grid.

The vertices in the network below represent the eight towns.
The arcs represent possible ways to link the towns to the grid, and the numbers on each arc represent the length, in km, of the power lines needed to link them.

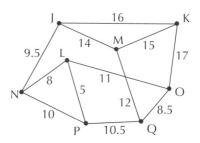

Using Prim's algorithm, and starting with town J, find the way to link the towns to the grid that keeps the total length of power lines as short as possible. State the total length of power lines used.

Q4 A new security system is being installed at a zoo. The diagram on the right shows the nine points where security cameras are to be placed, and the length of cabling, in metres, required to connect them.

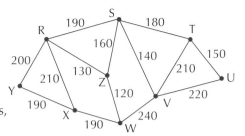

Listing the arcs carefully in the order in which they are chosen, use Prim's algorithm, starting from point R, to find the least possible length of cabling needed to join all nine cameras together. Calculate the total cost of linking up the cameras if the cabling costs £1.25 per metre to install.

Q5 The diagram on the right represents the possible routes and travelling times, in minutes, to walk between seven locations.

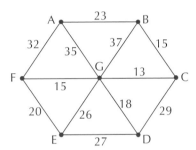

a) Using Prim's algorithm and starting at point G, find a minimum spanning tree for this network. Show the order in which the arcs are selected.

b) Veronica is at point G. She wants to visit points A–F today, and end up back at G. She can only return to G by retracing her steps along routes she has already walked.
Use your answer to a) to find the least time it would take Veronica to visit points A–F and return to G at the end.

Q5 b) Hint: Veronica can return to G more than once on her route if she needs to.

Q6 a) At an animal research centre in Africa, ten research sites need to be joined by wooden bridges, to allow the researchers access to each site. The network diagram below shows all the feasible locations for bridges and the prices, in £, of building bridges between these sites.

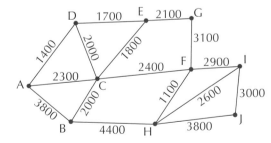

Apply Prim's algorithm to find a minimum spanning tree and hence state the minimum total cost of building bridges between the research sites. Start at site J.

b) During the rainy season a landslide destroys the bridge between sites C and F and the ground is not sufficiently firm for the bridge to be rebuilt. Between which two sites would you advise the researchers to build a bridge to ensure the network of bridges still provides access to and from all sites? Explain your answer.

Prim's algorithm on matrices

Tip: Kruskal's algorithm **doesn't** work on matrices.

The easiest way of putting a graph into a computer is to use a matrix. Prim's algorithm can be used on a distance matrix, which makes it very useful.

1. Pick **any vertex** to start the tree.
2. **Cross out** the **row** for the new vertex and **number** the corresponding **column**.
3. Find and circle the **smallest weight** that's in **any** numbered column **and** that hasn't been crossed out yet. (If more than one entry could be chosen, pick one at random.)
4. The entry you've just circled represents the **next arc** to add to the tree. The column it's in represents the **start vertex** of the arc, and the row it's in represents the **new vertex**.
5. Repeat steps 2-4 until all the rows are crossed out.

Example

Use Prim's algorithm to find a minimum spanning tree for the graph represented by this distance matrix.

List the arcs of the minimum spanning tree in the order you selected them.

	A	B	C	D	E
A	–	4	–	3	3
B	4	–	5	–	6
C	–	5	–	8	7
D	3	–	8	–	2
E	3	6	7	2	–

- Pick a **starting vertex** — A is as good as any.
- **Cross out** the 'A' row and **number** the 'A' column.

- The **smallest** number in the 'A' column that isn't deleted is 3. This appears twice, so **circle** either of them.
- The first arc to add is **AD** (A from column A, D from row D) — weight 3.

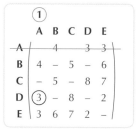

- D is the new vertex, so **cross out** the 'D' row and **number** the 'D' column.

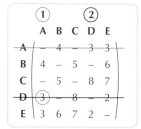

- The smallest number in the A or D columns that isn't deleted is 2, so **circle** it.
- The second arc to add is **DE** (weight 2).

- E is the new vertex, so **cross out** the 'E' row and **number** the 'E' column.

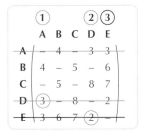

- The smallest number in the A, D or E columns that isn't deleted is 4, so **circle** it.
- The third arc to add is **AB** (weight 4).

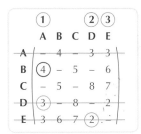

- B is the new vertex, so **cross out** the 'B' row and **number** the 'B' column.

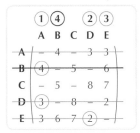

- The smallest number in the A, B, D or E columns that isn't deleted is 5.
- The fourth arc to add is **BC** (weight 5).

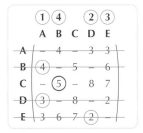

- After crossing out the **final row** and numbering the **final column**, you know you've finished.
- Remember to include an ordered list of the arcs of the minimum spanning tree.
- The total weight of the MST is: 2 + 3 + 4 + 5 = 14

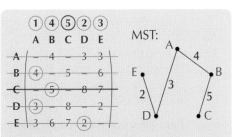

The arcs of the MST were added in the order: **AD, DE, AB, BC**

Tip: There's no need to show each step separately — I've just done it here to make things clearer. Your answer to a question like this should be the final matrix with all the circles and crossings-out, plus the list of arcs in the order they were added. You don't have to draw the MST unless you're asked for it — I've just included it here to show you what it looks like.

Q1 The matrix on the right shows the distances between six vertices. Use Prim's algorithm on this matrix, starting at vertex A, to find a minimum connector for the network represented by the matrix.

List the arcs in the order in which they are chosen and state the weight of your minimum connector.

	A	B	C	D	E	F
A	–	13	24	20	25	22
B	13	–	18	15	19	14
C	24	18	–	21	17	16
D	20	15	21	–	23	22
E	25	19	17	23	–	18
F	22	14	16	22	18	–

Q2 The matrix on the right represents a network of seven villages, labelled A-G, and the distances between them in km.
Using Prim's algorithm on this matrix, and starting with vertex C, find the weight of the minimum spanning tree required to join the seven villages. List the arcs in the order in which they are chosen and draw the minimum spanning tree.

	A	B	C	D	E	F	G
A	–	3.1	4.4	2.9	3.3	2.7	1.9
B	3.1	–	4.1	3.5	2.7	–	3.7
C	4.4	4.1	–	–	4.4	4.3	4.2
D	2.9	3.5	–	–	2.8	1.9	3.2
E	3.3	2.7	4.4	2.8	–	4.5	2.6
F	2.7	–	4.3	1.9	4.5	–	1.1
G	1.9	3.7	4.2	3.2	2.6	1.1	–

Q3 A college wants to install a number of photocopiers (A-E) which must be networked and linked to the main college computer system (F). The distances, in metres, between the locations are given in the matrix on the right.

	A	B	C	D	E	F
A	–	250	175	210	330	195
B	250	–	185	135	260	270
C	175	185	–	155	230	410
D	210	135	155	–	280	340
E	330	260	230	280	–	300
F	195	270	410	340	300	–

If cabling costs £3 per metre, find the minimum cost of connecting the photocopiers to the network.

Use Prim's algorithm on the matrix, starting at vertex F.

Q4 A cable TV company wishes to join the villages of Worsthorne (W), Cliviger (C), Furstwood (F), Roggerham (R) and Haggate (H) to its network.
The matrix on the right shows the distances in miles between the villages.

	W	C	F	R	H
W	–	2.4	1.3	1.2	3.1
C	2.4	–	2.6	3.9	6.1
F	1.3	2.6	–	2.5	4.3
R	1.2	3.9	2.5	–	1.9
H	3.1	6.1	4.3	1.9	–

Find the minimum length of cabling required to complete the job, using Prim's algorithm and starting at Worsthorne.

Q5 A new reservoir, R, is to be built to supply the water to five towns T1–T5. The matrix shows the distances in miles between the reservoir and the five towns.

Find the minimum length of piping needed to join all five towns to a network of pipes connected to the reservoir and draw your minimum spanning tree.
Use Prim's algorithm, starting at R.

	R	T1	T2	T3	T4	T5
R	–	13	22	15	24	9
T1	13	–	16	18	16	11
T2	22	16	–	31	26	14
T3	15	18	31	–	19	17
T4	24	16	26	19	–	20
T5	9	11	14	17	20	–

3. Dijkstra's Algorithm

Dijkstra's algorithm is a bit different to Kruskal's and Prim's — it's used for finding shortest paths between vertices instead of minimum spanning trees.

Learning Objectives:

- Be able to use Dijkstra's algorithm to find the shortest path between two vertices.

Dijkstra's algorithm

Dijkstra's algorithm is a foolproof way to find the **shortest path** between **any two vertices** in a graph. In other words, Dijkstra's is the algorithm you need when you want to find the shortest (or quickest, or cheapest) way to join **two specific points**.

- For example, if you're driving between **two cities** with a complicated **road network** between them, it's useful to know which route is **quickest**. Many satnav systems use a version of Dijkstra's algorithm to do this.

- Basically, the algorithm **labels** each vertex with the length of the **shortest path** found so far from the starting point. The labels are **updated** if you find a shorter path, until you're sure that you've got the shortest distance to that vertex. The algorithm works through the vertices in this way until the **end vertex** is reached.

Tip: Don't confuse this with finding the shortest route that visits **all** the vertices — this is covered in Chapter 4.

1. Give the **start vertex** the **final value '0'**.

2. Find all the vertices **directly connected** to the vertex you've just given a final value. Calculate a **working value** for each of these vertices using the formula:

$$\text{working value} = \frac{\text{final value at}}{\text{previous vertex}} + \frac{\text{weight of arc}}{\text{between previous}} \atop \text{vertex and this one}$$

If one of these vertices already has a working value, replace it **only** if the new working value is **lower**.

3. **Compare** the working values of all the vertices that **don't** have a final value yet. Pick the **smallest working value** and make this the **final value** of that vertex. (If two vertices have the same smallest working value, pick either.)

4. Repeat steps 2 and 3 until the **end vertex** has a final value (this is the length of the shortest path).

5. Trace the route **backwards** from the end vertex to the start vertex to find the shortest path. An arc is only included in the path if:

$$\frac{\text{weight}}{\text{of arc}} = \frac{\text{difference in final}}{\text{values of its vertices}}$$

Tip: Once you've given a vertex a **final value**, you can't change it.

Tip: Sometimes there's more than one shortest route. If there is, you'll find two possible arcs leading off from a vertex when you're tracing the route back. Read the question carefully — they might want both of the shortest routes.

In **questions** on Dijkstra's algorithm you'll usually be given a graph to do your working on.

At each vertex you write down the **working value**, then put a **box around it** when it becomes a **final value**.

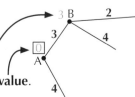

This will probably sound quite confusing at first.
Following through an **example** should help make things clearer.

Example

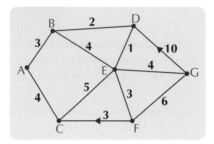

Use Dijkstra's algorithm to find the shortest route between A and G.

Tip: The working values are shown in green in this example.

- First label the **start vertex** with the **final value '0'**.

- **B** and **C** connect to A, so give them **working values**.

- E.g. at C:
    (previous final value) + (connecting arc weight) = 0 + 4 = 4

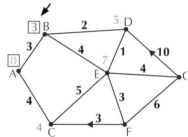

- Make the **smallest working value** a final value.

- 3 is the **lowest working value**, so make that a **final value**.

- Now give the vertices connecting to B (i.e. **D** and **E**) working values.

- E.g. at D:
    (previous final value)
        + (connecting arc weight)
            = 3 + 2 = 5

- Again, make the **smallest working value** a final value.

- 4 is the **lowest working value**, so make that a **final value**.

Tip: Watch out for sneaky directed edges — there's another one from G to D.

- Then give working values to any vertices without final values connecting to C. In this case that's only **E** — F is connected to C by a **directed edge** that only goes **from** F **to** C, not from C to F.

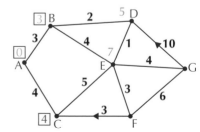

- 4 + 5 = 9, but this is greater than the current working value for E, so **don't** replace it.

- You're probably getting the idea now.
  Make the smallest working value a **final value** — in this case it's **5**.

- Give a working value to all
  vertices connecting to D
  without final values.
  Again, it's only E.
  (G is connected by a
  directed edge running in
  the opposite direction.)

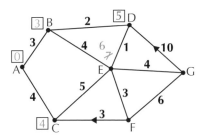

Tip: Just cross out the
old working value when
you find a better one.
Don't rub it out — leave
it there to show the
examiner that you've
used the correct method.

- The working value coming
  from D to E is 5 + 1 = 6.
  This is **smaller** than the current working value for E, so **replace it**.

- **E has the smallest working value** (6),
  (in fact, the only working value).
  Make that its **final value**.

- Give the vertices
  connecting to E
  (F and G) working values.

- So at F, 6 + 3 = 9
  and at G, 6 + 4 = 10

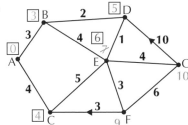

- **F has the smallest working value**
  of 9, so make that its final value.

- 9 + 6 = 15 is **greater** than G's
  current working value, so leave
  it as 10.

- G is the only vertex left. Make
  its working value the **final value**.

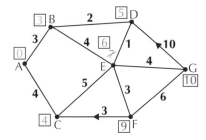

- You've now got a final value at the **end vertex**
  — this is the length of the **shortest route**.

- Now it's time to figure out the **route**. An arc's on the path if:

> Weight of arc = Difference in final values of arc's vertices

Working backwards from G (the **end vertex**):

- The arc **EG** is on the path,
  because the **difference**
  in the final values of E
  and G is **4**, which is the
  length of the arc **EG**.

- The arc **DE** is on the
  path, because the
  difference in the final
  values of D and E is **1**,
  which is the length of **DE**.

Tip: Remember, the
final value of the end
vertex is the length of
the shortest route.
You can use this to
check your route
is correct — in
this example, the
total weight of the
path A B D E G is
3 + 2 + 1 + 4 = 10,
which is the final value
of vertex G.

- And so on, all the way back to **A**.

So the **shortest route** from A to G is **A B D E G**.

Q1 a) For the network on the right, apply
        Dijkstra's algorithm to find the length
        of the shortest route from A to G.

    b) By working backwards through the
        network, identify the shortest route.

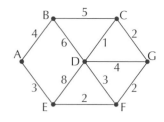

Q2 The network below represents a network of towns and possible
    routes between them. The numbers represent the times,
    in minutes, to travel between the towns.

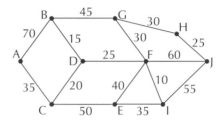

Apply Dijkstra's algorithm
to find the quickest route
from town A to town J.

State the time it would
take to travel this route.

Q3 The diagram below represents nine locations in a village, and the
    numbers represent the time, in minutes, needed to cycle between the
    locations. A newspaper delivery boy collects his newspapers from
    the shop at P at 6.30 am, and needs to deliver to house T first.

Q3 Hint: Don't forget
about the last part of this
question. Always read
the whole question —
you've not necessarily
finished once you've
found the shortest route.

By applying Dijsktra's algorithm,
find the optimal route that the
newspaper boy should take.

State whether the owner of house
T will get his newspaper before he
leaves for work at 6.40 am.

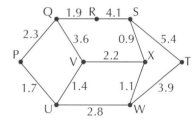

Q4 The city of Rochley is shown in the diagram below.
    Key locations in the city are indicated as follows:

    A = Airport   TH = Town Hall   S = Statue of Edsger Dijkstra
    P = Park   H = Hotel   SP = Swimming Pool
    CH = Church   GC = Golf Course   B = Bus Station

    The numbers indicate the times, in minutes,
    to walk between the various locations.

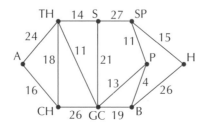

A pilot lands at the airport and
decides to walk to the hotel.

Apply Dijkstra's algorithm to
advise the pilot on the quickest
route to walk, and state how
long the journey will take.

Q5 The network below represents two storage depots (D1 and D2), a warehouse (W), and a number of other buildings (A – I), all located on an industrial estate. The distances between the buildings are given in metres.

A fork-lift truck is urgently required at the warehouse. It can be borrowed from either D1 or D2.

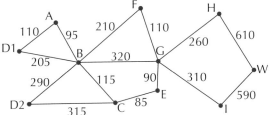

Q5 Hint: It looks like you have to run the algorithm twice here, starting from each depot. But if you start at the warehouse and work backwards, you only need to do it once to see which depot is nearest.

Apply Dijkstra's algorithm to find out which depot is nearest to the warehouse. State the optimal route that the fork-lift truck should take from your chosen depot to the warehouse.

Q6 The diagram on the right represents a network of university buildings within a city centre and the time taken to walk between them, in minutes.

David plans to walk from his Hall of Residence (A) to the Lecture Hall (J).

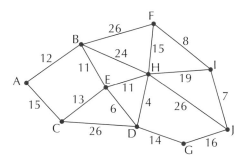

What is the latest time he could leave his Hall of Residence in order to arrive on time for a 9 am lecture?
State the optimal route he should take.

Q7 The network diagram on the right shows a number of bus routes around a city. The values are the costs of travelling by bus in pence. Ammar lives at location A and wishes to travel to the shopping centre, located at I.

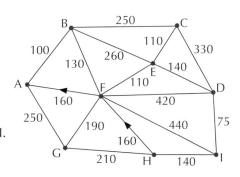

a) Using Dijkstra's algorithm, find the cheapest bus route Ammar could take, and state the total cost of his journey.

b) The bus company introduces a direct bus from A to C for £2. How, if at all, would this change your answer to part a)?

Q7 b) Hint: You don't need to run the whole algorithm again — just work out the new routes.

Q8 For the network diagram on the right, find the shortest possible route from B to G.

Show your working clearly and state the optimal length of route.

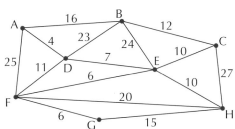

Q8 Hint: Remember to read the question carefully — don't assume you'll always be asked for a route from A to H.

Q9 During some roadworks in the town of Kentley (K), a large piece of equipment is needed. This piece of equipment is stored in Bington (B). The distances (in km) between the towns in the area are shown on the diagram below.

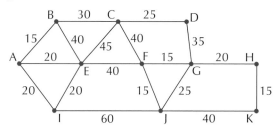

If the machinery can be transported at a maximum speed of 20 km/h, what is the shortest time needed to get the piece of equipment from Bington to Kentley?

Q10 The network diagram below shows a number of cities (D–M) and the cost, in £, of flying between the cities.

Ambreen plans to travel from her home at E, for a city break in city L.

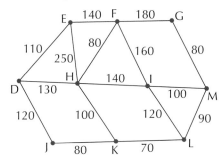

Using Dijkstra's algorithm, plan the most cost-effective route Ambreen could take, and state the total cost.

What other factors might Ambreen wish to take into account when planning her journey?

Q11 The network below represents a system of underground rail routes, and the time (in mins) to travel between the stations A-O.

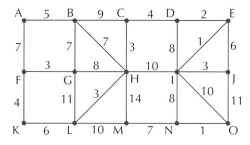

What is the minimal possible journey time from A to O, and which route should you take to make it in this time?

What assumptions have been made in your answer?

Review Exercise — Chapter 2

Q1 Explain what the following are: a) network b) digraph c) tree d) spanning tree

Q2

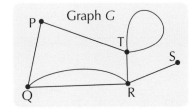

Graph G is shown on the left.

a) Draw a spanning tree of Graph G.

b) Which vertex would you have to remove to make G a Hamiltonian graph?

c) Which edges would you have to remove to make G a simple graph?

Q3 Padmaja is a town planner. She has prepared a scheme for a town centre road system that's entirely one-way. The one-way system connects five points, A, B, C, D and E. Padmaja's scheme has direct one-way streets from A to B, D to A, B to D, C to B, D to C, and E to A.

a) Draw a digraph to represent Padmaja's scheme.

b) How would you get from C to A?

c) Suggest a flaw in Padmaja's plan.

Q4 Doris and Harry are friends, Beryl and Harry are friends, Beryl and Melvyn are friends, Norman and Harry are friends, and Norman and Melvyn are friends.

a) Draw a bipartite graph to represent this information.

b) Which of the five friends is most popular within the group?

Q4 Hint: You'll need to draw each link twice here.

Q5 Graph G is shown on the right.

a) Draw two subgraphs of G.

b) How many arcs do you need to add to G to make it into a complete graph?

c) Describe a possible path in G.

d) Describe a possible cycle in G.

e) Graph G is currently connected. Delete some edges so that it isn't connected any more.

f) List the degree of each vertex of G.
    Explain the link between the number of edges and the sum of the degrees.

Q6

	P	Q	R	S	T	U
P	0	1	0	1	0	0
Q	1	0	1	0	0	1
R	0	1	0	1	2	0
S	1	0	1	2	0	0
T	0	0	2	0	2	0
U	0	1	0	0	0	0

This is the adjacency matrix for a graph. Without drawing the graph, find:

a) a path from P to T

b) a cycle starting from Q

c) the degree of vertex R

d) the number of edges in the graph

Q7 The arcs in the network shown on the right represent possible ways to lay pipes in a planned sewerage system. The numbers on each arc represent the cost, in hundreds of pounds, for laying the pipe. The vertices represent houses which must be connected to the sewerage system.

Using Kruskal's algorithm, plan the most cost-effective way to join all the houses to the sewerage system. State the cost of connecting the pipes in the way you have planned.

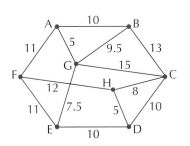

Q8 a) Describe the differences between Prim's algorithm and Kruskal's algorithm for finding the minimum connector of a network.

b) For the network shown on the right, apply Prim's algorithm to find a minimum connector, starting at:

(i) vertex A   (ii) vertex D

What do you notice about your answers?

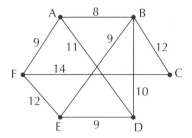

Q9 The distance matrix on the right represents a graph with six vertices. Starting at vertex S, apply Prim's algorithm to the matrix to find a minimum spanning tree of the graph.

Draw your minimum spanning tree, listing the arcs in the order in which they were added, and state its total weight.

	P	Q	R	S	T	U
P	–	12	–	15	9	–
Q	12	–	–	10	–	17
R	–	–	–	14	11	8
S	15	10	14	–	–	12
T	9	–	11	–	–	–
U	–	17	8	12	–	–

Q10 A rail network is being planned for a city and the surrounding area. Initially, seven stations are planned. The distances, in km, between the seven sites are given in the matrix on the right.

Apply Prim's algorithm, starting at X, to find the most efficient way to join the seven sites, and draw the minimum spanning tree.

	T	U	V	W	X	Y	Z
T	–	4.4	–	8.9	7.9	10.5	18.0
U	4.4	–	17.4	9.6	–	13.6	–
V	–	17.4	–	15.4	12.6	19.3	22.4
W	8.9	9.6	15.4	–	–	16.6	23.1
X	7.9	–	12.6	–	–	14.4	18.3
Y	10.5	13.6	19.3	16.6	14.4	–	3.9
Z	18.0	–	22.4	23.1	18.3	3.9	–

Q11 Using Dijkstra's algorithm on the graph on the right:

a) Find the shortest route from A to G.

b) Delete edge DE.

Now find the shortest route from A to G.

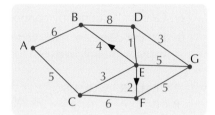

Q12 The network below indicates possible routes for laying electrical cable between locations S–Z in a furniture factory. The distances are given in metres.

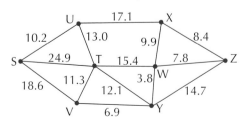

The manager of the factory needs to run a cable from S to Z.

State the optimal route for the cable and the minimum length of cabling required.

If cabling costs £2.50 per metre, state the cost of the cabling needed.

1   **Figure 1** shows the potential connections for a sprinkler system between greenhouses at a plant nursery. The numbers on each arc represent the cost in pounds of each connection.

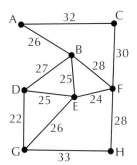

Figure 1

a)   Use Kruskal's algorithm to find a minimum spanning tree for the network in **Figure 1**. List the edges in the order that you consider them and state whether you are adding them to your minimum spanning tree.

(3 marks)

b)   State the minimum cost of connecting the sprinkler system.

(1 mark)

c)   Draw the minimum spanning tree obtained in a).

(2 marks)

d)   If Prim's algorithm had been used to find the minimum spanning tree, starting from E, find which edge would have been the final edge added. Show your working.

(2 marks)

e)   State two advantages of Prim's algorithm over Kruskal's algorithm for finding a minimum spanning tree.

(2 marks)

2   The table shows the lengths, in miles, of the roads between five towns.

a)   Use Prim's algorithm, starting from A, to find a minimum spanning tree for this table. Write down the arcs in the order that they are selected.

(3 marks)

b)   Draw your tree and state its total weight.

(2 marks)

c)   State the number of other spanning trees that are the same length as your answer in part (b).

(1 mark)

	A	B	C	D	E
A	–	14	22	21	18
B	14	–	19	21	20
C	22	19	–	21	15
D	21	21	21	–	24
E	18	20	15	24	–

3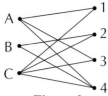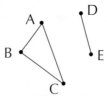

Figure 2   **Figure 3**

a) Name the type of graph drawn in **Figure 2**.

(1 mark)

b) State the number of edges that would need to be added to **Figure 2** to make the graph complete.

(1 mark)

c) State the number of edges that would need to be added to **Figure 3** to make the graph connected.

(1 mark)

d) What is the sum of the orders of the vertices in **Figure 3**?

(1 mark)

e) Explain why it is impossible to add edges to **Figure 3** so that all vertices have an odd order.

(2 marks)

4 The diagram below shows a network of forest paths. The number on each edge represents the time, in minutes, required to walk along the path.

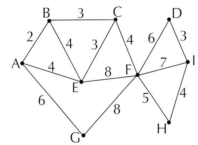

a) Write down the number of edges in a minimum spanning tree of the network shown.

(1 mark)

b) Use Dijkstra's algorithm to find the fastest route from A to I. State how long the route will take.

(6 marks)

c) A new path, taking x minutes to walk along, is to be made between G and H. The new path reduces the time required to walk between A and I. Find and solve an inequality for x.

(2 marks)

5 a) The graph G is complete and has n vertices. Find an expression for the number of edges of G in terms of n.

(1 mark)

b) The graph H is Hamiltonian and has m vertices. State the number of edges in a Hamiltonian cycle for H in terms of m.

(1 mark)

c) The graph J is connected and has p vertices. State the number of edges in a minimum spanning tree of J in terms of p.

(1 mark)

1. Eulerian Graphs

Route inspection problems are where you have to find the shortest possible route that travels along every edge of a network at least once — e.g. a postman's delivery route or a park ranger's patrol.

Eulerian and semi-Eulerian graphs

To find the **shortest route** through a network, first you decide if you'll have to **repeat** any **edges**. To do this, you need to work out if a graph is **traversable**:

> If a graph is traversable, it's possible to start at **any point** and draw along each edge **exactly once** (without taking your pen off the paper).

All the graphs in this section will be one of three things — **Eulerian**, **semi-Eulerian** or **neither**. Which of the three they are will tell you to what level the graphs are **traversable**. The graphs will also be **connected** — remember from page 31 that in a connected graph, there's a **path** between each pair of vertices.

To find if a graph is Eulerian, semi-Eulerian or neither, you look at the **degree** of each **vertex**. The degree of a vertex is the number of edges coming out of it (see page 34).

> If **all** the vertices in a graph have an **even** degree, the graph is **Eulerian**
>
> - The three graphs below are all **Eulerian**. Every vertex is **even**.
>
>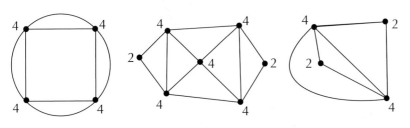
>
> - For a connected **Eulerian graph**, it's possible to find a route that goes along each edge **exactly once** and finishes back at the **starting point**, no matter which point you start at.
>
> - Or to look at it another way, if the graph represents **roads**, it's possible to walk down each of them **exactly once** before getting back to your **starting point**.
>
> - You find the routes by **inspection** (just by looking at the graph) and they all have the **same length** — the total weight of the network.

Learning Objectives:

- Be able to identify whether a graph is Eulerian, semi-Eulerian or neither.
- Find routes that traverse connected Eulerian or semi-Eulerian graphs.

Tip: A route that goes along every edge exactly once and ends up back at the starting point is called an **Eulerian cycle**. For an Eulerian graph with n edges, there will be n edges in the Eulerian cycle.

Tip: You find the total weight of the network by adding up the weights of each edge.

Example

Find a route for the graph below that traverses each arc exactly once.

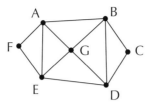

- All the vertices are even, so the graph is **Eulerian** — this means you can start at **any point**.
- A possible route is: A G D B C D E G B A F E A
- Another route is: E D C B D G A F E A B G E

Tip: No matter which route you take, it'll always involve passing through the same number of vertices (13 in this case).

If **exactly two vertices** have an **odd degree**, (and the rest are even), the graph is **semi-Eulerian.**

- The graphs below are all **semi-Eulerian**. There are **exactly two** odd vertices.

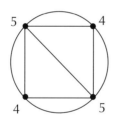 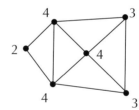 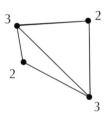

- For a connected **semi-Eulerian** graph, it's possible to find a route that goes along every edge on the graph **exactly once**, but only if you start at one odd vertex and end up at the **other** odd vertex.

Tip: A route that goes along every edge exactly once but doesn't end up at the starting point is called an **Eulerian trail**. For a semi-Eulerian graph with *n* edges, there will be *n* edges in the Eulerian trail.

Example

Find a route for the graph below that traverses each arc exactly once.

- The degrees of the vertices are: A = 5, B = 4, C = 4 and D = 5.

- Two vertices are odd and the rest are even, so this graph is semi-Eulerian — this means you have to start and end at the odd vertices (A and D).

- A possible route is A B D C A around the square, then A B D C A around the circle, then across the diagonal to D, i.e. A B D C A B D C A D

Tip: There's no way you could start and finish at A without repeating some edges, no matter which path you take.

- The graphs below are **neither** Eulerian nor semi-Eulerian.

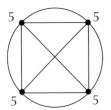 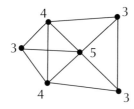 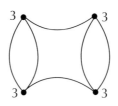

- If a graph is **neither** Eulerian nor semi-Eulerian, you **can't traverse it**.

- There's **no route** that travels along each edge exactly once. You'd have to go along some of them **twice**.

Tip: A graph can't have an odd number of odd vertices because the sum of the degrees is always even (see page 34) — if there were an odd number of odd vertices, the sum would be odd. This means you'd never end up with only 1 odd vertex.

The bridges of Königsberg is a famous example. The city of Königsberg was set on both sides of a river, with two islands in the middle. **Seven bridges** connected the **four different parts** of the city.

- The problem was to find a **route** that crossed **each bridge exactly once** and ended up back at the **starting point**. As only the **connections** between the different parts of the city were important, the problem could be **simplified** using a graph.

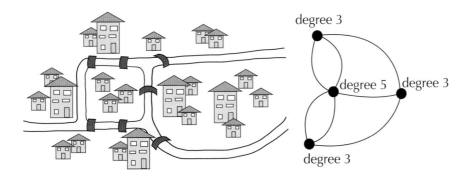

- The **vertices** represent the **land masses** (one for each side of the river and one for each island) and the **edges** represent the **bridge connections**.

- The Swiss mathematician Euler showed that there was **no solution** to the problem — there was **no way** to walk through the city and cross each bridge **once** and only once. There are **more than two** odd vertices, so the city is **not traversable**.

Tip: That's where the name Eulerian comes from.

Q1 For each of the following, say whether the graph is Eulerian, semi-Eulerian or neither. For the Eulerian graphs, state how many edges there would be in the Eulerian cycle, and for semi-Eulerian graphs state how many edges there would be in the Eulerian trail.

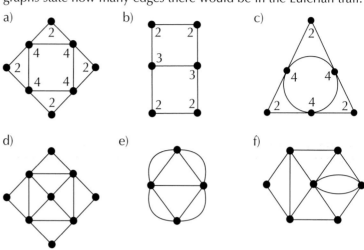

d)   e)   f)

Q2 The graph below is Eulerian. Find a route that traverses it, starting at vertex A.

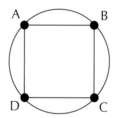

Q3 The graph below is semi-Eulerian. Find a route that traverses it, starting at vertex A and ending at vertex C.

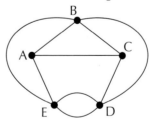

Q4 The graph below is Eulerian. Find a route that traverses it, starting at vertex A.

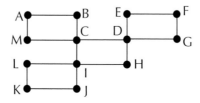

2. Route Inspection Problems

The route inspection problem is also called the Chinese postman problem because it was first discussed by a Chinese mathematician in the 1960s. His name was Kwan Mei Kwo, and he wasn't actually a postman.

Finding the shortest route

Route inspection problems ask you to find the **shortest route** through a connected network that goes along **each edge at least once** before returning to the **starting point**.

- It's the route that, say, a **railway engineer** would take if he had to **inspect** all the tracks in the most **efficient** way possible.

- In **Chinese postman** terms, the postman wants to find the **shortest route** that allows him to deliver letters to **every street** in a city, and brings him back to his **starting point** for a cup of tea.

- As you might expect, there are **algorithms** for finding the quickest route for each **type** of graph you might come across.

It's **not always possible** to find an inspection route without **repeating** some edges — in these cases, you'll need to choose **which** edges to repeat to make the route as short as possible. The first step is to consider whether the graph is **Eulerian**, **semi-Eulerian**, or **neither** (see pages 61-63).

Eulerian graphs

- In a connected **Eulerian graph**, you can travel along each edge **exactly once** and end up back at your **starting point**, no matter which point you start from.

- Because you've gone down **each** edge **once**, you find the length of the route by just **adding up** all the **edge weights**.

> **Length of inspection route in an Eulerian graph = weight of the network**

Learning Objectives:
- Be able to find an inspection route for a connected Eulerian network and calculate its weight.
- Be able to find an inspection route for a connected semi-Eulerian network and calculate its weight.
- Be able to work out the number of possible pairings for a non-Eulerian network with n odd vertices.
- Be able to find an inspection route for a non-Eulerian network and calculate its weight.
- Be able to find an inspection route with different start and end vertices for a non-Eulerian network.

Tip: Have a look back at page 61 if you need a reminder about Eulerian graphs.

Example

Find an inspection route for the network below.
Your route must start and finish at A. State the length of the route.

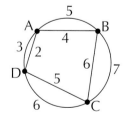

- The graph is Eulerian — the vertices all have even degrees (they're all 4).
  A possible inspection route is: A B C D A B C D A
  (once round the quadrilateral, then once around the circle).

- Length of the route = sum of weights
$$= 4 + 6 + 5 + 2 + 5 + 7 + 6 + 3$$
$$= 38$$

Q1   a) Find an inspection route starting at vertex C for the graph below and state its length.

b) Find an alternative inspection route starting at C and show that the two routes have the same length.

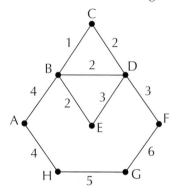

Q2   Find an inspection route starting at E for the Eulerian network below. State the length of the route.

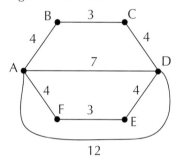

Q3   The paths in a park are represented by the network below. Each path needs to be checked for cracks. Find an inspection route and state its length (the numbers represent distance in hundreds of metres).

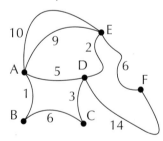

Q4   The network below represents the corridors in the school science block, which Kevin the caretaker has to patrol to make sure that no poisonous snails have escaped from their enclosures. Find an inspection route he can use, and state its length.

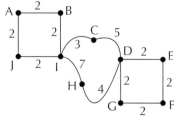

The numbers represent distance in tens of metres.

Semi-Eulerian graphs

For an inspection route in a semi-Eulerian network, you have to repeat the **shortest path** between the two **odd vertices**. You can think of it as **adding arcs** to the network so that all the vertices are **even**.

Length of inspection route in a semi-Eulerian graph	=	Weight of network	+	Weight of the shortest path between the two odd vertices

Examples

a) **Find an inspection route for the network on the right. Your route must start and finish at B. State the length of the route.**

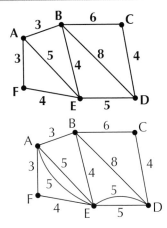

- The vertices have orders A = 3, B = 4, C = 2, D = 3, E = 4 and F = 2.

- So the graph is semi-Eulerian — the odd vertices are A and D.

- The shortest path between them is **AED**, of length 10 (5 + 5), so extra edges **AE** and **ED** are added (shown in pinky purple).

- A possible route is BCDEFAB<u>DEA</u>EB.

- The weight of the network = 3 + 6 + 4 + 5 + 4 + 3 + 5 + 4 + 8 = 42

- Length of inspection route = Weight of network + weight of shortest path between odd vertices

  = 42 + 10 = 52

Tip: There's no set method for finding the shortest path — you just do it by inspection. That means considering each option and working out which is the shortest.

Tip: The added paths have been underlined here to show when they've been used.

b) **Find an inspection route for the network on the right. Your route must start and finish at A. State the length of the route.**

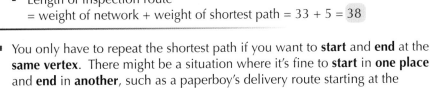

- The orders here are A = 2, B = 5, C = 2, D = 4, E = 3, F = 4, G = 4.

- Again, you have a semi-Eulerian graph, so you need to add a path between the two odd vertices (B and E).

- By inspection, the shortest path between them is BCDE, which has a length of 2 + 1 + 2 = 5.

- A possible route is ABCD<u>EDC</u>BDGEFGBFA.

- Length of inspection route = weight of network + weight of shortest path = 33 + 5 = 38

Tip: By effectively making the graph Eulerian, you can start from any vertex if you want to.

- You only have to repeat the shortest path if you want to **start** and **end** at the **same vertex**. There might be a situation where it's fine to **start** in **one place** and **end** in **another**, such as a paperboy's delivery route starting at the newsagents and ending at his house.

- You can only do this if you start at one **odd vertex** and end at the other. In this case, you don't repeat any paths, so the length of the route will just be equal to the **network weight**.

Q1 a) Find the shortest route between the two
    odd vertices in the semi-Eulerian
    network to the right.

    b) Find an inspection route for the
    network starting at A.

    c) Find the length of the route.

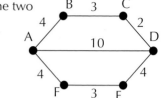

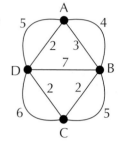

Q2 a) Find the shortest route between the two
    odd vertices in the semi-Eulerian
    network to the right.

    b) Find an inspection route for the
    network starting at B.

    c) Find the length of the route.

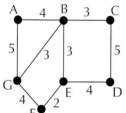

Q3 a) What are the two odd vertices in this graph?

    b) There are two possible shortest paths
    between these vertices. What are these
    and what is their weight?

    c) Find an inspection route for the graph,
    starting and finishing at vertex E.

    d) What is the total weight of this route?

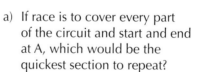

Q4 The network shows the relative amount of time
    each section of a racecourse takes.

    a) If race is to cover every part
    of the circuit and start and end
    at A, which would be the
    quickest section to repeat?

    b) The organisers want a complete
    circuit to last at least 1 hour.
    What would be the minimum value of t?

    c) Suggest a route starting and ending at A.

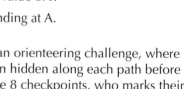

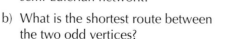

Q5 Some children are taking part in an orienteering challenge, where
    they must collect a flag that's been hidden along each path before
    reporting to a teacher at any of the 8 checkpoints, who marks their
    finishing time. Distances are in hundreds of metres.

    a) Which are the two odd vertices in this
    semi-Eulerian network?

    b) What is the shortest route between
    the two odd vertices?

    c) Find an optimal route around the network,
    starting at A and ending at any point.

    d) What is the length of your route?

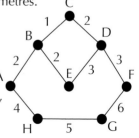

Q5 c) Hint: Be careful
here — this isn't a
typical question, as
you're not starting at an
odd vertex.

Other graphs

Finding inspection routes for graphs with **more than two** odd vertices
is a little trickier than for the Eulerian and semi-Eulerian networks
you saw in the previous sections.

However, in D1 you'll only have to **solve** problems with a **maximum** of
4 odd vertices. You'll need to know how to **deal with** networks with more
than 4 odd vertices (see page 70), but you won't actually have to solve these
problems. Remember that networks **never** have an odd number of odd
vertices (page 63).

For a network with 4 odd vertices:

> 1. Identify all of the **odd vertices** in the graph (say A, B, C and D).
>
> 2. Write down **all** the possible **pairs** you can make from the odd
>   vertices — there will only ever be **3 possible pairings**:
>   [AB and CD],   [AC and BD],   [AD and BC].
>
> 3. For each of the three combinations, find the **shortest path**
>   between **each pair** then **add** the two distances together.
>
> 4. Use the set of pairs that gives the **smallest combined** weight as
>   your **repeated paths**.

Tip: The order of the
pairs doesn't matter —
AC and BD is the same
as DB and CA.

This will make more sense with an example:

Example

**Find an inspection route for the network below. Your route must start
and finish at E. State the length of the route.**

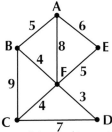

- First, find the **degrees** of the vertices: A = 3, B = 3, C = 3,
  D = 2, E = 2, F = 5.

- Then pick out the vertices with **odd degrees**.
  In this case, the vertices are A, B, C and F.

- Then **pair off** the vertices with **odd degrees** in **all** the possible ways:

  > AB and CF
  > AC and BF
  > AF and BC

- Once you've found all the pairings, work out the **minimum total
  distance** between each set of pairs:

  > AB + CF = 5 + 4 = 9
  > AC + BF = 12 + 4 = 16
  > AF + BC = 8 + 8 = 16

Tip: There are lots of
different paths from
A to C. By inspection,
AFC is the shortest (12).

- Now choose the **set** of pairs with the **smallest total distance**. Here it's AB and CF, with a total of 9. These are the two paths that will be **repeated** in the inspection route:

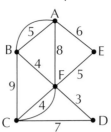

- The graph is now **Eulerian** so you can find an inspection route through it. A possible route is E A B C F A̲B̲ F D C̲F̲ E.

- To find the **length** of the route, add the **weight** of the network to the distance of the **added paths**.

$$\text{Length} = [5 + 8 + 6 + 5 + 4 + 9 + 4 + 3 + 7] + 9 = \boxed{60}$$

- Although you'll never be given route inspection problems with more than 4 odd vertices, you do need to know how many **possible sets of pairings** of vertices there would be for **any number** of odd vertices — say **n**.

- If you had **two** odd vertices (i.e. a semi-Eulerian graph), there's only **1** possible set of pairings. You saw on page 69 that for **four** odd vertices, there are **3** possible sets of pairings. For a problem with **six** odd vertices, there'd be **15** possible sets of pairings, and so on.

- There's a **formula** you can use to work out the number of sets of pairings:

> Number of sets of pairings for n odd vertices = $1 \times 3 \times 5 \times ... \times (n - 1)$

(basically, it's the **product** of all the **odd numbers** up to $n - 1$).

- You soon end up with **hundreds** of different sets of pairings to consider (for $n = 8$, there are 105 possible sets of pairings) — which is why you **won't** have to **solve** problems with this many odd vertices in the exam.

Tip: n has to be even — see p.63.

Tip: For 6 odd vertices (A, B, C, D, E and F), the pairings are:
AB, CD and EF,
AB, CE and DF,
AB, CF and DE,
AC, BD and EF,
AC, BE and DF,
AC, BF and DE,
and similar for AD, AE and AF — 15 in total.

Starting and finishing at different vertices

- In a network with 4 odd vertices you can **reduce** the distance of an inspection route if you're **not** restricted to starting and finishing at the **same vertex**.

- In this case, the shortest inspection route will **start** and end at **two** of the odd vertices, and will **repeat** the **shortest path** between the **other two** odd vertices.

To find the shortest inspection route with **different start and end points**:

Tip: If you're told a specific start or end point, just go through these steps but leave out any pairs that include the point(s) you need to start or end from. For example, if you need to start at A and end anywhere, just find the shortest paths between BC, BD, and CD.

1. Write down **each pair** of **odd** vertices. With 4 odd vertices you'll get 6 pairs — if your vertices are A, B, C, D, then the pairs would be AB, AC, AD, BC, BD and CD.

2. Find the **shortest distance** between each pair by **inspection**.

3. The pair with the **smallest value** is the path to **repeat** in your route inspection (starting and ending at either of the two **other** points). If the shortest path is AD, then your inspection route should start at B and end at C, or vice versa (and repeat AD).

Examples

A feather duster salesman wants to travel along each
street in a housing estate. He can start his journey
at any point, and end it at any point.
The graph represents the streets in the estate,
and the numbers represent the lengths of each street
in hundreds of metres.

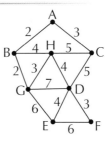

a) **Find the vertices that the salesman
could start at to minimise his journey.**

- There are four odd vertices, so you're going to **start and end** at **two
  of them**. You have to **repeat the path** between the other two odd
  vertices, so make sure it's the **shortest possible**.

- The odd vertices are B, C, D, E.
  The distance between each possible pair is:
  BC = 5, DE = 4, BD = 8, CE = 9, BE = 8, CD = 5

- The distance between **D and E** is shortest, at only 4, so that's
  the path you need to repeat — you start at **either** of vertices
  B or C, and end at the **other**.

b) **Find the length of his journey.**

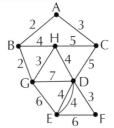

- To find the length of the journey, just add up
  the path lengths, remembering to include
  the one you've added (DE, 4 units long):

  $$[2 + 3 + 4 + 5 + 3 + 4 + 2 + 7 + 5 + 6 + 4 + 3 + 6] + 4 = \boxed{58}$$

- Remember to always **check the units** — the weights represent
  hundreds of metres, so the journey is actually 5800 metres long,
  or 5.8 km.

- Sometimes, the usual 'inspection route' or 'Chinese postman' problem is
  changed so that the person has to go down **each path twice**. Perhaps they'll
  be inspecting each **pavement**, or delivering leaflets to **both sides** of the streets.

- This actually makes it **easier** to solve. It effectively **doubles** the edges at each
  vertex, making all the vertices **even**. The network is now **Eulerian**, so you
  can **traverse** it, and the length of the inspection route will just be **double the
  weight** of the original network.

Example

The feather duster salesman decides to go down each street twice,
once on each side. What is the length of his new route?

- The original network weight is 54.

- As the salesman wants to go down each street twice, the network
  becomes Eulerian because the degree of each vertex is doubled.
  So the distance travelled must just be 54 × 2 = 108 units.

- The salesman therefore travels **10 800 metres** or **10.8 km**.

Tip: You know this from
the last example — the
weight was 58, so it's 54
without the added path.

Q1 a) Identify the odd vertices in the graph below.

b) Write down all the possible ways of pairing the odd vertices and work out the weight of each pairing.

c) Find an inspection route for the network, starting at vertex A, and state its length.

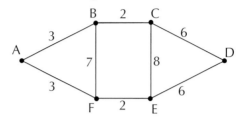

Q2 a) Identify the odd vertices in the graph below.

b) Write down all the possible ways of pairing the odd vertices and work out the weight of each pairing.

c) Find an inspection route for the network starting and ending at vertex G and state its length.

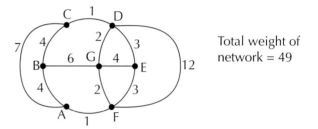

Total weight of network = 49

Q3 The number of market stalls in a town centre is shown in the network below. The weights represent the number of stalls on each street. A safety inspector wants to start at A and walk along each road, pass each stall at least once, and finish back at A, repeating the smallest possible number of stalls.

a) Why does she have to pass some stalls more than once?

b) Using the Chinese postman algorithm, find the minimum number of stalls she will have to pass more than once.

c) Give a possible route.

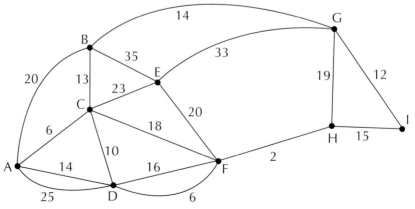

Q4 The network below shows the paths in a park. The numbers represent the length (in m) of each path. The total length of the paths shown is 2890 m. What is the length of the shortest route that the park keeper can take if he starts and ends at his hut (H) and walks along each path at least once?

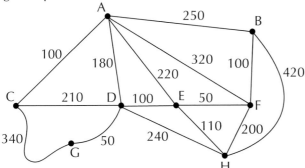

Q5 The diagram below shows the main roads in a town. The weights represent the length of each road in km, and the total weight of the network is 71. Peter has been asked to inspect these roads and so he needs to pass along each road at least once. He lives near K and wants to finish there, but he can start at any point. How long would the shortest possible inspection route be?

Q5 Hint: Remember, when you don't have to start and finish at the same vertex you only need to repeat one path, not two.

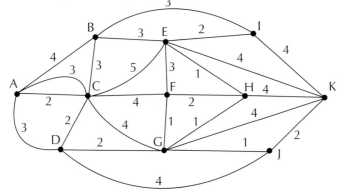

Q6 a) The network below represents the corridors in a building. The weights are the lengths of the corridors in metres. The total length is 765 m. In order to sweep the corridors the cleaner must go along each corridor at least once. If the cleaner can start and finish at different points, find an inspection route and calculate its length.

Q6 Hint: Remember, the shortest route will always be one that starts and ends at odd vertices.

b) The cleaner decides to go along each corridor twice, sweeping on the left the first time and on the right the second time. What would the length of a new inspection route be?

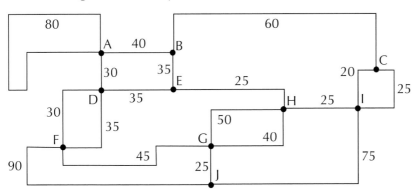

Review Exercise — Chapter 3

Q1 Say whether each of these graphs is Eulerian, semi-Eulerian or neither.

a)
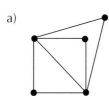

b)

c)
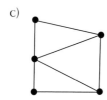

d)
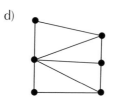

Q2 Identify the odd vertices in the graph below.
Write down all the possible ways of pairing the odd vertices.

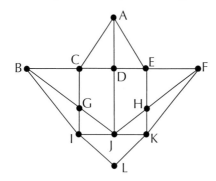

Q3 Find the length of the shortest "Chinese postman" route for each of these networks.
Start and end at vertex A.

a)
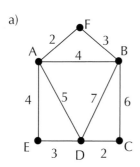

b)
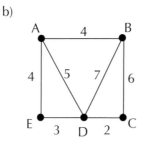

c)
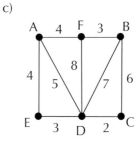

Q4 Repeat question 3. But this time you can start and finish at any vertices.
State which vertices you're starting and finishing at.

Q5 a) Find the shortest route between the two odd vertices in this semi-Eulerian network.

b) Find the length of an inspection route for this network, starting and ending at H. You don't need to find the route.

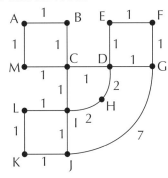

Total network weight = 25

Q6 a) Identify the odd vertices in the network below.

b) Write down all the possible ways of pairing the odd vertices and work out the weight of each pairing.

c) Find the length of an inspection route for the network starting and finishing at vertex A. You don't need to find the route.

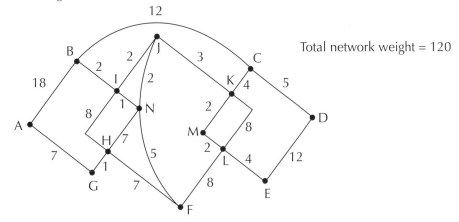

Total network weight = 120

Q7 The network below represents the paths in a funfair, where the entrance and exit are found at E.

a) Jonny wants to see the attractions on every path before leaving. Calculate the length of the shortest route he can take.

b) Suggest a possible inspection route starting and ending at E.

c) Jonny decides he wants to walk down each path twice to make sure he doesn't miss any attractions. What would be the distance of his new route?

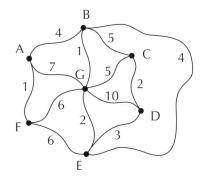

Numbers show distances in tens of metres.

Total weight = 560 m

1   A machinist is embroidering logos on sportsbags. The two logos are shown below.

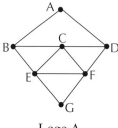

Logo A

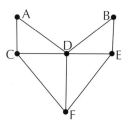

Logo B

(a)   Say whether each logo consists of an Eulerian graph,
       a semi-Eulerian graph or neither.

(2 marks)

(b)   The sewing machine needle is positioned at any starting point, and sews a route
       without stitching any line more than once. It can be lifted and moved to a
       new starting point.

   (i)   For each logo, how many times must the needle be lifted?

(2 marks)

   (ii)   For logo A, state an efficient starting vertex.

(1 mark)

(c)   Extra arcs are added to each logo to make them Eulerian.
       State the minimum number of arcs that must be added to each logo.

(2 marks)

2   The diagram on the right shows all the streets in a town,
    and their lengths in metres.

   Angus is considering moving to the town and
   wants to walk down each street at least once.
   He parks his car at K.

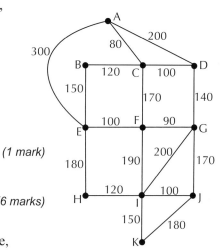

(a)   Explain why it is not possible to walk down each
       street only once and return to the starting point.   *(1 mark)*

(b)   Find the length of the shortest route Angus
       could follow, starting and finishing at K.   *(6 marks)*

(c)   Angus's friend offers to drop him off at any point,
       and after he's walked down each street at least once,
       to pick him up from any point.

   (i)   Find the length of the optimal route for Angus.   *(2 marks)*

   (ii)   State the vertices from which Angus could
           start in order to achieve this optimal route.

(1 mark)

Total length of all
the roads = 2740 m

3   The diagram below shows the paths in a park, and the time taken to walk them in minutes.

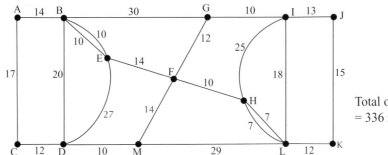

Total of all path times
= 336 minutes

Alice the park keeper needs to walk down each path to check for storm-damaged trees.
She parks her car at F.

(a)   Find the time for the quickest route Alice could follow,
      starting and finishing at F.

      (6 marks)

(b)   If Alice starts at point B, and can finish at any point:

      (i)   What point should she end at for the optimal route?
             Show your working.

             (2 marks)

      (ii)   How long will it take her to walk along all the paths now?

             (1 mark)

4   The diagram below shows the distances between towns in miles.
     The total road distance is 106 miles.

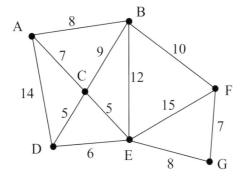

Jamie is inspecting the hedgerows along the roads.
He needs to go along each road, starting and finishing at A.

(a)   Find the length of the optimal 'Chinese postman' route for Jamie.

      (6 marks)

(b)   There are ice-cream shops at points C and E. If Jamie follows his optimal route,
      how many times will he pass an ice-cream shop?

      (2 marks)

(c)   Jamie decides it would be better if he went along each road twice.
      What is the length of his new optimal route?

      (2 marks)

1. Hamiltonian Cycles

In the last chapter, you saw how the Chinese postman problem requires you to cross every edge at least once. The travelling salesperson problem, on the other hand, wants you to visit each vertex at least once. A network that lets you do this without visiting vertices twice is called a Hamiltonian network.

Finding Hamiltonian cycles

- In a **travelling salesperson problem (TSP)**, you need to visit **every vertex** in a network and return to your starting point.

- A 'classical' TSP aims to find the **shortest route** that visits each vertex **exactly once** before returning directly to the **starting point** — such a route is a **Hamiltonian cycle** (see page 27) and so the classical TSP is to find the **shortest** Hamiltonian cycle for a given **Hamiltonian graph**.

- There isn't an algorithm guaranteed to find the **shortest** Hamiltonian cycle. And it's not always practical to test each one as the number of possible Hamiltonian cycles can **rise dramatically** as the number of vertices increases.

- Instead, you find a **lower and upper bound**, then a **reasonably good solution** between them. Luckily, there are **algorithms** for finding the lower and upper bound. These are covered later in this chapter.

Tip: All **complete graphs** (see p.30) are Hamiltonian — all the vertices are connected, so you can always find a Hamiltonian cycle.

Tip: 10 vertices means well over 100 000 Hamiltonian cycles for a complete graph — a lot for even a computer to consider.

Tip: There are loads of cycles you could choose here, and as you can see they're not always the same length. You just have to find one you're happy with by inspection.

Example

Find two Hamiltonian cycles through the network to the right, starting and finishing at A.

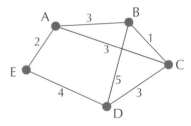

One possible cycle is:

  A E D C B A   (length 13)

Another possible cycle is:

  A C B D E A   (length 15)

Exercise 1.1

Q1 For each graph below, add edges to make the networks complete and then find a Hamiltonian cycle by inspection.

a)
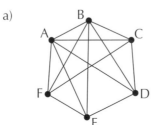

b)
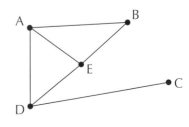

Q2 For each of these graphs, find by inspection a Hamiltonian cycle through the network.

a)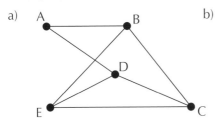

b)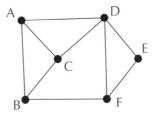

Q3 For each of these graphs, find by inspection two Hamiltonian cycles of different lengths.

a)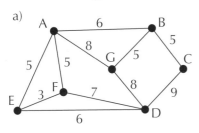

b)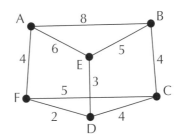

TSP in non-Hamiltonian networks

There are loads of cases in **real life** where you want to visit each vertex in a network at least once while covering the shortest possible distance, but in practice there **might not** always be a **Hamiltonian cycle** in the network.

For example, a tourist might want to visit **every** tourist attraction in the city before **returning** to their hotel. If there aren't direct routes between the attractions, they'll have to pass some places **more than once** in order to visit them all.

Tip: Don't get TSPs confused with the route inspection problem from Chapter 3 — this time you want to visit all the vertices (you don't necessarily have to go along every edge).

Example

Sandy wants to visit each tourist attraction on the map before ending up back at his hotel.

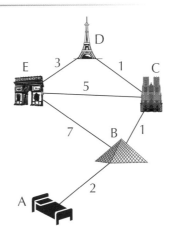

a) **Find by inspection the quickest route he can take.**

The quickest route Sandy can take is:

A B C D E D C B A (= 14)

b) **Which attractions would he have to walk past twice?**

He'd have to walk past B, C and D twice to get back to the hotel.

Quiz: Can you name the famous Parisian tourist attractions? Answers below!

D: Eiffel Tower E: Arc de Triomphe
B: The Louvre C: Notre Dame

In this kind of situation, you can **add edges** to turn the graph into a **complete graph** which you can tackle using the **classical method**.

Find the shortest route through the network to the right that visits each vertex at least once, starting and finishing at vertex A.

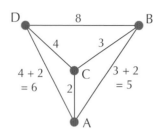

The network isn't Hamiltonian, so you're going to have to visit at least one of the vertices more than once.

To fix this, add edges to make the network complete. The two edges you add to do this are A D and A B.

Tip: The same route in reverse is also the quickest — this is always the case unless there are directed edges.

Tip: The weight of the actual route is the same — the only thing you change is the vertices.

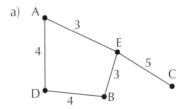

By making the network complete, you've reduced it to a classical TSP, so all you have to do is find the shortest Hamiltonian cycle. You can see by inspection that the quickest route is:

A D C B A (= 18)

Because this uses edges you added, you need to interpret it and write the actual route:

A C D C B C A

Exercise 1.2

Q1 For each graph below:
    (i) Find by inspection the shortest route for a TSP, starting at A, and give its length.
    (ii) State which vertices are visited twice (apart from A).

a) 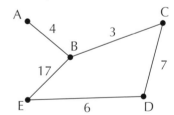   b)

Q2 For each graph below:
    (i) Add edges to the graph to make it complete.
    (ii) Find by inspection the shortest route for a TSP in your complete graph, starting at A, and give its length.
    (iii) Use your answer to (ii) to state the shortest route for a TSP in the original graph.

Q2 (iii) Hint: You need to interpret your route here and work out which edges were actually crossed, like in the example above.

a) 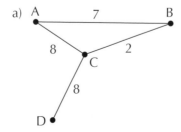   b)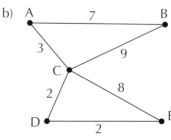

2. Nearest Neighbour Algorithm

For any travelling salesperson problem, it's good to have an idea of the kind of length a route should be. The nearest neighbour algorithm calculates an upper bound for the shortest Hamiltonian cycle in the network, giving the length of a route that is definitely possible. The shortest route will be the same or smaller.

Upper bounds

Because there's no algorithm for finding the shortest path in a travelling salesperson problem, it's good to have a **target length** that you need to try and **stay under** — this is called the **upper bound**.

As soon as you know the length of a tour through the network, that becomes your upper bound. The **smaller** the upper bound the **better**, so when you find the length of another tour:

- If it's bigger than your current upper bound, ignore it.

- If it's smaller than your current upper bound, replace it.

So, for example:

1. Say the first tour you find has a length of 20.
    This is your **initial upper bound**.

2. The next tour you find has a length of 22. The upper bound **stays** 20 as that's still your current **best solution**.

3. The next tour you find has a length of 17. This is a **better solution** than 20, so 17 becomes your **new upper bound**.

You can find an upper bound using the **nearest neighbour algorithm**.

Learning Objectives:

- Be able to find the upper bound for a travelling salesperson problem by using the nearest neighbour algorithm on a network.

- Be able to find the upper bound for a travelling salesperson problem by using the nearest neighbour algorithm on a matrix.

Tip: Normally the upper bound is the highest you **can** go, but here it's the highest you **want to** go, or the lowest you know is possible. It's the upper bound on the **shortest possible** route, not on all routes.

The nearest neighbour algorithm

The nearest neighbour algorithm is quite self-explanatory — you just choose the **unvisited vertex** closest to you each time. Once you've been through all of the vertices, you go along the edge that takes you **straight back** to the starting point.

> ### The Nearest Neighbour Algorithm
>
> 1. Choose a **starting vertex** (you'll usually be told which one to use in a question).
>
> 2. Choose the **nearest unused vertex**.
>
> 3. Repeat Step 2 until you've visited **each vertex**.
>
> 4. Finish the Hamiltonian cycle by **returning to the starting vertex**.

The nearest neighbour algorithm **doesn't always work** — it will find a Hamiltonian cycle for any starting vertex on a **complete** graph, but for a graph that **isn't** complete, the algorithm can **break down** for certain **starting vertices**. A question will sometimes tell you to **make** a graph complete, if it isn't already.

Example

The graph shows the durations in hours of train journeys between five Russian towns. Ben wants to visit all five towns, spending the minimum amount of time on trains. Apply the nearest neighbour algorithm, starting at vertex A, to find an upper bound for Ben's optimum route.

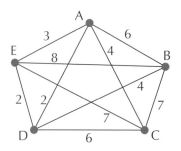

Applying the nearest neighbour algorithm **from A**:

1. The closest vertex to A is D (2 hours).

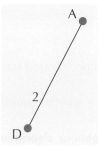

2. The closest unused vertex to D is E (2 hours).

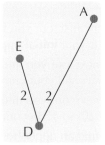

3. The closest unused vertex to E is C (7 hours).

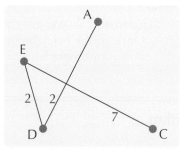

4. The closest unused vertex to C is B (7 hours).

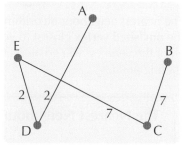

5. That's all the vertices visited, so back to A (6 hours).

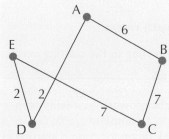

Upper bound = total duration of
A D E C B A

= 24 hours

Tip: Remember, you need to visit every vertex but not every edge. The network you get for the upper bound will often end up looking somewhat bare compared to the original network.

Starting from a **different vertex** can sometimes give a **different result**.

If you apply the nearest neighbour algorithm to a different vertex and get a result that's **lower** than your current upper bound, then you can **replace** the upper bound with the new number.

Example

Ben wants to find a better upper bound for his journey.
Apply the nearest neighbour algorithm starting at C and say whether this replaces the upper bound found in the last example.

Just go through the same process as the last example, but start from vertex C instead of vertex A:

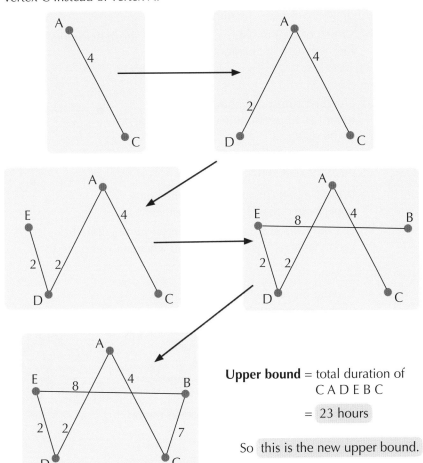

Upper bound = total duration of
C A D E B C

= 23 hours

So this is the new upper bound.

Tip: Ideally you'd do this for each vertex and find the smallest upper bound, but often that's too time consuming.

Exercise 2.1

Q1 a) Use the nearest neighbour algorithm starting at A to find an upper bound for the TSP on this network.

 b) Repeat part a), but start at vertex C.

 c) Which gives the better upper bound?

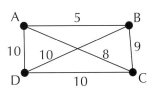

Q2 Shaniqua wants to visit all the places on the network below. Distances shown are in metres.

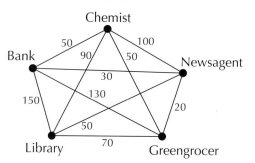

a) Apply the nearest neighbour algorithm starting at
(i) the bank, (ii) the library.

b) Which of your answers to part a) gives the better upper bound for the length of Shaniqua's journey?

Q3 a) Use the nearest neighbour algorithm to find an upper bound for the network to the right:

(i) Starting at vertex A
(ii) Starting at vertex E.

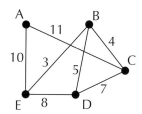

b) Which of parts (i) and (ii) gives the better upper bound for a TSP on this network?

Q3 c) Hint: Remember the nearest neighbour algorithm needs the next vertex to be connected by a direct edge.

c) Use the nearest neighbour algorithm starting from C. What happens if you do this, and what can you do to fix it?

Q4 a) Use the nearest neighbour algorithm to find an upper bound for a TSP on the network to the right, starting at D.

b) Carry out the nearest neighbour algorithm starting at A, adding an edge where necessary, and find an upper bound for a TSP on the network.

c) Which of the two upper bounds is better?

Q5 a) The zookeeper in charge of small mammals has five pens of animals to feed. Apply the nearest neighbour algorithm starting at each animal to find how long he'd have to travel for (times are in minutes).

b) What's the best upper bound for his route?

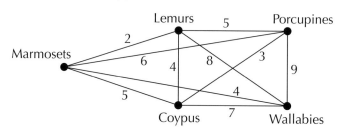

Nearest neighbour algorithm on a matrix

When you have more than about 5 vertices, the graph can get complicated. In these situations it's more likely to be represented on a matrix.

- The weights between vertices are given in **distance matrix** form (see pages 37-39).

- You might have to **complete** the matrix — fill in **missing distances** from a graph or find the **shortest route** between vertices if there's no **direct path** between them.

Here's an example of how to apply the **nearest neighbour algorithm** to a matrix:

Tip: The matrices in this section look a bit different from the ones in Chapter 2 as they're shown as tables. They work in just the same way though.

Example

Poppy is on holiday in New York and wants to see landmarks A-F. The time that it takes in minutes to get between each place on public transport is given in the matrix.
Use the nearest neighbour algorithm starting from C to find an upper bound for Poppy's tour.

From \ To	A	B	C	D	E	F
A	—	5	35	5	10	15
B	10	—	10	20	20	35
C	45	15	—	10	30	25
D	20	10	5	—	5	10
E	40	25	15	35	—	40
F	35	20	25	30	20	—

Tip: With a matrix, it's easier to show different weights for each edge going in different directions (A to B is 5 minutes but B to A is 10 minutes). This could be because of heavier traffic in a certain direction, more stops on the train, etc.

- Start by finding **vertex C** in the 'From' column, and look across to find the **lowest number** (the time taken to get to the closest vertex). It's **10 mins to D**, so D is the next vertex in the tour.

- You don't want to go to D again after that, so **cross out** the D **column**. You don't want to return to C until the end, so **cross out** the C **column** too.

Circle any rows you've started from already...

...and any numbers you've chosen.

From \ To	A	B	C	D	E	F
A	—	5	35	5	10	15
B	10	—	10	20	20	35
C	45	15	—	10	30	25
D	20	10	5	—	5	10
E	40	25	15	35	—	40
F	35	20	25	30	20	—

Tip: It might help to keep track of the order you visited the vertices (by numbering the columns or similar), but you can also read the route off the completed matrix if you remember where you started.

- Now you're at **D**, so find D in the 'From' column, and look across to find the shortest time to an **unvisited vertex** (i.e. not C). This is **5 minutes** (to E), so E is the **next vertex** in the tour. So far, the tour is **C D E**.

Cross out column E so you don't go there again.

Circle D

From \ To	A	B	C	D	E	F
A	—	5	35	5	10	15
B	10	—	10	20	20	35
C	45	15	—	10	30	25
D	20	10	5	—	5	10
E	40	25	15	35	—	40
F	35	20	25	20	20	—

Tip: If you circle the weight of the path every time you choose one, it makes it easier to add up the total length at the end.

- Keep going with this until **all** the vertices are visited, then **return** to the start vertex (C). F is the **last vertex** visited — it's then 25 mins back to C.

From \ To	A	B	C	D	E	F
A	—	5	35	5	10	15
B	10	—	10	20	20	35
C	45	15	—	10	30	25
D	20	10	5	—	5	10
E	40	25	15	35	—	40
F	35	20	25	20	20	—

The whole tour is **C D E B A F C**, which takes 90 minutes.

So 90 minutes is an upper bound.

Sometimes there are obvious better solutions than the one you get from the nearest neighbour algorithm.

- It's a '**greedy algorithm**', so you choose the best option at any one moment, rather than thinking about what's best in the long run.
- This can mean you end up having to go along really long edges at the end. You'll often be able to see a **better route** just by looking.

Example

a) **Use the nearest neighbour algorithm to find an upper bound for the Travelling Salesperson problem for the network represented by the matrix below, starting at vertex A.**

From \ To	A	B	C	D	E	F
A	—	5	16	8	—	2
B	5	—	6	—	5	4
C	16	6	—	22	4	—
D	8	—	22	—	5	6
E	—	5	4	5	—	5
F	2	4	—	6	5	—

Just go through the matrix like in the last example and work out an upper bound from the route it produces:

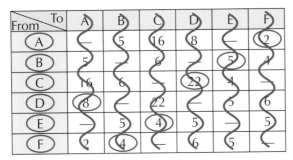

Upper bound = sum of the circled numbers = 2 + 4 + 5 + 4 + 22 + 8

$$= \boxed{45}$$

Route:

AFBECDA

b) The network represented by the matrix is on the right. Find a TSP route by inspection and use it to find an improved upper bound for the problem.

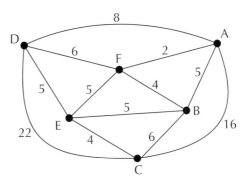

By inspection, you can just work your way clockwise or anticlockwise from A through each vertex (taking the straight lines instead of the curvy ones). The path is coloured light blue in the diagram:

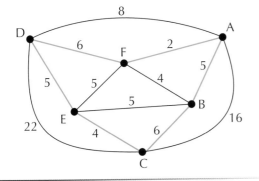

Route:

A B C E D F A

Upper bound:

5 + 6 + 4 + 5 + 6 + 2

$$= \boxed{28}$$

Tip: As you can see, the 'obvious' route found by inspection is much shorter than the route found with the nearest neighbour algorithm.

Exercise 2.2

Q1 Apply the nearest neighbour algorithm starting at A to the matrix below to find an upper bound for a TSP on this network.

From \ To	A	B	C	D	E
A	—	10	5	7	6
B	10	—	8	4	3
C	5	8	—	9	4
D	7	4	9	—	8
E	6	3	4	8	—

Q2 a) Apply the nearest neighbour algorithm to the matrix below, starting at A, to find an upper bound for a TSP on the network.

b) Repeat part a) starting at C.

c) Which of parts a) and b), if any, gives the better upper bound?

From\To	A	B	C	D	E	F
A	—	7	8	3	6	4
B	7	—	6	4	9	7
C	8	6	—	5	7	9
D	3	4	5	—	8	6
E	6	9	7	8	—	5
F	4	7	9	6	5	—

Q3 Matilda is delivering cakes to shops around the town, where the times (in minutes) between shops are shown in the matrix below.

From\To	A	B	C	D	E	F
A	—	8	7	11	18	12
B	15	—	6	4	10	11
C	12	6	—	21	27	5
D	18	26	8	—	7	12
E	13	21	18	24	—	5
F	8	16	14	17	22	—

a) She can start at either A or C. Use the nearest neighbour algorithm starting at each of these to find an upper bound for a TSP problem on the network.

b) Which starting point gives the better upper bound?

Q4 a) The matrix below shows the time taken to travel between 6 towns, represented by the graph. Make the graph complete and then use it to fill in the blanks in the matrix.

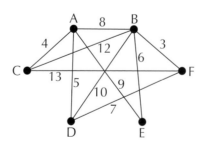

From\To	A	B	C	D	E	F
A	—	8	4	5	9	
B	8	—	12	10	6	3
C	4	12	—			13
D	5	10		—		7
E	9	6			—	
F		3	13	7		—

b) Use the nearest neighbour algorithm to find an upper bound for a TSP on the network:

(i) Starting at A

(ii) Starting at E

c) News is in that the road from B to F is closed, but not the road from F to B. How will this affect the upper bounds found in b)?

3. The Lower Bound Algorithm

Whereas the nearest neighbour algorithm gives you a maximum value, the lower bound algorithm gives you a minimum value that a travelling salesperson problem could take for the network. It uses Prim's or Kruskal's algorithms, so you'll need to make sure you're up to scratch with those before continuing.

The lower bound algorithm

Finding the **lower bound** for a travelling salesperson problem is completely different to finding the upper bound, and it involves finding the **minimum spanning tree** for a network (page 41). So you'll need to use **Prim's** or **Kruskal's** algorithms from Chapter 2 of this book (pages 41-49).

- The lower bound algorithm calculates a **minimum weight** for a Hamiltonian cycle in the network.

- There might not be a Hamiltonian cycle of this weight, but there definitely won't be a shorter one.

> ### The Lower Bound Algorithm
>
> 1. Choose a **vertex**, say A. Find the **two lowest weight edges** joined to vertex A. Call their weights x and y.
>
> 2. **Delete vertex A** and all the **edges** joined to it. This is your 'reduced network'. Now find a **minimum spanning tree** (minimum connector) for the rest of the network and work out its **weight**. Call this W.
>
> 3. The **lower bound** = $W + x + y$

Tip: You'll normally be told which vertex to delete.

Tip: You can find the MST with either Prim's or Kruskal's algorithm.

Example

By deleting vertex E, find a lower bound for the travelling salesperson problem on this network.

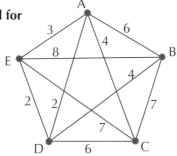

- The **two lowest weights** joined to E are AE (3) and DE (2). So $x = 3$ and $y = 2$.

- Next, **delete** vertex E and its incident edges.

- Now find a **minimum spanning tree** for the reduced network. Here we're going to use Prim's algorithm, but it doesn't matter if you'd rather use Kruskal's.

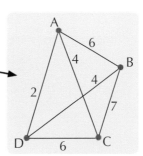

Tip: Edges that touch a vertex are said to be 'incident to' that vertex.

For Prim's algorithm, pick a vertex — here we'll pick A.

Next, choose the edge of least weight that will join the vertex in the tree to a vertex not yet in the tree:

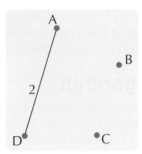

Repeat this process until you've joined all the vertices:

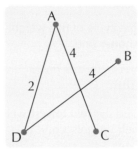

The weight W of the minimum spanning tree is $2 + 4 + 4 = 10$.

- Now you just need to add up the three numbers to get the lower bound:

$$\text{lower bound} = W + x + y = 10 + 3 + 2 = \boxed{15}$$

If you're asked to find a lower bound from a distance matrix, start by **crossing out** the row and column of the deleted vertex. Then just use Prim's algorithm to find the minimum spanning tree (as on page 48).

Example

Find a lower bound, deleting vertex A, for the network represented by the distance matrix below.

From \ To	A	B	C	D	E
A	—	4	—	6	2
B	4	—	3	—	1
C	—	3	—	7	5
D	6	—	7	—	3
E	2	1	5	3	—

- You're starting by deleting A, so cross out both the row and column to make sure you don't visit that vertex in your minimum spanning tree.

From \ To	A	B	C	D	E
A		4		6	2
B	4	—	3	—	1
C		3	—	7	5
D	6	—	7	—	3
E	2	1	5	3	—

- Then find a minimum spanning tree, using Prim's algorithm on a matrix (this was covered on page 48). I'm going to start with vertex B:

(this was covered on page 48).

	①	③	④	②	
From \ To	A	B	C	D	E
A		4		6	2
B	4	—	3	—	1
C		③	—	7	5
D	6	—	7	—	③
E	2	①	5	3	

Tip: You might get different MSTs if you start from different vertices here — but they'll all have the same weight.

- This gives you a minimum spanning tree with a weight W of $3 + 1 + 3 = 7$.
- The values of x and y are given by AB (4) and AE (2), so the lower bound is given by:

$$\text{Lower bound} = W + x + y = 7 + 4 + 2 = \boxed{13}$$

Unlike with upper bounds, the **larger** the lower bound the **better**.

- A **small range** of possible weights for the optimum tour is **more useful** than a large range — so you want your **lower bound** to be as **large** as possible.

- To get the best lower bound you should **repeat the algorithm**, deleting a **different vertex** each time. Then you can pick the **largest** of the lower bounds.

If you'd repeated the algorithm for the network above, you would have got lower bounds of 14, 14, 15 and 16 by deleting B, C, D and E respectively. This means deleting E would give you the best lower bound.

Remember (from p.89), there might not be a Hamiltonian cycle of the weight of the lower bound, but there definitely won't be a shorter one.

Remember (from p.89),

- If you find a tour which has the **same weight** as your lower bound, you know you've stumbled upon an **optimum tour**.

- Once you've found your upper and lower bounds, you can write an **inequality** for the weight of an optimum tour like this:

lower bound ≤ weight of optimum tour ≤ upper bound

- If your lower bound and your upper bound are the **same**, you know that value is the weight of the **optimum tour**.

Q1 Use Prim's algorithm to find a lower
    bound for this network, deleting
    vertex A.

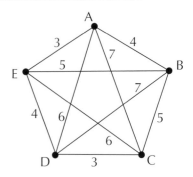

Q2 Use Kruskal's algorithm to find a lower
    bound for this network, deleting
    vertex A.

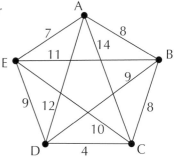

Q3 Use Prim's algorithm to find a lower
    bound for this network, deleting
    vertex C.

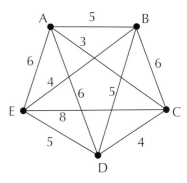

Q4 Use Kruskal's algorithm to find a
    lower bound for this network,
    deleting vertex A.

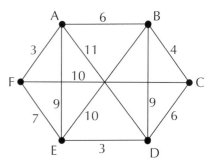

Q5 Carl is travelling around local
    garden centres promoting his
    range of garden sculptures.
    The distances between the garden
    centres, in km, are shown here.
    Delete vertex C and use Prim's
    algorithm to find a lower bound
    for a TSP problem on the network.

From \ To	A	B	C	D	E
A	—	8	7	11	18
B	8	—	6	4	10
C	7	6	—	21	27
D	11	4	21	—	7
E	18	10	27	7	—

Q6 Mrs Jones wants to visit all the stalls at the coffee morning exactly once.
The layout of the stalls and the distance between them, in m, is shown below.

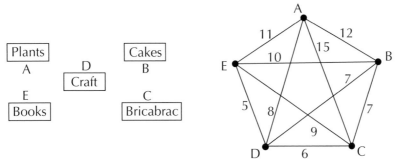

a) Find lower bounds for the network by deleting A and by deleting B.

b) Which gives the better lower bound? Explain why.

Q7 A network representing the time taken in minutes to travel between
road junctions in a town centre is shown by the matrix below.
Delete junction A and use an appropriate algorithm to find a lower
bound for the one-way system.

From\To	A	B	C	D	E	F
A	—	9	5	7	10	12
B	9	—	8	11	15	8
C	5	8	—	13	5	4
D	7	11	13	—	16	8
E	10	15	5	16	—	6
F	12	8	4	8	6	—

Q8 A computer game requires Pandora to collect items and put them
back in her box. There are weighted obstacles between the items,
given by the numbers on the network.

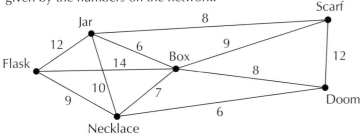

a) Complete the matrix and
find a lower bound for the
network. Begin by deleting
the box vertex.

From\To	J	S	D	N	F	B
J	—	8		10	12	6
S	8	—	12			9
D		12	—	6		8
N	10		6	—	9	7
F	12			9	—	14
B	6	9	8	7	14	—

b) Beginning at the box vertex, find an **upper** bound for her route
through the network.

Review Exercise — Chapter 4

Q1 Find by inspection 2 Hamiltonian cycles in this network, starting and ending at B.

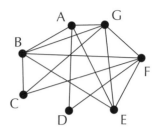

Q2 Add edges to make this network complete, then find 3 Hamiltonian cycles by inspection, starting and ending at C. Give the weights of the cycles.

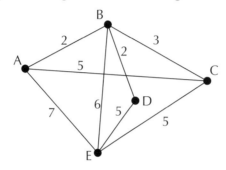

Q3 Use the nearest neighbour algorithm to find an upper bound for the travelling salesperson problem on the network below:

a) starting at A

b) starting at C

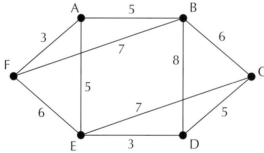

Q4 a) Use the nearest neighbour algorithm to find an upper bound for the travelling salesperson problem on the matrix below:

(i) starting at B   (ii) starting at F

b) Which, if either, gives the better upper bound?

From \ To	A	B	C	D	E	F
A	—	5	10	6	8	12
B	5	—	6	12	4	10
C	10	6	—	8	12	5
D	6	12	8	—	7	4
E	8	4	12	7	—	9
F	12	10	5	4	9	—

Q5 a) Represent this network on a matrix. Fill in the missing distances by finding the shortest route between vertices by inspection when there's no direct link.

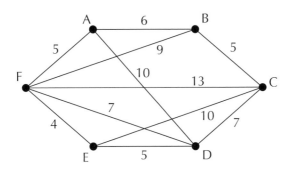

b) Find a lower bound for a TSP on the matrix by deleting vertex C.

Q6 a) Give three different Hamiltonian cycles for this network that start at A.

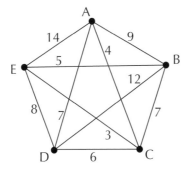

b) Apply the nearest neighbour algorithm from each vertex in turn.
What is your best upper bound?

c) Apply the lower bound algorithm five times, deleting each vertex in turn.
What is your best lower bound?

d) What do your answers to b) and c) tell you about the optimum solution to the travelling salesperson problem for this network?

Q7 a) Apply the nearest neighbour algorithm starting from F to find an upper bound for a TSP on this network.

From \ To	A	B	C	D	E	F
A	—	4	6	5	8	12
B	4	—	14	22	6	11
C	6	14	—	18	3	5
D	5	22	18	—	13	15
E	8	6	3	13	—	20
F	12	11	5	15	20	—

b) Find a lower bound for a TSP on this network by deleting vertex B.

1   The diagram below shows the main streets in a town centre, and their lengths in metres.
     Max wants to display a poster at each intersection.

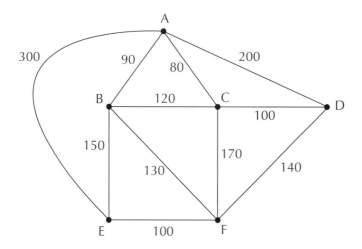

a)   Complete the matrix below to show the distance between each intersection.

(2 marks)

From \ To	A	B	C	D	E	F
A	—	90	80	170	210	
B	90	—	120		150	130
C	80	120	—	100		170
D	170		100	—		140
E	210	150			—	100
F		130	170	140	100	—

b)   Find the length of tour ABCDEFA.

(2 marks)

c)   Find the length of the tour produced when the nearest neighbour algorithm is
      applied from vertex A.

(3 marks)

d)   Which of your answers to b) and c) is the better upper bound for Max's tour
      around the town centre?

(1 mark)

e)   Find a lower bound for the distance by deleting vertex D.

(6 marks)

2   A network is shown to the right.

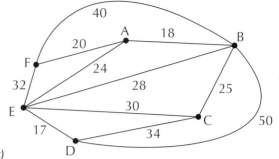

a)   (i)   State how many edges you
             would need to add to make
             this network complete.   *(1 mark)*

      (ii)   Complete the network.   *(3 marks)*

b)   By deleting vertex C and all incident edges, find a lower bound
      for this network.
                                                                    (5 marks)

c)   Draw the network that represents this lower bound.
                                                                    (1 mark)

d)   Find an upper bound for the travelling salesperson problem on this network
      by applying the nearest neighbour algorithm. Start from vertex A.
                                                                    (3 marks)

3   The diagram to the right shows the time taken
     to walk between park benches A-G in minutes.
     Alice the park keeper needs to inspect each
     bench for rot.

From \ To	A	B	C	D	E	F	G
A	—	15	10	7	6	7	4
B	15	—	8	5	12	13	14
C	10	8	—	6	15	18	2
D	7	5	6	—	7	5	13
E	6	12	15	7	—	3	10
F	7	13	18	5	3	—	6
G	4	14	2	13	10	6	—

a)   Give an example of a Hamiltonian
      cycle for this park.   *(2 marks)*

b)   Starting from A, use Prim's algorithm to find a minimum spanning tree.
      Show the order in which edges are added and draw your minimum
      spanning tree, giving its total weight.
                                                                    (6 marks)

c)   Using your answer to part b), calculate a lower bound for the duration of
      Alice's tour. You should delete vertex B and the edges incident to it.
                                                                    (3 marks)

d)   Use the nearest neighbour method starting from F to find an upper bound
      for Alice's tour.
                                                                    (3 marks)

e)   Using your previous answers, draw a conclusion about the duration of
      the optimum tour.
                                                                    (2 marks)

1. Linear Programs

Learning Objectives:

- Be able to understand and use all of the definitions used in linear programming.
- Be able to set up a linear program from a wordy problem, and vice versa.

Linear programming is a way of finding the optimal solution to a problem, subject to certain constraints. It's useful when a company wants to maximise profit (or time efficiency, etc.), but is limited by costs and resources.

Definitions

The **aim** of linear programming is to produce an **optimal solution** to a **problem** — e.g. to find the solution that gives the **maximum profit** to a manufacturer, based on **conditions** that would affect it, such as **limited time** or **materials**. Before you start having a go at linear programming problems, there are a few **terms** you need to know:

> **Decision variable**
>
> In any problem, you'll have things that are being **produced** (or **bought** or **sold** etc.) — e.g. jars of jam or different types of books.
> The **amount** of each thing is represented by letters — x, y, z etc.
> These are called the **decision variables**.

> **Constraints**
>
> The **constraints** are the **factors** that **limit** the problem, e.g. a limited number of workers available. The constraints are written as **inequalities** in terms of the **decision variables**. Most problems will have **non-negativity constraints**. This just means that the decision variables **can't** be **negative** — it wouldn't make sense to have a solution that produces –2 books.

Tip: The non-negativity constraints are usually written as x, $y \geq 0$.

> **Objective function**
>
> The **objective function** represents the thing you're trying to **maximise** or **minimise**, e.g. **profit** or **cost**. It's usually an **equation** written in terms of the **decision variables**.

> **Feasible solution**
>
> A **feasible solution** is a solution that **satisfies** all the **constraints**. It'll give you a **value** for each of the **decision variables**. On a **graph**, the **set** of feasible solutions lie inside the **feasible region** (see page 103).

> **Optimal solution**
>
> You're aiming to **optimise** the objective function — that's finding a solution within the feasible region that maximises (or minimises) the **objective function**. This is an **optimal solution**, and there can be **more than one**.

Example

In the following linear programming problem, identify the objective function, decision variables and constraints.

A company that produces inflatable penguins wants to maximise profits $£P$. They produce 3 types of penguin — emperor (E), gentoo (G) and Adélie (A). They must produce at least 10 of each type of penguin every day, but don't have the equipment to produce more than 50.

- The objective function is profit, $£P$, which needs to be maximised.

- The decision variables are the number of each type of penguin to be produced, i.e. the number of:

    emperor (E), gentoo (G) and Adélie (A).

- The constraints are the limits on production:

    The number of each type of penguin must be 10 or more.
    The total number of penguins must be no more than 50.

Tip: Determining the constraints is the trickiest part in setting up linear programming problems. There's more on this in the next section.

Exercise 1.1

Q1 For the following linear programming problems, state the decision variables, the objective function and the constraints.

a) Maximise $P = 5x + 7y$
Subject to $5x + 2y < 4$
$x + y \geq 1$
$x, y \geq 0$

b) Minimise $C = 200h + 250a$
Subject to $50h + 20a \leq 1200$
$h + a \leq 30$
$h, a \geq 0$

c) Maximise $W = 2x + 3y + 4z$
Subject to $x, y, z > 0$
$3x - y + z \leq 0$
$2x \geq y$

Q2 Briefly explain what is meant by non-negativity constraints.

Q3 A clothing company makes football shirts for both home and away kits. The company can produce up to 900 shirts per day (x home shirts and y away shirts) but is required to make at least twice as many home shirts as away shirts. Home shirts make £2 profit and away shirts make £1.50 profit, and the company wants to maximise its profits $£P$.

a) What are the decision variables?

b) What's the objective function?

c) Explain whether or not the problem needs non-negativity constraints, and if so write them down.

d) What are all the other constraints for this problem?

Setting up linear programming problems

Sometimes you'll have to set up the constraints and objective function yourself by **interpreting** the information given in the question. Often you'll be presented with a **wordy** problem and asked to turn the information into **inequalities** that describe the **constraints**.

Tip: If the question says 'at least' or 'no more than', you'll need a $\geq$ or $\leq$ sign. Don't get these confused with situations that need 'more than' or 'less than' (> or <) a certain number.

- A company might be **limited** by **how many** products they can make — say, for example, they produce x balls and y frisbees, but only have machinery to produce **100 units a day**. This is shown by the inequality $x + y \leq 100$.

- They might also have a **quota** as to how many they must produce — if they have to produce **at least** 50 units a day, then $x + y \geq 50$.

- Sometimes sales figures show that a certain product sells better than another. In this case, they decide they want to produce **at least 3 balls, x, for every 2 frisbees, y**. Be **careful** not to fall for the trap here — the inequality **isn't** $3x \geq 2y$ as you might expect. That would allow 2 balls and 2 frisbees ($6 \geq 4$), which **isn't** at least 3 balls for every 2 frisbees. Another way of looking at it is that the **number of balls** must be **at least $\frac{3}{2}$ (i.e. 1.5) times** the **number of frisbees**. This gives $x \geq 1.5y$, or $2x \geq 3y$.

- For the **objective function**, just look at **what** the company is trying to **maximise** or **minimise**, and how this is relevant to the **decision variables**. If the aim is to **maximise profit** (£P), then you'll want to know **how much** each variable makes when it sells. If balls (x) make £3 and frisbees (y) make £4 then the **objective function** is **£$P = 3x + 4y$**, which is to be **maximised**.

Sometimes when the question gives a **lot of information** all at once you might find it easier to set up a **table** to display it. This way you can just read off the inequalities from each row or column.

Example

Set up the following as a linear programming problem, identifying the objective function and writing out the constraints as inequalities.

A company makes garden furniture, and produces both picnic tables and benches. It takes 5 hours to make a picnic table and 2 hours to paint it. It takes 3 hours to make a bench and 1 hour to paint it. In a week, there are 100 hours allocated to construction and 50 hours allocated to painting. Picnic tables are sold for a profit of £30 and benches are sold for a profit of £10. The company wants to maximise their weekly profit.

- To make the information easier to process, put it into a table:

Item of furniture	Construction time	Painting time	Profit (£)
Picnic table	5	2	30
Bench	3	1	10
Total time available:	100	50	

- Now use the table to identify all the different parts of the problem and come up with the inequalities.
- The **decision variables** are the **number of picnic tables** and the **number of benches**, so let x = number of picnic tables and y = number of benches.

- The first **constraint** is for **construction** — making a picnic table takes 5 hours, so x tables will take $5x$ hours. Making a bench takes 3 hours, so y benches will take $3y$ hours. There are a **total** of 100 hours available, so this gives the inequality $5x + 3y \leq 100$.

- The second constraint is for **painting**. There are 50 hours available and a table takes 2 hours to paint and a bench takes 1 hour to paint, giving the inequality $2x + y \leq 50$.

- The **objective function** to be **maximised** is **profit**. Each picnic table makes a profit of £30, so x tables make a profit of £30x. Each bench makes a profit of £10, so y benches make a profit of £10y. Let P be the profit, then the aim is to maximise £$P = 30x + 10y$.

- So the problem can be written as:

Maximise   £$P = 30x + 10y$
Subject to the constraints $5x + 3y \leq 100$
                                                 $2x + y \leq 50$
                                                 $x, y \geq 0$

Tip: Don't forget the non-negativity constraints (you can't have a negative number of picnic benches).

You may also be asked to go in the **other direction** and write out **inequalities** in **words**. This is fairly easy if you already know how to form inequalities, but it's still worth making sure you know how to do it.

Example

Maureen runs a theatre and needs to order three types of snack before the next show — ice cream (x), sweets (y) and crisps (z).

The member of staff who normally deals with ordering products is off sick, but he's left the details he uses for ordering snacks on his desk. Maureen wants to understand the information before ordering so that she doesn't make any mistakes.

Tip: This example uses 3 variables, but it's no different to those with 2 — just deal with each of the inequalities one at a time and keep in mind which letter represents which snack.

Describe, in words, what the following information shows.

Maximise the profit   £$P = x + 0.5y + z$
Subject to the constraints $x, y, z \geq 20$
                                                 $x + y + z \leq 120$
                                                 $y \geq 2x$

- The objective function is **profit, £P**, and this needs to be **maximised**. Looking at the expression, ice cream and crisps make £1 profit and sweets make 50p.

- The first constraint says that x, y and z must be **at least** a certain value. Maureen must order at least 20 of each product.

- The next constraint is setting a limit on the number of products she orders (perhaps because they don't expect more than a certain number of customers, or they have limited space). The **combined total** of snacks ordered must be **no more** than 120.

- The final constraint shows that the number of bags of sweets bought must be **at least twice** the number of ice creams bought. Or, in other words, she must buy **at least** 2 bags of sweets for every ice cream.

Q1 A company produces milk frothers, and are buying two components
— heating elements (x) and frothing motors (y). The company
accountant has produced the following linear programming problem
for buying the two types of component:

Q1 Hint: Make sure you
don't get the numbers
the wrong way round
on the final constraint
(see page 100).

$$\begin{array}{ll} \text{Minimise} & \pounds C = 2x + 3y \\ \text{Subject to the constraints} & x, y \geq 5 \\ & x + y \leq 20 \\ & x + 2y \leq 30 \\ & 3y \leq 5x \end{array}$$

Describe, in words, what the objective function and constraints are.

Q2 An electronics company makes two MP3 players — one has a 16GB
capacity and the other 32GB. Loading software onto the MP3
players takes 5 mins for the 16GB model and 3 mins for the 32GB.
In a single production run there are 3 hours in total available for
loading software. Before leaving the factory, all MP3 players have
to be checked by quality control. It takes 2 mins to check the 16GB
model and 3 mins for the 32GB model. Quality control is available
for 2½ hours per production run.
The company makes £40 profit from the sale of each 16GB model
and £30 from the 32GB model — it wishes to maximise its potential
profit per production run.

Q2 Hint: This much text
might look scary — just
do it step by step and
use the table to help.

a) Complete the following table showing this information.

MP3 Player Size	Software	Quality control	Profit (£)
16GB			
32GB			
Total time			

b) Let x be the number of 16GB models produced per production run.
Let y be the number of 32GB models produced per production run.
Let £P be the total potential profit per production run. Write down
the objective function P in terms of x and y.

c) Write down the constraints for this linear programming problem.

Q3 A shop sells small and large boxes of fireworks. The suppliers charge
£3 for a small box of fireworks and £6 for a large box. The shop has
used information from pre-orders to come up with a list of constraints:

The shop wants to buy at least 90 boxes in total.
They will sell both small and large boxes.
They will sell at least twice as many small boxes as large.

The supplier can provide a maximum of 120 small boxes of fireworks
and 80 large boxes.

Q3 Hint: Optimising
doesn't necessarily
involve maximising
profits — in this case it
wants you to minimise
something.

Let x be the number of small boxes the shop buys from its suppliers
and y be the number of large boxes it buys.

Formulate this information as a linear programming problem, writing
out all the constraints as inequalities in terms of x and y and identifying
a suitable objective function, stating how it would be optimised.

2. Solving Linear Programming Problems

Now you know how to set up linear programming problems, you can start actually solving them. You need to know two ways of doing this — the objective line method and the vertex method. For both of these you need to start by plotting the constraints on a graph.

Feasible regions

Plotting the constraints on a **graph** helps you see the **feasible solutions** clearly (those that satisfy all of the constraints).

- Draw each of the **constraints** as a **line** on the graph. All you have to do is **change** the **inequality sign** to an **equals sign** and plot the line. If you find it easier, **rearrange** the equation into the form $y = mx + c$.

- Then you have to **decide** which bit of the graph you **want** — whether the solution will be **above** or **below** the line. This will depend on the **inequality sign**. If you're not sure, put the **coordinates** of a point (e.g. the origin) into the equation and see if it **satisfies** the inequality.

- Once you've decided which bit you want, **shade** the region you **don't want**. This way, when you put all the constraints on the graph, the **unshaded region** (the bit you want) is easy to see. Your finished graph should have an area, **bounded** by the lines of the **constraints**, that **hasn't** been **shaded**. This is the **feasible region**.

- If the inequality sign is < or >, use a **dotted line** — this means you **don't** include the line in the region. If the inequality sign is ≤ or ≥ then use a **solid** line, so the line **is included** in the range of solutions.

- Once you've drawn **all** the constraints on the graph, you'll be able to solve the problem. Don't forget the **non-negativity constraints** — they'll limit the graph to the **first quadrant**.

- The **coordinates** of any point inside the **unshaded area will satisfy all** the **constraints**.

Learning Objectives:

- Be able to plot the constraints of a linear programming problem on a graph and find the feasible region.
- Be able to use the objective line method to find the optimal solution to a problem.
- Be able to use the vertex method to find the optimal solution to a problem.
- Be able to find the optimal integer solution to a problem.

Tip: To see which bit of the graph you want, rearrange the inequality into the form $y = mx + c$, then think about which sign you'd use.
For $y \leq mx + c$ (or <), you want the bit **underneath** the line, and if it's $y \geq mx + c$ (or >) then you want the bit **above** the line.

Tip: Sometimes a 3-variable problem involves drawing a graph. If it does, you'll be given a way to eliminate one of the variables to reduce it to a 2-variable problem.

Example

On a graph, show the constraints $x + y \leq 5$, $3x - y \geq 2$, $y > 1$ and $x, y \geq 0$. Label the feasible region R.

- Rearranging the inequalities into '$y = mx + c$' form gives:
$$y \leq 5 - x$$
$$y \leq 3x - 2$$
$$y > 1$$

- The decision variables are represented by the x- and y-axes, and the non-negativity constraints $x, y \geq 0$ restrict us to the positive quadrant.

- Once you've sorted out your constraints, just draw a **set of axes** and plot each constraint on the **same** axes.

- For the first constraint, **replace** the ≤ with = and plot a straight line:

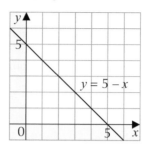

Tip: The regions that don't satisfy the non-negativity constraints are already shaded.

- To work out which section to **shade out**, choose a point **on one side** of the line and see if it **satisfies** the inequality — say the origin.

  $y \leq 5 - x \Rightarrow 0 \leq 5 - 0$ This is **correct**, so shade out the **other side**:
  (above the line)

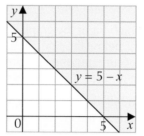

- The next inequality is $y \leq 3x - 2$ so draw the line of $y = 3x - 2$ and shade out the region that **doesn't** satisfy the inequality (in this case, shade everything above the line):

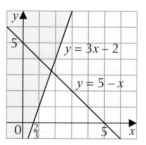

- For the final inequality, follow the usual method but notice the > sign — make the line **dotted** to show it's not included in the feasible region.

- The **feasible region** is the bit that's left **unshaded** — label this R.

Tip: You can check the feasible region is correct by choosing a point inside (say (2, 2)) and making sure it satisfies all the inequalities.

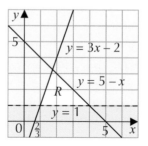

Q1   a) On the same set of axes, plot the following inequalities, shading out the region that doesn't satisfy the inequalities.

$$y \le 2x - 3 \qquad x \le 4 \qquad y \ge 1$$

     b) Label the unshaded feasible region R.

Q2   a) On the same set of axes, plot the following inequalities, shading out the region that doesn't satisfy the inequalities.

$$y < \frac{x}{2} + 2 \qquad x \le 5 \qquad y < 6 - x$$

     b) Label the unshaded feasible region R.

Q2 Hint: Remember to check if the lines should be solid or dashed (see page 103).

Q3   Write down the constraints represented by the diagram below.

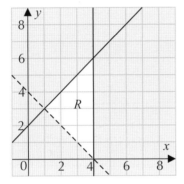

Q4   Write down the constraints represented by the diagram below.

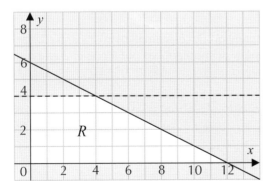

Q5   a) On the same set of axes, plot the following inequalities, shading out the region that doesn't satisfy the inequalities.

$$x > 1 \qquad y + 1 \ge x \qquad x + 2y - 10 \le 0$$

     b) Label the unshaded feasible region R.

Q5 Hint: Remember, rearranging them into the form '$y = mx + c$' will make graphing the inequalities easier.

Q6 Hint: This question uses c and d instead of x and y, but it's no different really. When you plot the graph, just treat c as x and d as y.

Q6 PawsPlayPets produce collars for both cats and dogs. In a single production run the company makes c cat collars and d dog collars. For every two cat collars they make at least three dog collars. A production run lasts two hours. A cat collar takes 3 minutes to produce and a dog collar takes 2 minutes.

a) Write a list of constraints the company must follow in terms of c and d, simplifying where possible.

b) Plot these constraints on a graph and label the feasible region R.

Q7 A small company produces two types of pen — black (y) and blue (x). They're limited as to how many of each type of pen they can produce each day by some constraints, shown on the graph below.

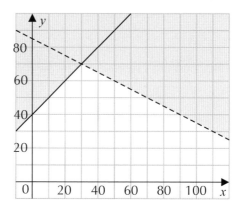

a) Write down the constraints shown by the graph.

b) An employee points out that they can't make more than 100 blue pens or more than 60 black pens in a day. Add these constraints to a copy of the graph.

c) There's another pair of constraints that haven't been taken into account. What are these? Add them to the copy of the graph.

Q8 A textiles company produces x small blankets and y large blankets in a day. The company accountant has put together a graph showing the various constraints on the number of blankets they can make each day.

Q8 Hint: Look for 'easy' points to use to work out the gradients of the lines — e.g. (0, 160) and (200, 0) for the solid sloping line and (100, 100) and (140, 0) for one of the dotted lines.

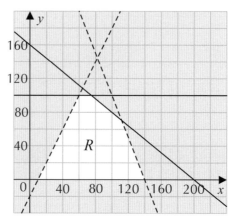

Write down all the constraints shown by the graph.

Optimal solutions — the objective line method

Once you've drawn a graph showing the constraints you can use it to **solve** the linear programming problem and find the **optimal solution**.

- All the points in the **feasible region** (see page 103) satisfy all the **constraints** in the problem.

- You need to be able to work out which point (or points) also **optimises** the **objective function**.

- The objective function is usually of the form **$Z = ax + by$**, where Z either needs to be **maximised** (e.g. profit) or **minimised** (e.g. cost) to give the **optimal solution**.

> **The Objective Line Method**
>
> 1. Draw the **straight line** $Z = ax + by$, choosing a **fixed value** of Z (a and b will be given in the question). This is called an **objective line**.
>
> 2. If you're trying to **maximise** Z, move the line to the **right**, keeping it **parallel** to the original line. As you do this, the value of Z **increases**. The **optimal solution** will be the **last point** within the **feasible region** that the objective line touches.
>
> 3. If you're trying to **minimise** Z, the **optimal solution** will be the **last point** within the **feasible region** that the objective line touches as you slide it to the **left**. As you move it to the left, the value of Z **decreases**.

Tip: This is sometimes called the ruler method, as a good way to do it is to slide a ruler over the graph parallel to the objective line.

When you draw your **first** objective line, you can use **any value** for Z. Pick one that makes the line **easier** to draw — e.g. let Z be a **multiple** of both a and b so that the **intercepts** with the axes are **easy** to find.

Example

Maximise the profit £$P = 2x + 3y$ in the linear programming problem from the example on pages 103-104. The graph below represents the constraints.

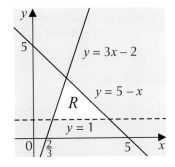

- Choose a value of P that's **divisible** by both 2 and 3 — say 6.
  If $P = 6$ then $6 = 2x + 3y$. When $x = 0$, $y = 2$ and when $y = 0$, $x = 3$.

- Now plot a **straight line** on the graph that goes through the points $(0, 2)$ and $(3, 0)$ — this is an **objective line**:

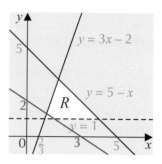

Tip: You might want to draw a few more lines using the ruler as you drag it along the page so you can keep track of where you are.

- Now take a **ruler** and place it along the line. Then **slide** it up and right keeping the ruler **parallel** to the line — as you do this, the value of P increases.

- Keep sliding the ruler until it's no longer within the **feasible region**. The **last point** within R it touches is the **optimal solution**.

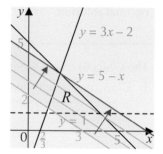

Tip: If you had to minimise P, you'd slide the ruler down and left.

- From the diagram you can see this point is the **intersection** between the lines $y = 3x - 2$ and $y = 5 - x$. To find the point of intersection, solve these **simultaneous equations**. This will give you the optimal solution.

- Substituting $y = 5 - x$ into $y = 3x - 2$ gives:

$$5 - x = 3x - 2 \ \Rightarrow\ 4x = 7 \ \Rightarrow\ x = \frac{7}{4}$$

- Putting $x = \frac{7}{4}$ into $y = 5 - x$ gives $y = \frac{13}{4}$

- Now put these values into the **objective function** to find P:

$$P = 2x + 3y = \frac{14}{4} + \frac{39}{4} = \frac{53}{4} = 13.25$$

- So the maximum value of P is 13.25, which occurs at $\left(\frac{7}{4}, \frac{13}{4}\right)$.

Sometimes the optimal solution isn't just a single point.

- If the objective line is **parallel** to one of the **constraints**, you might end up with a **section of a line** that gives the **optimal solution**.

- If this happens, **any point** along the line is an optimal solution (as long as it's **inside** the **feasible region**).

- This shows that there can be **more than one** optimal solution to a problem.

Tip: If the optimal solution is a dotted line then the actual solution will just be a line very close to it. You don't need to worry about this in D1 though.

Q1 The following graph shows the feasible region of a linear programming problem. The objective function to be maximised is $Z = 2x + y$.

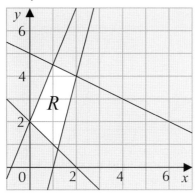

a) On a copy of the graph, show the objective line $2x + y = 2$.

b) Show at least two more objective lines, including the line that passes through the point that will give the optimal solution.

Q2 Use a copy of the graph below and the objective line method to maximise the following functions:

a) $Z = 2x + 3y$ b) $Z = 3x + 2y$ c) $Z = 3x - 2y$

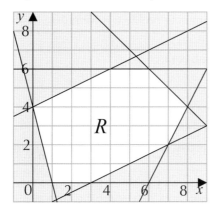

> **Q2 Hint:** You're not given the equations of the constraints here, but you can read the coordinates off the graph.

Q3 Use a copy of the graph below and the objective line method to minimise the following functions:

a) $Z = 4x + 3y$ b) $Z = 2x + 5y$ c) $Z = 3x + y$

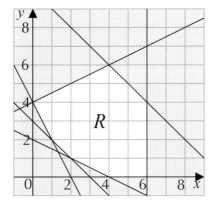

> **Q3 Hint:** Minimising is done the same way as maximising, but instead of sliding the ruler up and right you slide it down and left.

Q4 A company produces a linear programming problem. The decision variables x and y are subject to the constraints shown on the graph:

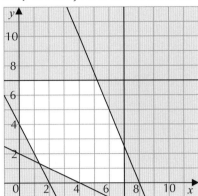

a) Two more constraints must be applied to the problem:

$$x + y \geq 3 \qquad x + y \leq 11$$

Add these to a copy of the graph and label the feasible region R.

b) The company wishes to maximise its takings $\pounds T = 3x + 2y$. Use the objective line method to find the maximum takings, stating the values of x and y at this point.

c) The company decides that instead it would rather minimise its costs, $\pounds C = x + 4y$. Use the objective line method and your graph from part a) to find the minimum cost, stating the values of x and y.

Q5 A linear programming problem is formulated as follows:

$$\begin{aligned}
\text{Minimise} \quad & C = 0.8x + 1.2y \\
\text{Subject to} \quad & x \geq 0 \\
& 12 \leq y \leq 50 \\
& x + y \geq 40 \\
& 6x + 5y \leq 300
\end{aligned}$$

a) Plot a graph showing these constraints.

b) Use the objective line method to solve the problem.

Q6 A company that grows Christmas trees grows them to two different heights — 'indoor' and 'outdoor'. The land available is sufficient to grow 300 indoor trees. Outdoor trees require twice as much space as indoor trees.
The cost of water throughout the growing season is £4 per indoor tree and £5 per outdoor tree. The company has a £1000 water budget.
The cost of insecticides is £2 per indoor tree and £8 per outdoor tree. The budget for chemicals is also £1000.
The company makes £2 on each indoor tree and £5 on each outdoor tree, and wishes to maximise its profit (assuming all trees are sold).

Q6 Hint: Another way of describing the land constraint would be "indoor trees take up 1 unit of space, outdoor trees take up 2 units of space, and there are 300 units in total."

a) If the company grows x indoor trees and y outdoor trees, write down the objective function stating clearly whether it should be maximised or minimised.

b) Show that the insecticide constraint is $x + 4y \leq 500$.

c) List all the other constraints.

d) Draw a graph of the feasible region.

e) Use the objective line method to solve the problem.

Optimal solutions — the vertex method

The **optimal solution** for the example on page 108 was found at a **vertex** of the **feasible region**. This isn't a coincidence — if you've had a go at some more linear programming problems, you'll have noticed that the optimal solutions **always** occur at a vertex (or an **edge**) of the feasible region. This gives you another way to solve the problem.

The Vertex Method

1. Find the x- and y-values of the **vertices** of the **feasible region**. You do this by solving the **simultaneous equations** of the **lines** that **intersect** at each vertex.

2. Put these values into the **objective function** $Z = ax + by$ to find the value of Z.

3. Look at the Z values and work out which is the **optimal value**. Depending on your objective function, this might be either the **smallest** (if you're trying to **minimise** Z) or the **largest** (if you're trying to **maximise** Z).

Tip: If two vertices A and B produce the same Z value, this means that all points along the edge AB are also optimal solutions.

Even if it looks **obvious** from the graph, you still have to **test** each vertex of the feasible region. Sometimes the **origin** will be one of the vertices — it's really easy to test, as the objective function will usually be equal to **0** there. Don't forget vertices on the **x-** and **y-axes** too.

Example

Minimise $Z = 8x + 9y$, subject to the constraints:

$$2x + y \geq 6$$
$$x - 2y \leq 2$$
$$x, y \leq 4$$
$$x, y \geq 0.$$

- Start by drawing the constraints on a graph. This way you'll be able to identify the vertices. Here A, B, C and D are the vertices of the feasible region R.

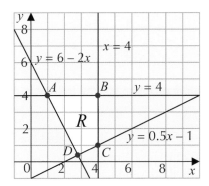

Point A is the intersection of the lines $y = 6 - 2x$ and $y = 4$, so A has coordinates $(1, 4)$.

Point B is the intersection of the lines $x = 4$ and $y = 4$, so B has coordinates $(4, 4)$.

Point C is the intersection of the lines $x = 4$ and $y = 0.5x - 1$, so C has coordinates $(4, 1)$.

Point D is the intersection of the lines $y = 6 - 2x$ and $y = 0.5x - 1$, which has coordinates $\left(\frac{14}{5}, \frac{2}{5}\right)$.

■ Putting these values into the objective function $Z = 8x + 9y$:

At A, $Z = (8 \times 1) + (9 \times 4) = 44$
At B, $Z = (8 \times 4) + (9 \times 4) = 68$
At C, $Z = (8 \times 4) + (9 \times 1) = 41$
At D, $Z = (8 \times 2.8) + (9 \times 0.4) = 26$

■ So the minimum value of Z is 26, which occurs at $\left(\frac{14}{5}, \frac{2}{5}\right)$.

Exercise 2.3

Q1 Solve the following simultaneous equations:
   a) $y = 2x - 3$ and $y = 6 - x$
   b) $x + 4y = 14$ and $9x - 2y + 26 = 0$
   c) $2y = 4x - 19$ and $6x + 2y - 23 = 0$

Q2 Find the value of $P = 2x + 3y$ at each vertex of the feasible region in the graph below.

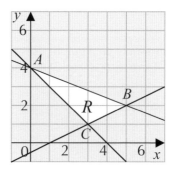

Q3 A linear programming problem has the following constraints:

$y \le 4$ $\quad$ $y \le x + 2$ $\quad$ $y \ge 2x - 8$ $\quad$ $y \le 12 - 2x$ $\quad$ $2y \ge 4 - x$

   a) Plot these constraints on a graph and label the feasible region R.
   b) The objective for this problem is to maximise $Z = x + 5y$. Use the vertex method to find an optimal solution.

Q4 A linear programming problem is formulated as follows:

Maximise $P = 3x + 7y$
Subject to the constraints
$x - y \leq 15$
$2x + 5y \geq 10$
$x - 2y + 40 \geq 0$
$y \leq 3x$
$2x + y \leq 60$
$x, y \geq 0$

a) Plot these constraints on a graph, labelling the feasible region R.

b) Use simultaneous equations to show that two of the vertices of the feasible region have coordinates (25, 10) and (16, 28).

c) One of these two vertices gives an optimal solution. Which is it?

Q4 b) Hint: Use your graph from part a) to work out which lines are meeting at the points (25, 10) and (16, 28).

Q5 A linear programming problem is formulated as follows:

Minimise $C = 3x + y$
Subject to the constraints
$y \leq 250$
$x - 2y + 400 \geq 0$
$y \leq 450 - x$
$y + 2x \geq 300$
$2y \geq 100 + x$

a) Plot these constraints on a graph, labelling the feasible region R.

b) Use the vertex method to solve the problem, giving the coordinates of the optimal solution and stating the value of C at this point.

Q5 Hint: Remember, if it's not clear from the graph what the coordinates of a vertex are you should use simultaneous equations.

Q6 A company makes two different types of model train, steam and electric, and has the capacity to make up to 60 trains per week. Assembling a steam train takes 2 hours, while an electric train takes 1 hour. Painting and inscribing a steam train takes 1 hour, while the same process takes 4 hours for an electric train.
In a week the company dedicates 100 hours to assembling trains and 180 hours to painting and inscribing.
Steam trains sell for £32 profit, while electric trains sell for £20 profit. The company wants to maximise its profit.

a) Formulate this as a linear programming problem.

b) Use the vertex method to find an optimal solution and say how many of each train should be made.

Q7 A factory manufactures two different types of china ornaments — a cat and a dog. The factory must manufacture between 30 and 70 ornaments per production run. Sales figures show the factory should produce at least 2 dogs for every 5 cats, and that twice the number of cats must be at least 20 more than the number of dogs.
It costs the factory £2 to produce a cat ornament and £4 for a dog ornament. The factory wants to minimise costs.
Let x be the number of cat ornaments and y be the number of dog ornaments produced per production run. Let the costs be £C.

Q7 Hint: 'At least 2 dogs for every 5 cats' is like saying 'the number of cats cannot be bigger than $\frac{5}{2}$ times the number of dogs (see page 100).

a) Formulate this as a linear programming problem, stating the objective function and listing all of the constraints.

b) Draw a graph to show the feasible region and use the vertex method to find the optimal solution of the problem formulated in a).

c) Comment on your solution — is this solution realistic?

Optimal integer solutions

- Sometimes it's fine to have **non-integer solutions** to linear programming problems — for example, if you were making different **fruit juices**, you could realistically have 3.5 litres of one type of juice and 4.5 litres of another.

- However, if you were making **garden furniture**, you couldn't make 3.5 tables and 4.5 benches — so you need **integer solutions**.

- You won't always be **told** whether a problem needs integer solutions, so you might have to **work it out** for yourself. It's common sense really — just think about whether you can have **fractions** of the **decision variables**.

You can use both the **objective line method** (page 107) and the **vertex method** (page 111) to find optimal integer solutions. It's important when using these that your **graph** is as **clear** as possible.

To use the **objective line method**:

- You use this method in exactly the **same way** as before, but instead of looking for the last **vertex** the line touches, you need to look for the last **point** with **integer coordinates** in the **feasible region**.

- This might be hard to do if your graph isn't very **accurate**, or if the scale isn't **clear**.

To use the **vertex method**

- Start by finding which **vertex** gives an optimal solution as before.

- Then, consider all the points with **integer coordinates** that are **close by**. Make sure you **check** whether these points still **satisfy** the **constraints** though — test this **before** you put the values into the objective function.

Tip: Some problems have optimal integer solutions that are far away from the vertices of the feasible region, but you don't need to worry about these for D1.

- To test the integer solutions that are close by, just **round** the coordinates of the optimal solution up and down to create **4 new sets of coordinates**, and test those.

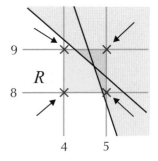

- Here, the optimal solution is **between** 4 and 5 on the x-axis and **between** 8 and 9 on the y-axis, so the 4 points you'd test are (4, 8), (4, 9), (5, 8) and (5, 9).

- It's easy to forget that **not all** the solutions near the optimal vertex will be **inside** the **feasible region** — you can check either **by eye** on an **accurate graph**, or put the **coordinates** into each of the **constraints**. In this case, (5, 8) and (5, 9) are outside the feasible region, so you'd just ignore those.

Example 1

The optimal solution to the problem on page 111 occurred at $\left(\frac{14}{5}, \frac{2}{5}\right)$ (= (2.8, 0.4)). Find the optimal integer solution.

- Looking at the integers nearby gives you the points
  (3, 0), (3, 1), (2, 0) and (2, 1) to test.

- However, the point (3, 0) doesn't satisfy the constraint $x - 2y \leq 2$,
  and (2, 0) and (2, 1) don't satisfy $2x + y \geq 6$.

- So the optimal integer solution is at (3, 1),
  where $Z = (8 \times 3) + (9 \times 1) = 33$

Tip: You won't always just end up with one solution — sometimes you'll have a few to test.

Example 2

A company makes designer dresses. It makes x ballgowns and y cocktail dresses, for a profit of £600 and £500 respectively, subject to the constraints $x + y \leq 9$, $3x - y \leq 9$, $y \leq 7$ and $x, y \geq 0$. Maximise the profit, $P = 600x + 500y$.

- Start by drawing the constraints on a graph:

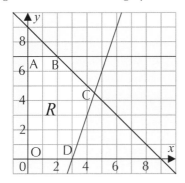

Tip: This example uses the vertex method, but you could also use the objective line method.

- The feasible region is the area $OABCD$, with coordinates
  $O(0, 0)$, $A(0, 7)$, $B(2, 7)$, $C\left(\frac{9}{2}, \frac{9}{2}\right)$ and $D(3, 0)$.

- The value of P at each vertex is O: £0, A: £3500, B: £4700,
  C: £4950 and D: £1800.

- The maximum value of P is £4950, which occurs at $\left(\frac{9}{2}, \frac{9}{2}\right)$ (= (4.5, 4.5)).
  However, making 4.5 dresses isn't possible, so an integer solution is needed.

- The integer coordinates near C are (4, 5), (5, 5), (5, 4) and (4, 4).
  (5, 5) and (5, 4) don't satisfy the constraint $3x - y \leq 9$ so are outside the feasible region.

- At (4, 5), $P = £4900$, and at (4, 4), $P = £4400$,
  so £4900 is the maximum profit.

- So the company needs to make 4 ballgowns and 5 cocktail dresses
  to make the maximum profit of £4900.

Q1 a) Identify the two constraints in the following graph
       (not including the non-negativity constraints).

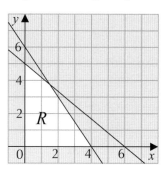

   b) The point of intersection, P, between these two constraints gives
      the optimal solution for maximising the objective function
      $Z = 4x + 3y$. Find its coordinates.

   c) Find the value of the objective function Z at P.

   d) Find the value of Z at the closest points to P inside
      the feasible region that have integer coordinates.

   e) Find the optimal integer solution.

Q2 The graph below shows the feasible region for a
    linear programming problem where Z is to be maximised.

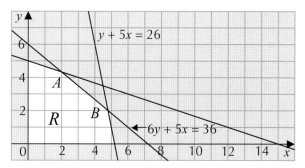

Q2 Hint: You may
need to identify some
of the constraints before
finding the coordinates
of the vertices.

   a) Find the coordinates of the points labelled A and B.

   b) Work out the value of $Z = 3x + 5y$ at the points A and B.

   c) Deduce the optimal integer solution.

Q3 A linear programming problem has the following constraints:

$$0 \le 2y - x \le 6$$
$$5x + 2y \ge 12$$
$$4x + y \le 15$$

   a) Plot these constraints on a graph and label the feasible region R.

Q3 Hint: You'll need to
plot 2 separate lines for
the first constraint.

   b) The objective for this problem is to maximise $Z = x + 5y$.
      Find the optimal solution.

   c) Find the optimal integer solution.

Q4 A linear programming problem is formulated as follows:

Maximise $Z = 9x + 8y$

Subject to the constraints

$x + 4y \leq 100$

$7x + 8y \leq 240$

$7x + 6y \leq 210$

$x, y \geq 0$

a) Plot the constraints on a graph, labelling the feasible region R.

b) Find the optimal integer solution, stating the value of Z.

Q5 A linear programming problem is formulated as follows:

Minimise $C = 3x + 5y$

Subject to the constraints $10 \leq x + y \leq 30$

$y \leq 3x$

$x + 4y \geq 20$

$x, y \geq 0$

a) Plot the constraints on a graph, labelling the feasible region R.

b) Find the optimal integer solution, stating the value of C.

Q6 A company makes two types of calculators — basic and scientific. In each production cycle they can manufacture a total of 70 calculators. The production involves two stages — construction and packaging. The basic model takes 10 minutes to go through construction and 4 minutes to be packaged, while the scientific model takes 30 minutes to go through construction but only 1 minute to be packaged. The company has a maximum of 22½ hours for the construction stage and 4 hours for packaging.
A basic calculator sells for £2.80 profit while a scientific calculator sells for £4.60 profit, and the company wants to maximise profits.

a) Formulate this as a linear programming problem, defining the decision variables and the objective function.

b) Plot the constraints on a graph and identify the feasible region.

c) Solve the problem and find an optimal solution.

Q6 c) Hint: Remember, you can't make a non-integer number of calculators.

Q7 Car Group Premium produce two types of car, offroad and hatchback, by purchasing individual parts and assembling them at the factory.
In a single production run they must manufacture between 4 and 14 cars in total. From past sales figures they know they should produce at least 3 offroaders for every 5 hatchbacks. The total production cost of an offroader is £6000, while the production cost of a hatchback is £3000. The company wants to minimise its costs.

Let x be the number of offroaders they produce per production run and y the number of hatchbacks. Let the production cost be £C.

a) Formulate this as a linear programming problem, stating the objective function and listing all of the constraints.

A further constraint is given by $2x \leq 3y + 4$.

b) Draw a graph to show the feasible region and solve the problem.

Review Exercise — Chapter 5

Q1   A company making photo frames has to purchase two raw materials: glass and wood. They buy these in bulk — a pallet of glass costs £300 and a pallet of wood costs £200. When ordering they must order a minimum of 5 pallets of glass and a minimum of 10 pallets of wood. The total number of pallets purchased at a time must be at least 20. A further constraint is given by $5x + 2y > 60$, where x is the number of pallets of glass and y is the number of pallets of wood. The company wishes to minimise the cost of purchasing pallets of raw materials.

Formulate this as a linear programming problem, stating the objective function and all of the constraints. You don't need to solve this problem.

Q2   Write down all constraints shown on the graph below.

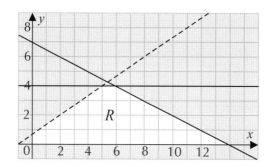

Q3   A company produces sticky notes in two varieties: standard size and jumbo size. Their production process is subject to the following constraints, where x is the number of standard packs and y is the number of jumbo packs:

$$x, y \geq 100$$
$$x + y \leq 500$$
$$y \leq 2x$$
$$x \leq 3y$$

a)   Describe, in words, what each of these constraints shows.

b)   Plot the constraints on a graph, labelling the feasible region R.

Q4   Use the graph below and the objective line method to maximise the following objective functions:

a) $Z = x + y$ b) $Z = 2x + 5y$ c) $Z = 4x + y$

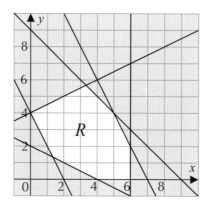

Q5 A linear programming problem is formulated as follows

Maximise $\qquad\qquad$ $Z = 3x + 2y$

Subject to the constraints $\qquad$ $x \geq 0$

$\qquad\qquad\qquad\qquad\qquad$ $2 \leq y \leq 6$

$\qquad\qquad\qquad\qquad\qquad$ $x + y \geq 4$

$\qquad\qquad\qquad\qquad\qquad$ $y \leq 9 - x$

a) Plot a graph showing these constraints.

b) Use the objective line method to solve the problem.

Q6 DontGetLost Ltd make satellite navigation systems for cars. They produce two models — square screen and widescreen. In each production run the company can manufacture a total of 25 machines but only a maximum of 10 can be widescreen. The square screen model takes half as long to produce as the widescreen model which takes 40 minutes. A production run lasts ten hours.

The company wishes to maximise its profit — a square screen model generates £40 profit whilst the widescreen model generates £32 profit.

a) Formulate this as a linear programming problem. Define the decision variables and the objective function stating clearly whether this is to be maximised or minimised.

b) Plot the constraints on a graph and use the vertex method to solve the problem.

Q7 a) A linear programming problem has its optimal solution at (3.2, 2.8). Draw a diagram to illustrate this solution and the four closest points with integer solutions.

b) State, with reason(s), whether or not you would need to test all four points in part b) in order to determine the optimal integer solution.

Q8 A company makes posters in two sizes: large and small. Large posters takes 10 minutes to print and small posters take 5 minutes to print. Each day has 250 minutes printing time.

It takes 6 minutes to laminate a large poster and 4 minutes to laminate a small poster. There are a total of 200 minutes laminating time each day.

The company wants to sell at least as many large posters as small, and they need to sell at least 10 small posters each day. Large posters are sold for a profit of £6 and small posters are sold for a profit of £3.50.

a) Write this out as a linear programming problem. Identify the decision variables, constraints and objective function.

b) Show the constraints for this problem graphically. Label the feasible region R.

c) Maximise the profit, using either the objective line method or the vertex method. Don't worry about integer solutions for now.

d) Use your answer to part c) to find the optimal integer solution.

1   Anna is selling red and white roses at a flower stall. She buys the flowers from a
     wholesaler, where red roses cost 75p each and white roses cost 60p each.
     Based on previous sales, she has come up with the following constraints:

- She will sell both red roses and white roses.

- She will sell more red roses than white roses.

- She will sell a total of at least 100 flowers.

- The wholesaler has 300 red roses and 200 white roses available.

Let x be the number of red roses she buys and y be the number of white roses she buys.
Formulate this information as a linear programming problem.

Write out the constraints as inequalities and identify a suitable objective function,
stating how it should be optimised. You do not need to solve this problem.

(7 marks)

2   The graph below shows the constraints of a linear programming problem.
     The feasible region is labelled R.

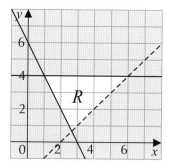

a)   Find the inequalities that produce R.

(4 marks)

b)   Find the coordinates of each vertex of R.

(4 marks)

The aim is to minimise $C = 4x + y$.

c)   Find the optimal solution and state where this value occurs.

(3 marks)

3   A company sells three packs of craft paper: bronze, silver and gold. Each pack is made up of three different types of paper: tissue paper, sugar paper and foil.

- The gold pack is made up of 6 sheets of foil, 15 sheets of sugar paper and 15 sheets of tissue paper.

- The silver pack is made up of 2 sheets of foil, 9 sheets of sugar paper and 4 sheets of tissue paper.

- The bronze pack is made up of 1 sheet of foil, 6 sheets of sugar paper and 1 sheet of tissue paper.

- Each day, there are 30 sheets of foil available, 120 sheets of sugar paper available and 60 sheets of tissue paper available.

- The company is trying to reduce the amount of foil used, so it uses at least three times as many sheets of sugar paper as of foil.

The company makes x gold packs, y silver packs and z bronze packs in a day.

a)   Apart from the non-negativity constraints, write out the other four constraints as inequalities in terms of x, y and z. Simplify each inequality where possible.

(8 marks)

b)   On Monday, the company decides to make the same number of silver packs as bronze packs.

(i)   Show that your inequalities from part (a) become
$$2x + y \leq 10$$
$$x + y \leq 8$$
$$3x + y \leq 12$$
$$2y \geq x$$

(3 marks)

(ii)   On graph paper, draw a graph showing the constraints from part (i) above, as well as the non-negativity constraints. Label the feasible region R.

(5 marks)

(iii)   Use your graph to work out the maximum number of packs the company can make on Monday.

(3 marks)

(iv)   Gold packs are sold for a profit of £3.50, silver packs are sold for a profit of £2 and bronze packs are sold for a profit of £1. Use your answers to parts (ii) and (iii) to maximise the profit they make, and state how many of each type of pack they need to sell.

(3 marks)

1. Matchings

Matchings are a way of allocating one set of nodes to another, taking into account what can and can't be matched. You'll often have to match people to tasks, based on what they can and can't do. The best way to work out a matching is to start with a bipartite graph — which you came across on p.26.

Bipartite graphs

The points in a graph are called **nodes** (or **vertices**) and the lines are called **arcs** (or **edges**) — this was covered in Chapter 2 (see page 26).

- A **bipartite graph** is made up of **two sets** of **nodes** that are **linked** by **arcs**. The arcs go from **one set** of nodes to the **other** — nodes within the **same set** can't be joined to each other.

- In lots of the examples you'll come across, one set of nodes will be the **people** and the other will be the **jobs** or **tasks** they have to do. You'll be told **who** can do which **job**.

- You might also come across bipartite graphs that have **two** sets of **people** — e.g. **girls** and **boys** being paired off for a dance.

- There doesn't have to be the **same number** of nodes in each set (like in the example below).

Example 1

Jenny, Katie, Latika, Martyn and Nikki are planning a picnic. Jenny can bring sandwiches and crisps, Katie can bring sandwiches and pork pies, Latika can bring drinks, Martyn can bring pork pies and biscuits and Nikki can bring biscuits, quiche and crisps. Draw a bipartite graph to show this information.

First, list all the people on one side of the graph, and all the food (and drink) on the other side. Then draw lines connecting each person to all the items they can bring.

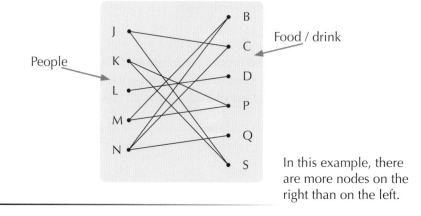

People

Food / drink

In this example, there are more nodes on the right than on the left.

Example 2

A teacher knows that some of her pupils are a bad influence on each other, so has drawn a bipartite graph (below) to help her work out a seating plan. Use the bipartite graph to work out who Poppy can sit by.

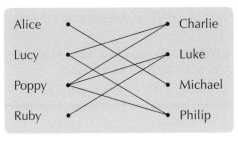

Just follow the arcs coming from Poppy's node — so

Poppy can sit by Charlie, Luke or Philip.

Tip: In this example, the lines show who each pupil can sit by.

Exercise 1.1

Q1 Four toddlers have the following preferences for snacks at nursery:
   Ellie likes biscuits and satsumas
   Isaac likes yoghurt and biscuits
   Leah likes raisins
   Rory likes biscuits, raisins and yoghurt
Draw a bipartite graph to show this information.

Q2 Draw a bipartite graph to show the following information:
   A group of students play a variety of instruments. Jack can play the piano and saxophone, Kate plays the violin and flute, Andrea plays the guitar, saxophone and piano, Tom plays the cello and violin and Nicky plays the piano and flute.

Q3 In a factory, a group of workers can only undertake a job if they are trained for it. The table on the right details which jobs (labelled A-E) each worker is trained for.
Show this information in a bipartite graph.

	A	B	C	D	E
Toby	X				
Bill	X			X	
Anna		X			X
Sam	X	X	X	X	
Eve		X	X		

Q4 A family shares out household chores. Use the bipartite graph below to answer the following questions:

a) Which chores is David willing to do?

b) Who is happy to feed the dog?

c) Who is only prepared to do one chore?

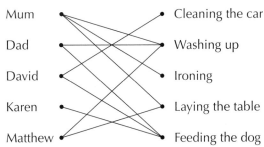

Matchings

Once you've drawn your bipartite graph showing who can do what, you need to work out a **solution** that assigns **one person** to **one job**. This is called a **matching**.

- In a matching, you can only have **one arc** for **each node** — so each person only does **one job** (and each job only has **one person** doing it). Matchings are **one-to-one**.

- You won't always be able to match **all** the nodes in one set with all the nodes in the other — it depends on who can do which tasks.

- If there are the **same number** of people as jobs, and each **job** is assigned to a **person**, the matching is said to be **complete**. So if there are x **nodes** in each set, a complete matching has x **arcs**.

- It's **not always possible** to have a complete matching — e.g. if there are **two jobs** that can only be done by the **same person**, one of the jobs **won't** be included in the matching.

Tip: You don't need to worry about the difference between 'maximal' and 'maximum' for D1.

- If a complete matching can't be done, you might have to find a **maximum** (or 'maximal') **matching** — a matching that has the **greatest number** of arcs possible (so as many jobs as possible are being done). There can be **more than one** possible maximum matching.

Example 1

Use the bipartite graph from the previous page to come up with a complete matching for the teacher's seating plan.

- Start with the people who have the most **restrictions** — Alice can **only** sit by Michael and Ruby can **only** sit by Luke.

- Lucy and Poppy can both sit by either Charlie or Philip, so there are **two** complete matchings.

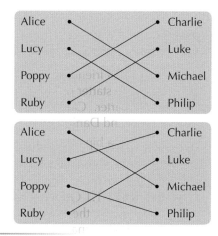

Example 2

Tip: In an adjacency matrix a 1 means there's an arc between that pair of nodes in the bipartite graph, and a 0 means there isn't.

	Big Wheel	Log Flume	Roller-coaster	Teacups
Andy	1	0	0	1
Bahir	0	0	1	1
Carys	0	1	1	0
Daniel	1	0	0	0

Andy, Bahir, Carys and Daniel are going to a theme park. They can only afford to go on one ride each, and they each want to try out a different ride. Their choices are shown in the adjacency matrix.

Draw a bipartite graph to show this information, then use it to find a complete matching.

- List all the **people** on one side of the graph, and all the **rides** on the other side. Then draw lines linking each person to the rides they want to go on.

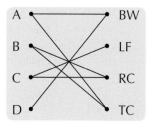

- To find a **complete matching**, you need to link **each person** to just **one ride**. Start with Daniel, as he **only** wants to go on the big wheel. This means that Andy will have to go on the teacups, then Bahir has to go on the rollercoaster and finally Carys has to go on the log flume.

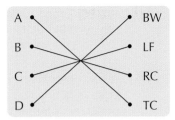

After a bad experience, Andy flatly refuses to go on the teacups again, so a complete matching is no longer possible.
Find a maximum matching for their next visit to the theme park.

- Now, **both** Andy and Daniel **only** want to go on the big wheel — so you **won't** be able to find a complete matching. Just match as many people as you can for a **maximum matching**.

- You don't always have to draw your matching — you can just **write it out** instead. So this maximum matching would be Andy = big wheel, Bahir = rollercoaster and Carys = log flume.

Tip: Here, the information has changed, so you have to come up with a new matching. If it helps, draw out the new bipartite graph and work from that.

Tip: This isn't the only maximum matching — you could have had Daniel = big wheel or Bahir = teacups instead.

Exercise 1.2

Q1 A group of friends are having a dinner party. Annabel is happy to make the starter or the dessert. Brendan is willing to provide drinks or the starter. Caroline is happy to make the main course or the dessert and Daniel is only willing to make the dessert.

   a) Draw a bipartite graph to illustrate this information.

   b) Find a complete matching for the model.

Q2 In Exercise 1.1 Question 1, the nursery has one snack available of each type for the toddlers. Find a complete matching so that every toddler has a snack that they like.

Q2 Hint: Use your bipartite graph from the previous exercise to help you answer this question.

Q3 In a project team there are 5 roles, team leader, facilitator, recorder, timekeeper and team member. The table below shows which roles a group of people are suited to.

	Team leader	Facilitator	Recorder	Timekeeper	Team member
Lamarr		X			X
Marcus	X	X			
Nadia			X	X	X
Oliver			X		X
Pippa	X				

   a) Show this information in a bipartite graph.

   b) Find a complete matching for the project team so that each person works in one role which they are suited to.

Q4 In Exercise 1.1 Question 4, every chore needs to be completed by one member of the family. Use the bipartite graph from that question to find a complete matching, if possible.

Q5 A row of six beach huts at the seaside are to be repainted in different colours to brighten them up. The owners are allowed to choose two preferences for the colours. Their choices are shown below:

	Pink	Blue	Yellow	Green	Orange	Red
No. 1	1	1	0	0	0	0
No. 2	0	1	1	0	0	0
No. 3	0	0	0	1	1	0
No. 4	0	0	0	1	0	1
No. 5	0	0	1	0	1	0
No. 6	1	0	0	0	0	1

a) Draw a bipartite graph to represent the possible colours for each beach hut.

The owners of No. 5 have decided they are not willing to be flexible and insist their hut is yellow.

b) Find a complete matching according to the owners' preferences so that every hut is painted a different colour.

Q5 Hint: Even if you draw out the complete matching, it's a good idea to write down the matching as well.

Q6 In Exercise 1.1 Question 3, is it possible to form a complete matching? If yes, show the matching on a bipartite graph.

Q7 A group of workers A-F are to be allocated six tasks 1-6. The table on the right shows the tasks each worker is qualified to do.

a) Draw a bipartite graph to illustrate this information.

b) Find a complete matching so that every job is completed by a qualified worker.

A	1, 4, 5
B	1
C	2, 3, 4, 5
D	4, 6
E	2
F	1, 3, 5

Q8 Some neighbours want to hold a street party and need to share out the jobs. The jobs each house can do are in the adjacency matrix below.

	Food	Drink	Music	Decorations	Tables/ Chairs
No. 1	0	1	0	1	0
No. 2	1	0	1	0	1
No. 3	0	0	1	0	1
No. 4	1	1	0	1	0
No. 5	0	0	0	1	1

a) Draw a bipartite graph to illustrate who can do which jobs.

The people at no. 5 have a very busy week and decide they don't have time to organise decorations after all.

b) Find a complete matching so that all jobs are done and the street party can go ahead.

2. Maximum Matchings

It can sometimes be hard to find a complete matching, especially if the bipartite graph is really complicated. If your original matching isn't complete, you can often improve it by using the alternating path method.

Alternating paths

To find an alternating path, you start by drawing **any** matching from a bipartite graph. This is the **initial matching** — you're trying to **improve** it.

This is how the alternating path method works:

- An alternating path **starts** at a node on one side of the graph that **isn't included** in the **initial matching** and **finishes** at a node on the **other side** of the graph that also **isn't** in the initial matching.

- To get from the **start node** to the **finishing node**, you have to **alternate** between arcs that are **not in** and **in** the initial matching. So the **first** arc you use (from the **unmatched** starting node) is **not in** the initial matching, the second arc is, the third one isn't and so on until you get to a finish node.

- When you reach a finish node (one not in the initial matching), you can **stop** — you've made a '**breakthrough**'.

- Now use your alternating path to construct an **improved matching**. Take the path and **change** the **status** of the arcs, so any arcs **not in** the initial matching are **in** the new matching, and the arcs that were **in** the initial matching are **not in** the new one. Any arcs in the initial matching that aren't in the alternating path just **stay as they are**.

- The **improved matching** should include **two nodes** that weren't in the initial matching, and have **one extra arc**.

The alternating path **can't change** the **original information** — you can't make people do jobs in the **alternating path** that they weren't doing in the **bipartite graph**. Sometimes an alternating path **won't work** — you end up getting **stuck** somewhere. If this happens, go back to the starting node and try a **different path**.

Learning Objectives:

- Be able to use the alternating path method to improve an initial matching.

- Be able to use the maximum matching algorithm to find a maximum matching.

Tip: If it helps, think of it as making new arcs and 'breaking' existing ones.

Example

Anne, Dick, George, Julian and Timmy are on an adventure holiday. They have a choice of five activities: abseiling, canoeing, diving, mountain biking and rock-climbing

Anne wants to go mountain biking or rock-climbing, Dick wants to go canoeing or diving, George wants to go abseiling or mountain biking, Julian wants to go diving or rock-climbing and Timmy just wants to go abseiling.

Find an alternating path that improves on this initial matching: Anne – mountain biking, Dick – canoeing, George – abseiling, Julian – rock climbing

- Start by drawing a **bipartite graph** so you can see all the preferences:

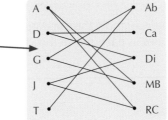

- Then draw the **initial matching**:

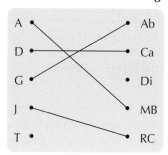

- For the **alternating path**, start at T and find a path that connects it to Di, the other unmatched node (it **won't** be a **direct path**, as Timmy doesn't want to go diving).

  One alternating path goes like this:

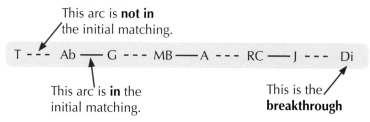

- **Changing the status** of the arcs gives:

$$T \;—\; Ab \;---\; G \;—\; MB \;---\; A \;—\; RC \;---\; J \;—\; Di$$

- Now use this to construct the **improved matching**:

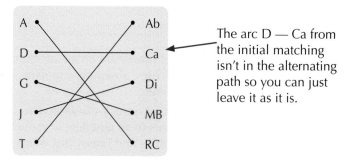

  The arc D — Ca from the initial matching isn't in the alternating path so you can just leave it as it is.

A = RC, D = Ca, G = MB, J = Di, T = Ab

There are now the same number of arcs as there are nodes in each set, so this is a **complete matching**.

Q1 A dance teacher must pair up 8 members of the class. She wants to ensure they are suited and makes a list of the members that might match as a couple.

	Paul	Qasim	Richard	Steven
Tina	X	X		
Ursula		X		X
Vanya	X		X	X
Wendy	X		X	

a) Show this information on a bipartite graph.

b) She initially matches up the couples as follows: Tina and Paul, Ursula and Qasim, Vanya and Richard. Find an alternating path that improves on this matching and state the resulting matching.

Q2 Five workers A to E are qualified to do tasks 1 to 5. A bipartite graph representing the tasks the workers are qualified for is shown below. An initial matching for the tasks is A – 2, B – 1, C – 3 and D – 5. Find an alternating path that improves on the initial matching. List the improved matching obtained.

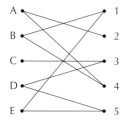

Q3 The students from Exercise 1.1 Question 2 are going to put on a concert. It is decided by the Head of Music that Andrea is not quite good enough to play guitar at a concert and that only one student should play each instrument. An initial matching is Jack – piano, Kate – flute, Andrea – saxophone and Tom – cello.

Q3 Hint: The original information's changed, so you might find it easier to draw a new bipartite graph.

a) Draw a bipartite graph to represent the initial matching.

b) Find an alternating path that improves on the initial matching and list your new matching.

Q4 Alan, Bobby, Charlotte, Dylan and Emily are film critics who are asked to review five films (1 to 5) for a magazine. Due to their busy schedules they are not all free to see all of the films. Their availability is shown in the adjacency matrix.

	1	2	3	4	5
Alan	0	0	1	1	0
Bobby	1	0	0	0	1
Charlotte	0	1	0	1	0
Dylan	1	0	0	0	1
Emily	0	0	1	0	0

a) Draw a bipartite graph to illustrate the information in the matrix.

The editor of the magazine allocates Alan to film 3, Bobby to film 1, Charlotte to film 4 and Dylan to film 5.

b) Show this initial matching clearly on a bipartite graph.

c) Find an alternating path that improves on this matching and list the improved matching achieved.

Maximum matchings

A **maximum matching** is one that uses the **greatest number** of arcs possible. To find the maximum matching, you need to keep finding **alternating paths** and **improved matchings** — this is the **maximum matching algorithm**.

1. Start with **any** initial matching.
2. Try to find an **alternating path** (using the method on p.127). If you find one, use this to form an **improved matching**. If there isn't one, then this is a **maximum matching** — so **stop**.
3. If there are no **unmatched** nodes, **stop** — the matching is **complete**. If there are still unmatched nodes, **repeat step 2)** using the **improved matching** as the new **initial matching**.

In some alternating paths, you have a **choice** between different nodes. You should draw a **tree diagram** to show the possible paths, then pick the route that gets you to a **breakthrough** the **fastest**.

Example

A music school offers tuition in the following instruments: clarinet, flute, piano, saxophone, trumpet and violin. Six children want to start lessons, but the school only takes on one pupil per instrument.
Their preferences are:

Student	First choice	Second choice	Third choice
Chad	Saxophone	Trumpet	—
Elly	Trumpet	Piano	Clarinet
Karen	Flute	Piano	—
Mike	Trumpet	Saxophone	—
Pascal	Clarinet	Violin	Piano
Stuart	Trumpet	Clarinet	—

a) **Draw a bipartite graph to show this information.**

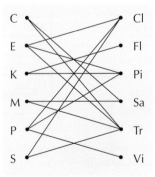

Initially, Chad, Elly, Karen and Pascal are matched to their first choice.

b) Draw this initial matching, then use the maximum matching algorithm to improve the matching as much as possible.

- The **initial matching** looks like this:

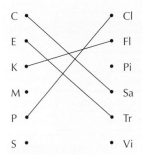

- You can see that there are **4 unmatched nodes** (Mike, Stuart, Piano and Violin), so you can probably find an **improved matching**.

- From the **initial matching**, find an **alternating path** from Mike to an unmatched instrument:

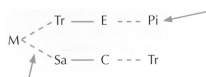

This route reaches a breakthrough first, so use this.

Use a tree diagram to show the possible routes.

Tip: You could have started with Stuart instead of Mike if you wanted.

- This produces the matching:
  Chad = saxophone, Elly = piano,
  Karen = flute, Mike = trumpet and
  Pascal = clarinet, which looks like this:

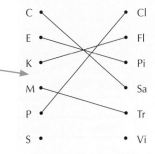

Tip: Don't forget to change the status of the arcs in the alternating path to form the new matching. You also need to include any arcs from the initial matching that haven't been changed.

- But there are still **two unmatched nodes**, so you need to look for **another** alternating path.

- Using this **new matching**, find an alternating path from Stuart to an unmatched instrument:

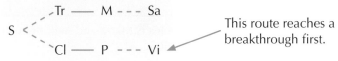

This route reaches a breakthrough first.

- This produces the matching:
  Chad = saxophone, Elly = piano,
  Karen = flute, Mike = trumpet,
  Pascal = violin, Stuart = clarinet.

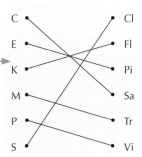

- There are no more unmatched nodes, so this is a **complete matching**.

Q1   Ahmed, Brad, Caleb, Danny and Eric play for a basketball team.
There are five positions in basketball: Point Guard, Shooting Guard,
Small Forward, Power Forward and Centre. The players have the
following preferences for positions:

	First choice	**Second choice**
Ahmed	Power Forward	Centre
Brad	Point Guard	Power Forward
Caleb	Centre	Small Forward
Danny	Shooting Guard	Point Guard
Eric	Power Forward	Centre

Initially everyone except Eric is given their first preference for position.

a) Draw a bipartite graph to show the preferences of the players
and state the initial matching.

b) Use the maximum matching algorithm to find a complete
matching, showing your alternating paths clearly.

c) Find another alternating path from the initial matching
and hence an alternative complete matching.

Q2 Hint: Remember
that the owners of
No. 5 insist that their
hut is painted yellow.

Q2   In Exercise 1.2, Question 5 starting from the initial matching:
no. 1 – pink, no. 2 – yellow, no. 3 – orange, no. 4 – red,
use the maximum matching algorithm to ensure every beach hut is
painted a different colour. Show your alternating paths clearly.

Q3   After a speed dating night, a group of women write down their
preferences for which of the men they would like to see again.
This is illustrated in the adjacency matrix below:

	Joe	**Raj**	**Troy**	**Akil**	**Chris**	**George**
Lian	0	1	1	0	0	0
Eva	0	1	0	0	0	0
Sophie	0	0	0	1	0	0
Kim	0	0	1	0	1	0
Betty	1	0	0	0	1	0
Maria	0	0	0	1	0	1

The initial matching of couples is Maria and Akil, Betty and Chris,
Kim and Troy and Lian and Raj.

a) Draw a bipartite graph to illustrate the information from the table
and show clearly on it the initial matching.

Q3 Hint: For part a),
draw the bipartite graph
and make the arcs for
the initial matching bold
or a different colour.

b) Starting from the initial matching use the maximum matching
algorithm to find a complete matching where everyone has a
date. Show your alternating paths clearly.

Q4   In Exercise 1.2, Question 7 the six workers are allocated to the
six tasks with an initial matching of A – 1, C – 2, D – 4 and F – 5.
Starting with the initial matching, use the maximum matching
algorithm to find a complete matching, showing your alternating
paths clearly.

Review Exercise — Chapter 6

Q1 The bipartite graph below shows the languages a group of friends can speak:

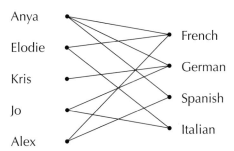

a) Which of the friends can speak French?
b) Who speaks the most languages?
c) What languages can Jo speak?

Q2 Elizabeth, Jane, Kitty, Lydia and Mary are going to an art gallery. Elizabeth likes Renaissance art, portraits and sculptures, Jane likes portraits, sculptures and modern art, Kitty likes the cafe, Lydia likes modern art and the cafe and Mary likes Renaissance art.

a) Draw this information on a bipartite graph.

b) Each girl is going to look at one thing, and they're all going to look at different things. Use your bipartite graph to find a complete matching.

Q3 At a school dance, Alice, Bella, Charlotte, Daisy, Evie and Felicity have to be paired with Gerwyn, Hector, Iago, Jason, Kyle and Liam. The adjacency matrix below shows who the girls want to dance with.

	G	H	I	J	K	L
A	1	0	1	0	0	0
B	0	0	1	1	0	0
C	0	1	0	0	1	0
D	0	0	0	0	1	1
E	1	1	0	0	0	0
F	0	0	0	1	0	1

a) Draw a bipartite graph to show this information.

The initial matching pairs Alice with Gerwyn, Bella with Jason, Charlotte with Hector and Daisy with Liam.

b) Draw the initial matching.

c) Using the maximum matching algorithm, find alternating paths so that everyone has someone to dance with and they aren't left sitting by themselves and looking sad.

Q4 Using the bipartite graph from Question 1 of this exercise:
a) Explain why it is not possible to form a complete matching.
b) Find a maximum matching so that there is one person speaking each language.

Q5   A travel company wants its members of staff to write reviews of cities they've visited.
     The bipartite graph below shows who has visited which city.

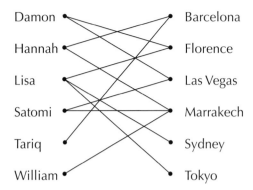

The initial matching has Damon reviewing Las Vegas, Hannah reviewing Marrakech, Lisa
reviewing Florence and Tariq reviewing Barcelona.

a) What would happen if you tried to find an alternating path starting Satomi - - Marrakech?

b) Use the alternating path method to find a maximum matching.

c) Explain why a complete matching is not possible.

Hannah visits Sydney.

d) Starting with the initial matching, use the alternating path method to find a maximum
   matching based on this new information. Is this matching complete?

Q6   A group of 4 children, Isabel, Sophie, Charlie and James, want to play dressing up.
     There are five outfits in the dressing up box: fairy, fireman, doctor, princess and monster.
     The table below shows the children's preferences:

	First choice	Second choice	Third choice
Isabel	Fairy	Fireman	—
Sophie	Doctor	Princess	Monster
Charlie	Doctor	Fairy	—
James	Princess	Monster	—

a) Draw a bipartite graph to illustrate this information.

b) Find a maximum matching so that every child has an outfit they like to dress up in.
   Is your solution the only possible maximum matching?

c) Explain why it is not possible to achieve a complete matching in this situation.

A new child, Harvey, joins the group and as he is new is allowed to have first choice of
dressing up outfits. He chooses the fireman.

d) What effect does this have? Is it now possible to achieve a complete matching,
   and if so what is it?

Harvey, Isabel, Sophie and James are allowed to dress up in the first outfit on their list.

e) Show this initial matching on a bipartite graph.

f) Find an alternating path that improves on the initial matching
   and show your improved matching.

1

	Class 1	Class 2	Class 3	Class 4	Class 5
Jamal	0	1	0	1	0
Kelly	1	1	0	0	0
Lee	0	0	1	0	1
Mia	0	0	0	1	0
Nick	1	0	0	1	0

Five tutors, Jamal, Kelly, Lee, Mia and Nick need to be assigned to classes 1 - 5. The adjacency matrix above shows their preferences.

a) Draw a bipartite graph to represent this information.

(2 marks)

b) An initial matching pairs Jamal with class 4, Kelly with class 1 and Lee with class 3.
Find an alternating path starting from Mia and ending with class 2.
Write out the improved matching that your path gives.

(3 marks)

c) A complete matching is not possible for this bipartite graph. Explain why.

(1 mark)

Mia agrees to teach class 3.

d) Starting with the matching found in part b), use the maximum matching algorithm to find a complete matching. Write out the alternating path and the final matching.

(3 marks)

Answers

Chapter 1: Algorithms

1. Algorithms

Exercise 1.1 — Algorithms in words

Q1 a) Input: radish seeds, water, sunlight, soil;
Output: radishes

b) Input: wool, knitting needles;   Output: scarf

c) Input: flour, sugar, eggs, (any other ingredients);
Output: cake

d) Input: sales figures, costs;   Output: profit

With these questions it's hard to say for definite what the inputs should be, but as long as your answers are sensible then you should be fine.

Q2

	a)	b)	c)	d)
Input	0	20	100	−35
× 9	0	180	900	−315
÷ 5	0	36	180	−63
+ 32	32	68	212	−31
Output	32 °F	68 °F	212 °F	−31 °F

Your trace table might look slightly different — as long as it clearly shows the output and you can understand the working, it should be fine.

Q3

	a)	b)	c)
Step 1	300	460	320
Step 2	0.12	0.09	0.23
Step 3	15	42	22
Step 4	36	41.4	73.6
Step 5	51	83.4	95.6
Step 6	61.2	100.08	114.72
Output	£61.20	£100.08	£114.72

d) Step 6 (multiply by 1.2) represents 20% tax, so it the tax rate changed to 15%, step 6 should change to 'multiply by 1.15'.

Q4 a) $n = 5$

a	b
1	5
5	25
25	125
125	625
625	3125

Stop

b) $n = 10$

a	b
1	10
10	100
100	1000

Stop

c) $n = 3$

a	b
1	3
3	9
9	27
27	81
81	243
243	729
729	2187

Stop

d) $n = 8$

a	b
1	8
8	64
64	512
512	4096

Stop

e) The algorithm generates powers of n until the value is at least 1000.

Q5 a)

Input	Working out	Output
18	1 + 8	9

The output is 9, so 18 is divisible by 3.

b)

Input	Working out	Output
239	2 + 3 + 9	14
14	1 + 4	5

The output is 5, so 239 is not divisible by 3.

c)

Input	Working out	Output
928 741	9 + 2 + 8 + 7 + 4 + 1	31
31	3 + 1	4

The output is 4, so 928 741 is not divisible by 3.

d)

Input	Working out	Output
298 218 744	2 + 9 + 8 + 2 + 1	45
	+ 8 + 7 + 4 + 4	
45	4 + 5	9

The output is 9, so 298 218 744 is divisible by 3.

Q6 a)

x	y
29	41
~~14~~	~~82~~
7	164
3	328
1	656
Total	1189

b)

x	y
~~102~~	~~87~~
51	174
25	348
~~12~~	~~696~~
~~6~~	~~1392~~
3	2784
1	5568
Total	8874

c)

x	y
57	67
~~28~~	~~134~~
~~14~~	~~268~~
7	536
3	1072
1	2144
Total	3819

Exercise 1.2 — Pseudo-code and flow charts

Q1 a) (i)

$a + b$	$c < 0$?	output c	$a =$
10 − 3	no	7	7
7 − 3	no	4	4
4 − 3	no	1	1
1 − 3	yes		

(ii)

$a + b$	$c < 0$?	output c	$a =$
30 − 7	no	23	23
23 − 7	no	16	16
16 − 7	no	9	9
9 − 7	no	2	2
2 − 7	yes		

b) E.g. It outputs all the non-negative terms of an arithmetic sequence with first term $a - b$ and common difference b.

Q2 a) (i)

$a + n$	$b \geq 40$?	output b	$a =$
0 + 6	no	6	6
6 + 6	no	12	12
12 + 6	no	18	18
18 + 6	no	24	24
24 + 6	no	30	30
30 + 6	no	36	36
36 + 6	yes		

(ii)

$a + n$	$b \geq 40$?	output b	$a =$
0 + 13	no	13	13
13 + 13	no	26	26
26 + 13	no	39	39
39 + 13	yes		

b) It finds all the multiples of input number n up to 40.

Q3 a)

n	b	Output	$n = a$?
1	15	1	No
2	$7\frac{1}{2}$		No
3	5	3	No
4	$3\frac{3}{4}$		No
5	3	5	No
6	$2\frac{1}{2}$		No
7	$2\frac{1}{7}$		No
8	$1\frac{7}{8}$		No
9	$1\frac{2}{3}$		No
10	$1\frac{1}{2}$		No
11	$1\frac{4}{11}$		No
12	$1\frac{1}{4}$		No
13	$1\frac{2}{13}$		No
14	$1\frac{1}{14}$		No
15	1	15	Yes

So the factors of 15 are 1, 3, 5 and 15.

b)

n	b	Output	$n = a$?
1	12	1	No
2	6	2	No
3	4	3	No
4	3	4	No
5	$2\frac{2}{5}$		No
6	2	6	No
7	$1\frac{5}{7}$		No
8	$1\frac{1}{2}$		No
9	$1\frac{1}{3}$		No
10	$1\frac{1}{5}$		No
11	$1\frac{1}{11}$		No
12	1	12	Yes

So the factors of 12 are 1, 2, 3, 4, 6 and 12.

Q4 **a)**

C	P	N	C ≤ N?	A	T
800	7	200	no		
600	7	300	no		
300	7	500	yes	120	£840

The maximum grant available is £840.

b) For Venue A:

C	P	N	C ≤ N?	A	T
350	6	200	no		
150	6	300	yes	82.5	£495

For Venue B:

C	P	N	C ≤ N?	A	T
600	4	200	no		
400	4	300	no		
100	4	500	yes	110	£440

Q5 e.g.

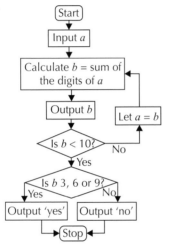

Q6 **a)**

A	B	C	D
6	8		
		6	
			8
		12	
			16
		18	
			24
		24	

24 is the LCM

b)

A	B	C	D
4	11		
		4	
			11
		8	
		12	
			22
		16	
		20	
		24	
			33
		28	
		32	
		36	
			44
		40	
		44	

44 is the LCM

2. Sorting Algorithms

Exercise 2.1 — Bubble sort

Q1 **a)** The first pass:

5 2 7 6 3 5		swap	
2 5 7 6 3 5		no swap	
2 5 7 6 3 5		swap	
2 5 6 7 3 5		swap	
2 5 6 3 7 5		swap	
2 5 6 3 5 7		end of first pass	

After the second pass, the list is:
2 5 3 5 6 7

After the third pass, the list is:
2 3 5 5 6 7

There are no swaps in the fourth pass, so the list in order is:
2 3 5 5 6 7

b) There were 4 swaps on the first pass.

c) 4 passes were needed.

Q2 **a)** The first pass:

3 11 5 0 7 6 4		swap	
11 3 5 0 7 6 4		swap	
11 5 3 0 7 6 4		no swap	
11 5 3 0 7 6 4		swap	
11 5 3 7 0 6 4		swap	
11 5 3 7 6 0 4		swap	
11 5 3 7 6 4 0		end of first pass	

After the second pass, the list is:
11 5 7 6 4 3 0

After the third pass, the list is:
11 7 6 5 4 3 0

There are no swaps in the fourth pass, so the list in descending order is:
11 7 6 5 4 3 0

b) There were 5 swaps on the first pass.

c) 4 passes were needed.

Q3 a) The first pass:

Z W T S M L K	swap
W Z T S M L K	swap
W T Z S M L K	swap
W T S Z M L K	swap
W T S M Z L K	swap
W T S M L Z K	swap
W T S M L K Z	end of first pass

After the second pass, the list is:
T S M L K W Z

After the third pass, the list is:
S M L K T W Z

After the fourth pass, the list is:
M L K S T W Z

After the fifth pass, the list is:
L K M S T W Z

After the sixth pass, the list is:
K L M S T W Z

There are no changes in the seventh pass,
so the list in alphabetical order is:
K L M S T W Z

b) The maximum number of passes was needed as
the list was in reverse alphabetical order.

Q4 The first pass:

A F B J M B C	swap
F A B J M B C	swap
F B A J M B C	swap
F B J A M B C	swap
F B J M A B C	swap
F B J M B A C	swap
F B J M B C A	end of first pass

After the second pass, the list is:
F J M B C B A

After the third pass, the list is:
J M F C B B A

After the fourth pass, the list is:
M J F C B B A

There are no swaps in the fifth pass,
so the list in reverse alphabetical order is:
M J F C B B A

Q5 a) The maximum number of passes for 5 items is 5.
(4 to sort the list plus 1 to check no more swaps
are possible.)

b) The maximum number of comparisons for 5 items
is $4 + 3 + 2 + 1 = 10$

Q6 a) The maximum number of passes for 8 items is 8.
(7 to sort the list plus 1 to check no more swaps
are possible.)

b) The maximum number of swaps for 8 items is
$\frac{1}{2}(7 \times 8) = 28$.
*If you'd have worked out the maximum number of
comparisons instead, you'd have found it was the same
as the maximum number of swaps.*

Q7 The first pass:

6 7 9 4 5 6 2	no swap
6 7 9 4 5 6 2	no swap
6 7 9 4 5 6 2	swap
6 7 4 9 5 6 2	swap
6 7 4 5 9 6 2	swap
6 7 4 5 6 9 2	swap
6 7 4 5 6 2 9	end of first pass

After the second pass:
6 4 5 6 2 7 9

After the third pass:
4 5 6 2 6 7 9

After the fourth pass:
4 5 2 6 6 7 9

After the fifth pass:
4 2 5 6 6 7 9

After the sixth pass:
2 4 5 6 6 7 9

There are no swaps in the seventh pass,
so the list in ascending order is:
2 4 5 6 6 7 9

Q8 The first pass:

59 39 89 79 69 29 39	no swap
59 39 89 79 69 29 39	swap
59 89 39 79 69 29 39	swap
59 89 79 39 69 29 39	swap
59 89 79 69 39 29 39	no swap
59 89 79 69 39 29 39	swap
59 89 79 69 39 39 29	end of first pass

After the second pass:
89 79 69 59 39 39 29

There are no swaps in the third pass,
so the list in descending order is:
89 79 69 59 39 39 29

Q9 The first pass:

E L E P H A N T	no swap
E L E P H A N T	swap
E E L P H A N T	no swap
E E L P H A N T	swap
E E L H P A N T	swap
E E L H A P N T	swap
E E L H A N P T	no swap
E E L H A N P T	end of first pass

After the second pass:
E E H A L N P T

After the third pass:
E E A H L N P T

After the fourth pass:
E A E H L N P T

After the fifth pass:
A E E H L N P T

There are no swaps in the sixth pass,
so the list in alphabetical order is:
A E E H L N P T

Q10 a) The first pass:

<u>1 5</u> 2 3 11 10 9 3 4 7   no swap
1 <u>5 2</u> 3 11 10 9 3 4 7   swap
1 2 <u>5 3</u> 11 10 9 3 4 7   swap
1 2 3 <u>5 11</u> 10 9 3 4 7   no swap
1 2 3 5 <u>11 10</u> 9 3 4 7   swap
1 2 3 5 10 <u>11 9</u> 3 4 7   swap
1 2 3 5 10 9 <u>11 3</u> 4 7   swap
1 2 3 5 10 9 3 <u>11 4</u> 7   swap
1 2 3 5 10 9 3 4 <u>11 7</u>   swap
1 2 3 5 10 9 3 4 7 11   end of first pass

After the second pass:
1 2 3 5 9 3 4 7 10 11

After the third pass:
1 2 3 5 3 4 7 9 10 11

After the fourth pass:
1 2 3 3 4 5 7 9 10 11

There are no swaps in the fifth pass,
so the list in ascending order is:
1 2 3 3 4 5 7 9 10 11

b) The numbers form the words:
BUBBLE SORT

Exercise 2.2 — Shuttle sort

Q1 a) First pass: <u>12, 6</u>, 7, 3, 11   swap
Second pass: 6, <u>12, 7</u>, 3, 11   swap
             <u>6, 7</u>, 12, 3, 11   no swap
Third pass: 6, 7, <u>12, 3</u>, 11   swap
             6, <u>7, 3</u>, 12, 11   swap
             <u>6, 3</u>, 7, 12, 11   swap
Fourth pass: 3, 6, 7, <u>12, 11</u>   swap
             3, 6, <u>7, 11</u>, 12   no swap

The list in ascending order is: 3, 6, 7, 11, 12

b) First pass: <u>22, 54</u>, 76, 43, 66, 19   no swap
Second pass: 22, <u>54, 76</u>, 43, 66, 19   no swap
Third pass: 22, 54, <u>76, 43</u>, 66, 19   swap
             22, <u>54, 43</u>, 76, 66, 19   swap
             <u>22, 43</u>, 54, 76, 66, 19   no swap
Fourth pass: 22, 43, 54, <u>76, 66</u>, 19   swap
             22, 43, <u>54, 66</u>, 76, 19   no swap
Fifth pass: 22, 43, 54, 66, <u>76, 19</u>   swap
             22, 43, 54, <u>66, 19</u>, 76   swap
             22, 43, <u>54, 19</u>, 66, 76   swap
             22, <u>43, 19</u>, 54, 66, 76   swap
             <u>22, 19</u>, 43, 54, 66, 76   swap

The list in ascending order is:
19, 22, 43, 54, 66, 76

c) First pass: <u>16, 1</u>, 7, 8, 3, 17, 12, 15   swap
Second pass: 1, <u>16, 7</u>, 8, 3, 17, 12, 15   swap
             <u>1, 7</u>, 16, 8, 3, 17, 12, 15   no swap
Third pass: 1, 7, <u>16, 8</u>, 3, 17, 12, 15   swap
             1, <u>7, 8</u>, 16, 3, 17, 12, 15   no swap
Fourth pass: 1, 7, 8, <u>16, 3</u>, 17, 12, 15   swap
             1, 7, <u>8, 3</u>, 16, 17, 12, 15   swap
             1, <u>7, 3</u>, 8, 16, 17, 12, 15   swap
             <u>1, 3</u>, 7, 8, 16, 17, 12, 15   no swap

Fifth pass: 1, 3, 7, 8, <u>16, 17</u>, 12, 15   no swap
Sixth pass: 1, 3, 7, 8, 16, <u>17, 12</u>, 15   swap
             1, 3, 7, 8, <u>16, 12</u>, 17, 15   swap
             1, 3, 7, <u>8, 12</u>, 16, 17, 15   no swap
Seventh pass: 1, 3, 7, 8, 12, 16, <u>17, 15</u>   swap
             1, 3, 7, 8, 12, <u>16, 15</u>, 17   swap
             1, 3, 7, 8, <u>12, 15</u>, 16, 17   no swap

The list in ascending order is:
1, 3, 7, 8, 12, 15, 16, 17

Q2 a) First pass: <u>2, 3</u>, 1, 4, 8, 5, 7, 6   swap
Second pass: 3, <u>2, 1</u>, 4, 8, 5, 7, 6   no swap
Third pass: 3, 2, <u>1, 4</u>, 8, 5, 7, 6   swap
             3, <u>2, 4</u>, 1, 8, 5, 7, 6   swap
             <u>3, 4</u>, 2, 1, 8, 5, 7, 6   swap
Fourth pass: 4, 3, 2, <u>1, 8</u>, 5, 7, 6   swap
             4, 3, <u>2, 8</u>, 1, 5, 7, 6   swap
             4, <u>3, 8</u>, 2, 1, 5, 7, 6   swap
             <u>4, 8</u>, 3, 2, 1, 5, 7, 6   swap
Fifth pass: 8, 4, 3, 2, <u>1, 5</u>, 7, 6   swap
             8, 4, 3, <u>2, 5</u>, 1, 7, 6   swap
             8, 4, <u>3, 5</u>, 2, 1, 7, 6   swap
             8, <u>4, 5</u>, 3, 2, 1, 7, 6   swap
             <u>8, 5</u>, 4, 3, 2, 1, 7, 6   no swap
Sixth pass: 8, 5, 4, 3, 2, <u>1, 7</u>, 6   swap
             8, 5, 4, 3, <u>2, 7</u>, 1, 6   swap
             8, 5, 4, <u>3, 7</u>, 2, 1, 6   swap
             8, 5, <u>4, 7</u>, 3, 2, 1, 6   swap
             8, <u>5, 7</u>, 4, 3, 2, 1, 6   swap
             <u>8, 7</u>, 5, 4, 3, 2, 1, 6   no swap
Seventh pass: 8, 7, 5, 4, 3, 2, <u>1, 6</u>   swap
             8, 7, 5, 4, 3, <u>2, 6</u>, 1   swap
             8, 7, 5, 4, <u>3, 6</u>, 2, 1   swap
             8, 7, 5, <u>4, 6</u>, 3, 2, 1   swap
             8, 7, <u>5, 6</u>, 4, 3, 2, 1   swap
             8, <u>7, 6</u>, 5, 4, 3, 2, 1   no swap

The list in descending order is: 8, 7, 6, 5, 4, 3, 2, 1

b) There were 26 comparisons and 22 swaps.
For this list the shuttle sort is only slightly quicker than the bubble sort (you have to make 28 comparisons to sort a list of 8 numbers with the bubble sort).

Q3 85%, 66%, 40%, 75%, 56%, 58%, 81%

First pass: <u>85, 66</u>, 40, 75, 56, 58, 81   no swap
Second pass: 85, <u>66, 40</u>, 75, 56, 58, 81   no swap
Third pass: 85, 66, <u>40, 75</u>, 56, 58, 81   swap
             85, <u>66, 75</u>, 40, 56, 58, 81   swap
             <u>85, 75</u>, 66, 40, 56, 58, 81   no swap
Fourth pass: 85, 75, 66, <u>40, 56</u>, 58, 81   swap
             85, 75, <u>66, 56</u>, 40, 58, 81   no swap
Fifth pass: 85, 75, 66, 56, <u>40, 58</u>, 81   swap
             85, 75, 66, <u>56, 58</u>, 40, 81   swap
             85, 75, <u>66, 58</u>, 56, 40, 81   no swap
Sixth pass: 85, 75, 66, 58, 56, <u>40, 81</u>   swap
             85, 75, 66, 58, <u>56, 81</u>, 40   swap
             85, 75, 66, <u>58, 81</u>, 56, 40   swap
             85, 75, <u>66, 81</u>, 58, 56, 40   swap
             85, <u>75, 81</u>, 66, 58, 56, 40   swap
             <u>85, 81</u>, 75, 66, 58, 56, 40   no swap

The list in descending order is:
85%, 81%, 75%, 66%, 58%, 56%, 40%

Q4 a) First pass: 23, 56, 4, 17, 60   no swap
        Second pass: 23, 56, 4, 17, 60   swap
                     23, 4, 56, 17, 60   swap
        Third pass: 4, 23, 56, 17, 60   swap
                     4, 23, 17, 56, 60   swap
                     4, 17, 23, 56, 60   no swap
        Fourth pass: 4, 17, 23, 56, 60   no swap

        The list in ascending order is: 4, 17, 23, 56, 60

b) 1 comparison was made, 0 swaps were made.

Q5 a) First pass:
        17.0, 16.8, 17.4, 15.9, 16.5, 18.0   swap
        Second pass:
        16.8, 17.0, 17.4, 15.9, 16.5, 18.0   no swap
        Third pass:
        16.8, 17.0, 17.4, 15.9, 16.5, 18.0   swap
        16.8, 17.0, 15.9, 17.4, 16.5, 18.0   swap
        16.8, 15.9, 17.0, 17.4, 16.5, 18.0   swap
        Fourth pass
        15.9, 16.8, 17.0, 17.4, 16.5, 18.0   swap
        15.9, 16.8, 17.0, 16.5, 17.4, 18.0   swap
        15.9, 16.8, 16.5, 17.0, 17.4, 18.0   swap
        15.9, 16.5, 16.8, 17.0, 17.4, 18.0   no swap
        Fifth pass:
        15.9, 16.5, 16.8, 17.0, 17.4, 18.0   no swap

        The list in ascending order is:
        15.9, 16.5, 16.8, 17.0, 17.4, 18.0

b) 10 comparisons were needed in total.

Q6 The list has 12 items so 12 − 1 = 11 passes are needed.

Q7 a) First pass: 13, 20, 5, 7, 25   swap
        Second pass: 20, 13, 5, 7, 25   no swap
        Third pass: 20, 13, 5, 7, 25   swap
                     20, 13, 7, 5, 25   no swap
        Fourth pass: 20, 13, 7, 5, 25   swap
                     20, 13, 7, 25, 5   swap
                     20, 13, 25, 7, 5   swap
                     20, 25, 13, 7, 5   swap

        The list in descending order is:
        25 mins, 20 mins, 13 mins, 7 mins, 5 mins

b) First pass: 1 exchange
    Second pass: 0 exchanges
    Third pass: 1 exchange
    Fourth pass: 4 exchanges

Q8 a) First pass: M, S, A, T, O, L   no swap
        Second pass: M, S, A, T, O, L   swap
                     M, A, S, T, O, L   swap
        Third pass: A, M, S, T, O, L   no swap
        Fourth pass: A, M, S, T, O, L   swap
                     A, M, S, O, T, L   swap
                     A, M, O, S, T, L   no swap
        Fifth pass: A, M, O, S, T, L   swap
                     A, M, O, S, L, T   swap
                     A, M, O, L, S, T   swap
                     A, M, L, O, S, T   swap
                     A, L, M, O, S, T   no swap

b) First pass: 1 comparison, 0 swaps
    Second pass: 2 comparisons, 2 swaps
    Third pass: 1 comparison, 0 swaps

Q9 First pass:
    12.1, 11.7 ,12.8, 11.3, 12.5, 13.0, 12.6   swap
    Second pass:
    11.7, 12.1, 12.8, 11.3, 12.5, 13.0, 12.6   no swap
    Third pass
    11.7 ,12.1, 12.8, 11.3, 12.5, 13.0, 12.6   swap
    11.7, 12.1, 11.3, 12.8, 12.5, 13.0, 12.6   swap
    11.7, 11.3, 12.1, 12.8, 12.5, 13.0, 12.6   swap
    Fourth pass
    11.3, 11.7, 12.1, 12.8, 12.5, 13.0, 12.6   swap
    11.3, 11.7, 12.1, 12.5, 12.8, 13.0, 12.6   no swap
    Fifth pass:
    11.3, 11.7, 12.1, 12.5, 12.8, 13.0, 12.6   no swap
    Sixth pass:
    11.3, 11.7, 12.1, 12.5, 12.8, 13.0, 12.6   swap
    11.3, 11.7, 12.1, 12.5, 12.8, 12.6, 13.0   swap
    11.3, 11.7, 12.1, 12.5, 12.6, 12.8, 13.0   no swap

    The list in ascending order is:
    11.3 s, 11.7 s, 12.1 s, 12.5 s, 12.6 s, 12.8 s, 13.0 S

Q10 a) £1.10, 85p, 90p, 99p, £1.30, 78p, 88p, 87p, 95p, £1.05

It's a bit easier to work with if the prices are all in the same units. Here we'll use pence, but you could also rewrite them all in pounds.

    First pass:
    110, 85, 90, 99, 130, 78, 88, 87, 95, 105   swap
    Second pass:
    85, 110, 90, 99, 130, 78, 88, 87, 95, 105   swap
    85, 90, 110, 99, 130, 78, 88, 87, 95, 105   no swap
    Third pass:
    85, 90, 110, 99, 130, 78, 88, 87, 95, 105   swap
    85, 90, 99, 110, 130, 78, 88, 87, 95, 105   no swap
    Fourth pass:
    85, 90, 99, 110, 130, 78, 88, 87, 95, 105   no swap
    Fifth pass:
    85, 90, 99, 110, 130, 78, 88, 87, 95, 105   swap
    85, 90, 99, 110, 78, 130, 88, 87, 95, 105   swap
    85, 90, 99, 78, 110, 130, 88, 87, 95, 105   swap
    85, 90, 78, 99, 110, 130, 88, 87, 95, 105   swap
    85, 78, 90, 99, 110, 130, 88, 87, 95, 105   swap
    Sixth pass:
    78, 85, 90, 99, 110, 130, 88, 87, 95, 105   swap
    78, 85, 90, 99, 110, 88, 130, 87, 95, 105   swap
    78, 85, 90, 99, 88, 110, 130, 87, 95, 105   swap
    78, 85, 90, 88, 99, 110, 130, 87, 95, 105   swap
    78, 85, 88, 90, 99, 110, 130, 87, 95, 105   no swap
    Seventh pass:
    78, 85, 88, 90, 99, 110, 130, 87, 95, 105   swap
    78, 85, 88, 90, 99, 110, 87, 130, 95, 105   swap
    78, 85, 88, 90, 99, 87, 110, 130, 95, 105   swap
    78, 85, 88, 90, 87, 99, 110, 130, 95, 105   swap
    78, 85, 88, 87, 90, 99, 110, 130, 95, 105   swap
    78, 85, 87, 88, 90, 99, 110, 130, 95, 105   no swap
    Eighth pass:
    78, 85, 87, 88, 90, 99, 110, 130, 95, 105   swap
    78, 85, 87, 88, 90, 99, 110, 95, 130, 105   swap
    78, 85, 87, 88, 90, 99, 95, 110, 130, 105   swap
    78, 85, 87, 88, 90, 95, 99, 110, 130, 105   no swap
    Ninth pass:
    78, 85, 87, 88, 90, 95, 99, 110, 130, 105   swap
    78, 85, 87, 88, 90, 95, 99, 110, 105, 130   swap
    78, 85, 87, 88, 90, 95, 99, 105, 110, 130   no swap

The list in ascending order is:
78p, 85p, 87p, 88p, 90p, 95p, 99p, £1.05, £1.10, £1.30

b) First pass: 1 swap
   Second pass: 1 swap
   Third pass: 1 swap
   Fourth pass: 0 swaps
   Fifth pass: 5 swaps
   Sixth pass: 4 swaps
   Seventh pass: 5 swaps
   Eighth pass: 3 swaps
   Ninth pass: 2 swaps

Exercise 2.3 — Shell sort

Q1 a) $n = 6$, so there are 3 subsets in the first pass:
Whole list: 14   3   7   15   8   5
First subset: 14   15
Second subset: 3   8
Third subset: 7   5
Reorder each subset:
First subset: 14   15
Second subset: 3   8
Third subset: 5   7
Put the list back together:
Whole list: 14   3   5   15   8   7
$3/2 = 1.5$ so now there's just one subset, so order the list using a shuttle sort:
First pass: <u>14   3</u>   5   15   8   7   swap
Second pass: 3   <u>14   5</u>   15   8   7   swap
                <u>3   5</u>   14   15   8   7   no swap
Third pass: 3   5   <u>14   15</u>   8   7   no swap
Fourth pass: 3   5   14   <u>15   8</u>   7   swap
                3   5   <u>14   8</u>   15   7   swap
                3   <u>5   8</u>   14   15   7   no swap
Fifth pass: 3   5   8   14   <u>15   7</u>   swap
                3   5   8   <u>14   7</u>   15   swap
                3   5   <u>8   7</u>   14   15   swap
                3   <u>5   7</u>   8   14   15   no swap
The list in ascending order is: 3, 5, 7, 8, 14, 15

b) $n = 8$, so there are 4 subsets in the first pass.
Whole list: 3.5   3.8   3.6   3.5   3.9   3.0   3.7   3.7
1st subset: 3.5   3.9
2nd subset: 3.8   3.0
3rd subset: 3.6   3.7
4th subset: 3.5   3.7
Reorder the subsets:
1st subset: 3.5   3.9
2nd subset: 3.0   3.8
3rd subset: 3.6   3.7
4th subset: 3.5   3.7
Whole list: 3.5   3.0   3.6   3.5   3.9   3.8   3.7   3.7
Now break the list up into $4/2 = 2$ subsets:
1st subset: 3.5   3.6   3.9   3.7
2nd subset: 3.0   3.5   3.8   3.7
Reorder the subsets:
1st subset: 3.5   3.6   3.7   3.9
2nd subset: 3.0   3.5   3.7   3.8
Whole list: 3.5   3.0   3.6   3.5   3.7   3.7   3.9   3.8

Using the shuttle sort on this list gives:
3.0, 3.5, 3.5, 3.6, 3.7, 3.7, 3.8, 3.9
The method for the shuttle sort is shown in part a).
When there's a repeated number, don't swap them.

c) $n = 11$, so there are 5 subsets in the first pass.
Whole list: 22 45 74 21 56 18 46 34 24 60 43
1st subset: 22   18   43
2nd subset: 45   46
3rd subset: 74   34
4th subset: 21   24
5th subset: 56   60
Reorder the subsets:
1st subset: 18   22   43
2nd subset: 45   46
3rd subset: 34   74
4th subset: 21   24
5th subset: 56   60
Whole list: 18 45 34 21 56 22 46 74 24 60 43
Now break the list up into 2 subsets ($5/2 = 2.5$):
1st subset: 18   34   56   46   24   43
2nd subset: 45   21   22   74   60
Reorder the subsets:
1st subset: 18   24   34   43   46   56
2nd subset: 21   22   45   60   74
Whole list: 18 21 24 22 34 45 43 60 46 74 56
Now use a shuttle sort to reorder and get:
18, 21, 22, 24, 34, 43, 45, 46, 56, 60, 74

Q2 $n = 8$, so there are 4 subsets in the first pass.
Whole list: 6   3.5   8   2.5   4.5   7.5   5.5   5
1st subset: 6   4.5
2nd subset: 3.5   7.5
3rd subset: 8   5.5
4th subset: 2.5   5
Reorder the subsets:
1st subset: 4.5   6
2nd subset: 3.5   7.5
3rd subset: 5.5   8
4th subset: 2.5   5
Whole list: 4.5   3.5   5.5   2.5   6   7.5   8   5
Now break the list up into 2 subsets ($4/2 = 2$):
1st subset: 4.5   5.5   6   8
2nd subset: 3.5   2.5   7.5   5
Reorder the subsets:
1st subset: 4.5   5.5   6   8
2nd subset: 2.5   3.5   5   7.5
Whole list: 4.5   2.5   5.5   3.5   6   5   8   7.5
Now use a shuttle sort to reorder: 2.5 min, 3.5 min, 4.5 min, 5 min, 5.5 min, 6 min, 7.5 min, 8 min

Q3 $n = 10$, so there are 5 subsets in the first pass.

Whole list:	3	6	7	1	10	12	2	8	13	4
1st subset:	3					12				
2nd subset:		6					2			
3rd subset:			7					8		
4th subset:				1					13	
5th subset:					10					4

Reorder the subsets:

1st subset:	12					3				
2nd subset:		6					2			
3rd subset:			8					7		
4th subset:				13					1	
5th subset:					10					4
Whole list:	12	6	8	13	10	3	2	7	1	4

Now break the list up into 2 subsets (5/2 = 2.5):

1st subset:	12		8		10		2		1	
2nd subset:		6		13		3		7		4

Reorder the subsets:

1st subset:	12		10		8		2		1	
2nd subset:		13		7		6		4		3
Whole list:	12	13	10	7	8	6	2	4	1	3

Reorder using a shuttle sort to get:
13 years, 12 years, 10 years, 8 years, 7 years, 6 years, 4 years, 3 years, 2 years, 1 year

Q4 a) $n = 8$, so there are 4 subsets in the first pass.

Whole list:	10	4	0	2	8	3	5	4
1st subset:	10				8			
2nd subset:		4				3		
3rd subset:			0				5	
4th subset:				2				4

Reorder the subsets:

1st subset:	8				10			
2nd subset:		3				4		
3rd subset:			0				5	
4th subset:				2				4
Whole list:	8	3	0	2	10	4	5	4

Now break the list up into 2 subsets (4/2 = 2):

1st subset:	8		0		10		5	
2nd subset:		3		2		4		4

Reorder the subsets:

1st subset:	0		5		8		10	
2nd subset:		2		3		4		4
Whole list:	0	2	5	3	8	4	10	4

Reorder using a shuttle sort to get: 0 cups, 2 cups, 3 cups, 4 cups, 4 cups, 5 cups, 8 cups, 10 cups

b) 4 comparisons   **c)** 2 swaps

Q5 $n = 8$, so there are 4 subsets in the first pass.

Whole list:	N	P	E	S	B	M	T	O
1st subset:	N				B			
2nd subset:		P				M		
3rd subset:			E				T	
4th subset:				S				O

Reorder the subsets:

1st subset:	B				N			
2nd subset:		M				P		
3rd subset:			E				T	
4th subset:				O				S
Whole list:	B	M	E	O	N	P	T	S

Now break the list up into 4/2 = 2 subsets:

1st subset:	B		E		N		T	
2nd subset:		M		O		P		S

Reorder the subsets (in fact they're in order):

1st subset:	B		E		N		T	
2nd subset:		M		O		P		S
Whole list:	B	M	E	O	N	P	T	S

Reordering using the shuttle sort gives:
B, E, M, N, O, P, S, T

Q6 $n = 9$, so you need 4 subsets on the first pass.

Whole list:	10	8	12	12	20	15	7	10	18
1st subset:	10				20				18
2nd subset:		8				15			
3rd subset:			12				7		
4th subset:				12				10	

Reorder the subsets:

1st subset:	20				18				10
2nd subset:		15				8			
3rd subset:			12				7		
4th subset:				12				10	
Whole list:	20	15	12	12	18	8	7	10	10

Now break the list up into 4/2 = 2 subsets:

1st subset:	20		12		18		7		10
2nd subset:		15		12		8		10	

Reorder the subsets:

1st subset:	20		18		12		10		7
2nd subset:		15		12		10		8	
Whole list:	20	15	18	12	12	10	10	8	7

Reorder using a shuttle sort to get: 20 km, 18 km, 15 km, 12 km, 12 km, 10 km, 10 km, 8 km, 7 km.

The Shell sort has worked particularly well here — you only had to make one swap in the shuttle sort at the end.

Q7 $n = 10$, so you need 5 subsets on the first pass.

List: 8.39 6.02 4.27 4.24 4.04 4.12 4.41 5.03 2.50 3.48

1st:	8.39	4.12	
2nd:	6.02	4.41	
3rd:	4.27	5.03	
4th:	4.24	2.50	
5th:	4.04	3.48	

Reorder the subsets:

1st:	4.12	8.39	
2nd:	4.41	6.02	
3rd:	4.27	5.03	
4th:	2.50	4.24	
5th:	3.48	4.04	

List: 4.12 4.41 4.27 2.50 3.48 8.39 6.02 5.03 4.24 4.04

Now break the list up into 2 subsets (5/2 = 2.5):

1st:	4.12	4.27	3.48	6.02	4.24
2nd:	4.41	2.50	8.39	5.03	4.04

Reorder the subsets:

1st:	3.48	4.12	4.24	4.27	6.02
2nd:	2.50	4.04	4.41	5.03	8.39

List: 3.48 2.50 4.12 4.04 4.24 4.41 4.27 5.03 6.02 8.39

Reorder using a shuttle sort to get:
2.50, 3.48, 4.04, 4.12, 4.24, 4.27, 4.41, 5.03, 6.02, 8.39

Q8   **a)** $n = 7$, so you need 3 subsets on the first pass.

Whole list:	1.45 1.25 1.30 1.10 1.05 1.50 1.35		
1st subset:	1.45	1.10	1.35
2nd subset:	1.25	1.05	
3rd subset:	1.30	1.50	

Reorder the subsets:

1st subset:	1.10	1.35	1.45
2nd subset:	1.05	1.25	
3rd subset:	1.30	1.50	
Whole list:	1.10 1.05 1.30 1.35 1.25 1.50 1.45		

Reorder using a shuttle sort to get:
1.05, 1.10, 1.25, 1.30, 1.35, 1.45, 1.50

b)   9 comparisons were made.

The second pass was the final pass, so you're being asked for the number of comparisons made in the shuttle sort of the whole list.

Q9   **a)**   **(i)**   32 ÷ 2 = 16 subsets

   (ii)   5 (16, 8, 4 and 2 subsets, and the final shuttle sort)

b)   **(i)**   18/2 = 9, so 9 subsets are needed.

   (ii)   List: 2 7 5 9 2 5 9 1 3 1 6 9 5 6 4 2 8 0

1st:	2	1		
2nd:	7	6		
3rd:	5	9		
4th:	9	5		
5th:	2	6		
6th:	5	4		
7th:	9	2		
8th:	1	8		
9th:	3	0		

Reorder the subsets:

1st:	1	2		
2nd:	6	7		
3rd:	5	9		
4th:	5	9		
5th:	2	6		
6th:	4	5		
7th:	2	9		
8th:	1	8		
9th:	0	3		

List: 1 6 5 5 2 4 2 1 0 2 7 9 9 6 5 9 8 3

That's one pass.

Now break the list up into 4 subsets (9/2 = 4.5):

1st:	1	2	0	9	8
2nd:	6	4	2	6	3
3rd:	5	2	7	5	
4th:	5	1	9	9	

Reorder the subsets:

1st:	0	1	2	8	9
2nd:	2	3	4	6	6
3rd:	2	5	5	7	
4th:	1	5	9	9	

List: 0 2 2 1 1 3 5 5 2 4 5 9 8 6 7 9 9 6

Exercise 2.4 — Quick sort

Q1 a) Use the first item as the first pivot.

First step:
3, 4, 6, 2, <u>7</u>, 8, 9

Second step:
2, <u>3</u>, 4, 6, <u>7</u>, <u>8</u>, 9

Third step:
2, <u>3</u>, <u>4</u>, 6, <u>7</u>, **8**, 9

The only remaining list has 1 item, so the numbers in ascending order are:
2, 3, 4, 6, 7, 8, 9

Here the pivot being used was underlined, and any items whose position was definite were made bold. We'll use this system throughout the rest of this exercise.

b) 7, 3, 8, 4

Q2 a) First step:
A, F, G H, <u>M</u>, N, Q

Second step:
<u>A</u>, F, G, H, **M**, <u>N</u>, Q

Third step:
<u>A</u>, <u>F</u>, G, H, **M**, **N**, **Q**

Fourth step:
A, **F**, <u>G</u>, H, **M**, **N**, **Q**

The remaining list only has 1 item, so the letters in alphabetical order are:
A, F, G, H, M, N, Q

b) M, A, N, F, G

Q3 a) First step:
103, 107, <u>101</u>, 96, 94, 98

Second step:
107, <u>103</u>, **101**, 98, <u>96</u>, 94

All the remaining lists only have 1 item, so the numbers in descending order are:
107, 103, 101, 98, 96, 94

b) 101, 103, 96

Q4 a) First step:
3.9, 3.3, 3.7, 4.1, 3.2, 4.2, 3.8, <u>4.4</u>

Second step:
3.3, 3.7, 3.2, 3.8, <u>3.9</u>, 4.1, 4.2, **4.4**

Third step:
3.2, <u>3.3</u>, 3.7, 3.8, **3.9**, <u>4.1</u>, 4.2, **4.4**

Fourth step:
3.2, **3.3**, <u>3.7</u>, 3.8, **3.9**, **4.1**, <u>4.2</u>, **4.4**

The remaining list only has 1 item, so the weights in ascending order are:
3.2, 3.3, 3.7, 3.8, 3.9, 4.1, 4.2, 4.4

b) 4.4, 3.9, 3.3, 4.1 and 3.7

Q5 First step:
T, <u>S</u>, O, R, I, N, G

Second step:
T, **S**, R, <u>O</u>, I, N, G

Third step:
T, **S**, **R**, <u>O</u>, N, <u>I</u>, G

All the remaining lists have only 1 item, so the letters in reverse alphabetical order are:
T, S, R, O, N, I, G

Q6 a) First step:
11.0, 11.3, 12.3, 11.7, 12.9, 12.8, <u>13.1</u>

Second step:
<u>11.0</u>, 11.3, 12.3, 11.7, 12.9, 12.8, **13.1**

Third step:
11.0, <u>11.3</u>, 12.3, 11.7, 12.9, 12.8, **13.1**

Fourth step:
11.0, **11.3**, 11.7, <u>12.3</u>, 12.9, 12.8, **13.1**

Fifth step:
11.0, **11.3**, **11.7**, <u>12.3</u>, 12.8, <u>12.9</u>, **13.1**

The remaining list only has 1 item, so the times in ascending order are:
11.0 s, 11.3 s, 11.7 s, 12.3 s, 12.8 s, 12.9 s, 13.1 s

b) 13.1, 11.0, 11.3, 12.3 and 12.9

Q7 a) First step:
18.0, 15.4, 23.0, <u>14.4</u>, 7.6, 10.6

Second step:
23.0, <u>18.0</u>, 15.4, **14.4**, 10.6, <u>7.6</u>

All the remaining lists only have 1 item, so the weights in descending order are:
23.0 kg, 18.0 kg, 15.4 kg, 14.4 kg, 10.6 kg, 7.6 kg

b) 14.4, 18.0, 7.6

Q8 a) First step:
Babatunde, <u>Ben</u>, Jane, Mary, Pete, Rob, Ian, Freda, Lorna, Kim

Second step:
Babatunde, **Ben**, Ian, Freda, <u>Jane</u>, Mary, Pete, Rob, Lorna, Kim,

Third step:
Babatunde, **Ben**, Freda, <u>Ian</u>, **Jane**, Lorna, Kim, <u>Mary</u>, Pete, Rob

Fourth step:
Babatunde, **Ben**, **Freda**, <u>Ian</u>, **Jane**, Kim, <u>Lorna</u>, **Mary**, <u>Pete</u>, Rob

All the remaining lists have only 1 item, so the names in alphabetical order are:
Babatunde, Ben, Freda, Ian, Jane, Kim, Lorna, Mary, Pete, Rob

It's a good idea to code the names (e.g. Be, Ja, Ma etc.) so you don't have to write them out in full each time.

b) Ben, Jane, Ian, Mary, Lorna, Pete

Review Exercise — Chapter 1

Q1 **a)** Input: raw ingredients (vegetables, water etc.)
Output: vegetable soup.

b) Input: starting point (Leicester Square)
Output: final destination (the Albert Hall)

c) Input: components (e.g. shelves, screws etc.)
Output: finished TV cabinet

Q2

x	y
17	56
8	112
4	224
2	448
1	896
Total	952

So 17 × 56 = 952.

Q3 $a = 16$

n	b	Output	n = a?
1	16	1	No
2	8	2	No
3	$5\frac{1}{3}$		No
4	4	4	No
5	$3\frac{1}{5}$		No
6	$2\frac{2}{3}$		No
7	$2\frac{2}{7}$		No
8	2	8	No
9	$1\frac{7}{9}$		No
10	$1\frac{3}{5}$		No
11	$1\frac{5}{11}$		No
12	$1\frac{1}{3}$		No
13	$1\frac{3}{13}$		No
14	$1\frac{1}{7}$		No
15	$1\frac{1}{15}$		No
16	1	16	Yes

So the factors of 16 are 1, 2, 4, 8 and 16.

Q4
<u>72, 57</u>, 64, 54, 68, 71   swap
57, <u>72, 64</u>, 54, 68, 71   swap
57, 64, <u>72, 54</u>, 68, 71   swap
57, 64, 54, <u>72, 68</u>, 71   swap
57, 64, 54, 68, <u>72, 71</u>   swap
57, 64, 54, 68, 71, 72   end of first pass.
After the second pass, the list is:
57, 54, 64, 68, 71, 72.
After the third pass, the list is:
54, 57, 64, 68, 71, 72.
There are no swaps on the fourth pass,
so the list is in order. 4 passes were needed
(the final pass with no swaps is included).

Q5 The maximum number of comparisons is
½ × 11 × 12 = 66.

Q6 First pass: <u>21, 11</u>, 23, 19, 28, 26   swap
Second pass: 11, <u>21, 23</u>, 19, 28, 26   no swap
Third pass: 11, 21, <u>23, 19</u>, 28, 26   swap
               11, <u>21, 19</u>, 23, 28, 26   swap
               <u>11, 19</u>, 21, 23, 28, 26   no swap
Fourth pass: 11, 19, 21, <u>23, 28</u>, 26   no swap
Fifth pass: 11, 19, 21, 23, <u>28, 26</u>   swap
               11, 19, 21, <u>23, 26</u>, 28   no swap

Q7 $n = 7$, so you want 7/2 = 3.5 = 3 subsets:
Whole list: 101   98   79   113   87   108   84
Subset 1:   101   113   84
Subset 2:   98   87
Subset 3:   79   108
Sorting these subsets gives:
Subset 1:   84   101   113
Subset 2:   87   98
Subset 3:   79   108
Whole list: 84   87   79   101   98   108   113
Now divide the list up into 3/2 = 1.5 = 1 subset and
use a shuttle sort to sort the numbers:
First pass: <u>84, 87</u>, 79, 101, 98, 108, 113 no swap
Second pass: 84, <u>87, 79</u>, 101, 98, 108, 113 swap
               <u>84, 79</u>, 87, 101, 98, 108, 113 swap
Third pass: 79, 84, <u>87, 101</u>, 98, 108, 113 no swap
Fourth pass: 79, 84, 87, <u>101, 98</u>, 108, 113 swap
               79, 84, <u>87, 98</u>, 101, 108, 113 no swap
Fifth pass: 79, 84, 87, 98, <u>101, 108</u>, 113 no swap
Sixth pass: 79, 84, 87, 98, 101, <u>108, 113</u> no swap
The shuttle sort is completed, so the list is in order.

Q8 **a)** First pass:
<u>23, 29</u>, 17, 23, 24, 30, 19, 252   swap
Second pass:
29, <u>23, 17</u>, 23, 24, 30, 19, 252   no swap
Third pass:
29, 23, <u>17, 23</u>, 24, 30, 19, 252   swap
29, <u>23, 23</u>, 17, 24, 30, 19, 252   no swap
Fourth pass:
29, 23, 23, <u>17, 24</u>, 30, 19, 252   swap
29, 23, <u>23, 24</u>, 17, 30, 19, 252   swap
29, <u>23, 24</u>, 23, 17, 30, 19, 252   swap
<u>29, 24</u>, 23, 23, 17, 30, 19, 252   no swap
Fifth pass:
29, 24, 23, 23, <u>17, 30</u>, 19, 252   swap
29, 24, 23, <u>23, 30</u>, 17, 19, 252   swap
29, 24, <u>23, 30</u>, 23, 17, 19, 252   swap
29, <u>24, 30</u>, 23, 23, 17, 19, 252   swap
<u>29, 30</u>, 24, 23, 23, 17, 19, 252   swap
Sixth pass:
30, 29, 24, 23, 23, <u>17, 19</u>, 252   swap
30, 29, 24, 23, <u>23, 19</u>, 17, 252   no swap

Seventh pass:
30, 29, 24, 23, 23, 19, <u>17, 252</u>   swap
30, 29, 24, 23, 23, <u>19, 252</u>, 17   swap
30, 29, 24, 23, <u>23, 252</u>, 19, 17   swap
30, 29, 24, <u>23, 252</u>, 23, 19, 17   swap
30, 29, <u>24, 252</u>, 23, 23, 19, 17   swap
30, <u>29, 252</u>, 24, 23, 23, 19, 17   swap
<u>30, 252</u>, 29, 24, 23, 23, 19, 17   swap

So the list in descending order is:
252, 30, 29, 24, 23, 23, 19, 17

b) The list is in descending order, so to sort it into ascending order you would need to make the maximum number of comparisons.

For 8 items, this is $7 + 6 + 5 + 4 + 3 + 2 + 1 = 28$ (or $\frac{1}{2}(7 \times 8) = 28$)

Q9 $n = 7$, so you want $7/2 = 3.5 = 3$ subsets:
Whole list: 0.8   1.2   0.7   0.5   0.4   1.0   0.1

Subset 1:   0.8   0.5   0.1
Subset 2:   1.2   0.4
Subset 3:   0.7   1.0

Sorting these subsets gives:
Subset 1:   0.1   0.5   0.8
Subset 2:   0.4   1.2
Subset 3:   0.7   1.0

Whole list: 0.1   0.4   0.7   0.5   1.2   1.0   0.8

Now divide the list up into $3/2 = 1.5 = 1$ subset and use a shuttle sort to sort the numbers:

First pass:
<u>0.1, 0.4</u>, 0.7, 0.5, 1.2, 1.0, 0.8   no swap

Second pass:
0.1, <u>0.4, 0.7</u>, 0.5, 1.2, 1.0, 0.8   no swap

Third pass:
0.1, 0.4, <u>0.7, 0.5</u>, 1.2, 1.0, 0.8   swap
0.1, <u>0.4, 0.5</u>, 0.7, 1.2, 1.0, 0.8   no swap

Fourth pass:
0.1, 0.4, 0.5, <u>0.7, 1.2</u>, 1.0, 0.8   no swap

Fifth pass:
0.1, 0.4, 0.5, 0.7, <u>1.2, 1.0</u>, 0.8   swap
0.1, 0.4, 0.5, <u>0.7, 1.0</u>, 1.2, 0.8   no swap

Sixth pass:
0.1, 0.4, 0.5, 0.7, 1.0, <u>1.2, 0.8</u>   swap
0.1, 0.4, 0.5, 0.7, <u>1.0, 0.8</u>, 1.2   swap
0.1, 0.4, 0.5, <u>0.7, 0.8</u>, 1.0, 1.2   no swap

The shuttle sort is completed, so the list, in order, is:
0.1, 0.4, 0.5, 0.7, 0.8, 1.0, 1.2

Q10 carrot leek endive <u>onion</u> parsnip swede turnip

<u>carrot</u> leek endive **onion** <u>parsnip</u> swede turnip

carrot endive <u>leek</u> **onion parsnip** <u>swede</u> turnip

So the list in alphabetical order is:
carrot endive leek onion parsnip swede turnip

Exam-Style Questions — Chapter 1

Q1 a) First step:
<u>77</u>, 83, 96, 105, 78, 89, 112, 80, 98, 94 *[1 mark]*
Second step:
<u>77</u>, 78, 80, <u>83</u>, 96, 105, 89, 112, 98, 94 *[1 mark]*
Third step:
<u>77</u>, <u>78</u>, 80, <u>83</u>, 89, 94, <u>96</u>, 105, 112, 98 *[1 mark]*
Fourth step:
<u>77</u>, <u>78</u>, 80, <u>83</u>, 89, 94, <u>96</u>, 98, <u>105</u>, 112 *[1 mark]*

All the remaining lists have 1 item, so the list is in order.

b) (i) After the first pass, the largest number in the list will be in the correct position. *[1 mark]*

(ii) There are 6 items, so the items will all be in order after 5 passes. *[1 mark]*

(iii) The maximum number of swaps is $5 + 4 + 3 + 2 + 1 = 15$ *[1 mark]*

Q2 a) 1st pass: <u>1.3, 0.8</u>, 1.8, 0.5, 1.2, 0.2, 0.9 swap
2nd pass: 0.8, <u>1.3, 1.8</u>, 0.5, 1.2, 0.2, 0.9 no swap
3rd pass: 0.8, 1.3, <u>1.8, 0.5</u>, 1.2, 0.2, 0.9 swap
0.8, <u>1.3, 0.5</u>, 1.8, 1.2, 0.2, 0.9 swap
<u>0.8, 0.5</u>, 1.3, 1.8, 1.2, 0.2, 0.9 swap
[1 mark]
4th pass: 0.5, 0.8, 1.3, <u>1.8, 1.2</u>, 0.2, 0.9 swap
0.5, 0.8, <u>1.3, 1.2</u>, 1.8, 0.2, 0.9 swap
0.5, <u>0.8, 1.2</u>, 1.3, 1.8, 0.2, 0.9 no swap
[1 mark]
5th pass: 0.5, 0.8, 1.2, 1.3, <u>1.8, 0.2</u>, 0.9 swap
0.5, 0.8, 1.2, <u>1.3, 0.2</u>, 1.8, 0.9 swap
0.5, 0.8, <u>1.2, 0.2</u>, 1.3, 1.8, 0.9 swap
0.5, <u>0.8, 0.2</u>, 1.2, 1.3, 1.8, 0.9 swap
<u>0.5, 0.2</u>, 0.8, 1.2, 1.3, 1.8, 0.9 swap
[1 mark]
6th pass: 0.2, 0.5, 0.8, 1.2, 1.3, <u>1.8, 0.9</u> swap
0.2, 0.5, 0.8, 1.2, <u>1.3, 0.9</u>, 1.8 swap
0.2, 0.5, 0.8, <u>1.2, 0.9</u>, 1.3, 1.8 swap
0.2, 0.5, <u>0.8, 0.9</u>, 1.2, 1.3, 1.8 no swap
[1 mark]

There are 7 numbers, so $7 - 1 = 6$ passes *[1 mark]*.

b) On the first pass, there was 1 comparison and 1 swap *[1 mark]*.

Q3 First step:
Adam, Dan, James, Helen, <u>Mark</u>, Stella, Robert
[1 mark]
Second step:
Adam, Dan, James, Helen, **Mark**, Robert, <u>Stella</u>
[1 mark]
Third step:
Adam, <u>Dan</u>, James, Helen, **Mark**, **Robert**, **Stella**
[1 mark]
Fourth step:
Adam, **Dan**, Helen, <u>James</u>, **Mark**, **Robert**, **Stella**
[1 mark]

The remaining list has 1 item so the list is in order.

Q4 **a)**

N	C	D	Output	N = A?
1	8	12	1	No
2	4	6	2	No
3	$2\frac{2}{3}$	4		No
4	2	3	4	No
5	$1\frac{3}{5}$	$2\frac{2}{5}$		No
6	$1\frac{1}{3}$	2		No
7	$1\frac{1}{7}$	$1\frac{5}{7}$		No
8	1	$1\frac{1}{2}$		Yes

The results are 1, 2 and 4.

[3 marks available — 1 mark for correct values of C, 1 mark for correct values of D, 1 mark for correct outputs (there should be 3 outputs)]

b) **(i)** This algorithm produces the common factors of the inputs *[1 mark]*.

(ii) The output would be 1 *[1 mark]*, as 19 and 25 have no common factors except 1 *[1 mark]*.

c) E.g. if $A = 0$, the algorithm will fail because C will always be 0 *[1 mark]*.
Anything sensible will do here — you could have said that the algorithm will never stop as N will never equal A.

Q5 **a)** On the first pass, there were 4 comparisons *[1 mark]* and 3 swaps *[1 mark]*.

You can work this out by calculating how many subsets are needed — 8/2 = 4 subsets, each with 2 numbers in, so there will be 4 comparisons. You have to see how many numbers have swapped places — in this case, 71 and 59 have swapped, 63 and 60 have swapped and 72 and 55 have swapped, so there were 3 swaps.

b) On the second pass, you need 4/2 = 2 subsets:
First subset: 54   60   68   63
Second subset: 59   55   71   72

[1 mark]

Putting these in order gives:
First subset: 54   60   63   68
Second subset: 55   59   71   72

[1 mark]

Putting the list back together gives:
54, 55, 60, 59, 63, 71, 68, 72 *[1 mark]*.

You now need 2/2 = 1 subset, this is just the list above. Sort this using a shuttle sort:

1st pass: <u>54, 55</u>, 60, 59, 63, 71, 68, 72   no swap

2nd pass: 54, <u>55, 60</u>, 59, 63, 71, 68, 72   no swap

3rd pass: 54, 55, <u>60, 59</u>, 63, 71, 68, 72   swap
              54, <u>55, 59</u>, 60, 63, 71, 68, 72   no swap

4th pass: 54, 55, 59, <u>60, 63</u>, 71, 68, 72   no swap

5th pass: 54, 55, 59, 60, <u>63, 71</u>, 68, 72   no swap

6th pass: 54, 55, 59, 60, 63, <u>71, 68</u>, 72   swap
              54, 55, 59, 60, <u>63, 68</u>, 71, 72   no swap

7th pass: 54, 55, 59, 60, 63, 68, <u>71, 72</u>   no swap

[2 marks for correct shuttle sort, or 1 mark for correct method but with mistakes made]

Chapter 2: Algorithms on Graphs

1. Graphs

Exercise 1.1 — Paths and cycles

Q1 E.g.

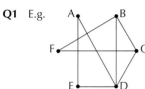

Your graph might look quite different to this — for example, you could have put the vertices in a completely different arrangement. The important thing is that all the connections are right.

Q2 a) Not a path, as there is no edge UR in the graph.

b) Is a path.

c) Not a path, as R is repeated.

Q3 E.g.

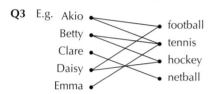

Q4 a) 7   **b)** 11   **c)** 67

Q5 E.g.

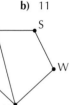

a) KNWS or KNLS

b) WNLSW or WSLNW

c) There is no cycle starting with K, because you'd have to pass through N twice to get back to K.

Only Nelly likes Kevin. Poor Kevin.

d)

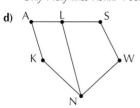

E.g. ALSWNKA is a Hamiltonian cycle.
You could have started at any node here, or gone the other way round — e.g. AKNWSLA.

Q6 E.g.

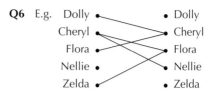

Q7 ABCDEA, AEDCBA, ABCEDA, ADECBA, ABECDA, ADCEBA, ADCBEA, AEBCDA

Q8 a) 2 (ACA and ACA (going the other way))

b) 8 — CDEC, CEDC, CDFGC, CGFDC, CEDFGC, CGFDEC, CAC and CAC (going the other way).

c) B

Exercise 1.2 — Networks and digraphs

Q1 a) E.g.

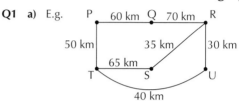

b) 30 km + 70 km = 100 km

Q2 a) Complete. Every vertex is connected to every other vertex.

b) Not complete. There are no connections for AD, BE, and CF.

Q3 a)   **b)**

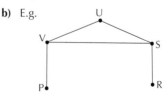

Q4 Each of the 40 vertices is connected by an edge to 39 other vertices, giving 40 × 39 = 1560 — but this counts each edge twice (once at each end), so the actual number of vertices is (40 × 39) ÷ 2 = 1560 ÷ 2 = 780

Q5 a) (ii) is not a subgraph of *G* because it contains an edge (QS) which is not in *G*.

b) E.g.

Q6 a) Simple   **b)** Not simple

c) Not simple   **d)** Simple

Exercise 1.3 — Trees and spanning trees

Q1 **a)** Yes. E.g. they are connected by the path ECF.

    b) **(i)** ECD   **(ii)** BCD, BAFCD

Q2 **a)** Tree.

    b) Not a tree — not connected.

    c) Not a tree — not connected (there is no vertex in the middle).

    d) Tree.

    e) Not a tree — the graph contains cycles.

Q3 **a)** Connected

    b) Not connected

    c) Not connected

Q4 E.g.

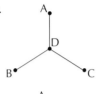 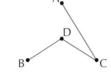

Q5 E.g.

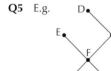

Exercise 1.4 — Degree of a vertex

Q1 **a)**

Vertex	A	B	C	D	E	F	G
Degree	1	2	1	1	4	2	3

    b)

Vertex	A	B	C	D	E	F	G	H
Degree	1	2	3	3	5	2	4	0

    c)

Vertex	H	I	J	K	L
Degree	2	4	4	2	4

    d)

Vertex	A	B	C	D	E	F	G	H	I	J	K	L	M
Degree	3	2	6	2	3	3	4	4	2	4	2	1	4

Q2 The sum of the degrees in Aroon's table is 11. This must be wrong, because the sum of the degrees in a graph is always an even number.

Q3 **a)** 14   **b)** 28

Q4 **a)** E.g.   **b)** E.g.

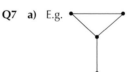 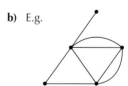

    c) E.g.   **d)** E.g.

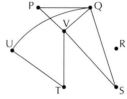

Q5 $(3 + 5 + 6 + 2) \div 2 = 16 \div 2 = 8$

Q6 Edges deleted: UV, RT

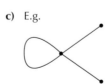

Q7 **a)** E.g.   **b)** E.g.

    c) E.g.   **d)** E.g.

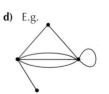

Q8 **a)** The sum of the degrees of the vertices is 14, so the number of edges is $14 \div 2 = 7$. So Sara's graph has 4 vertices and 7 edges, but a tree with 4 vertices would have only 3 edges.

    b) 4

Exercise 1.5 — Adjacency matrices and distance matrices

Q1 a)

	A	B	C	D	E	F
A	0	1	0	0	0	0
B	1	0	1	2	0	1
C	0	1	0	1	0	1
D	0	2	1	0	1	0
E	0	0	0	1	0	2
F	0	1	1	0	2	0

b)

	P	Q	R	S	T
P	0	1	0	0	1
Q	1	0	1	0	1
R	0	1	0	0	0
S	0	0	0	2	1
T	1	1	0	1	2

c)

	A	B	C	D	E	F	G	H	I
A	0	1	0	0	1	0	0	0	0
B	1	0	1	0	2	0	0	0	0
C	0	1	0	2	0	0	0	0	0
D	0	0	2	0	1	0	0	0	0
E	1	2	0	1	0	0	0	0	0
F	0	0	0	0	0	0	1	1	1
G	0	0	0	0	0	1	0	1	0
H	0	0	0	0	0	1	1	0	0
I	0	0	0	0	0	1	0	0	0

d)

	S	T	U	V	W	X	Y	Z
S	0	1	1	0	1	0	0	1
T	1	0	1	1	1	0	0	0
U	1	1	0	1	0	1	0	0
V	0	1	1	0	1	0	1	0
W	1	1	0	1	0	1	0	0
X	0	0	1	0	1	2	0	0
Y	0	0	0	1	0	0	0	3
Z	1	0	0	0	0	0	3	0

This one's pretty tricky — it would be easy to get confused. You just have to take your time and try not to get caught out when the edges cross over each other.

Q2 a) E.g.

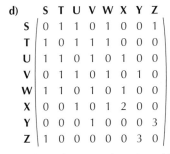

b) E.g.

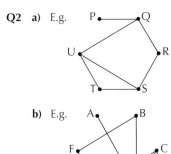

c) E.g.

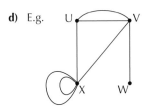

d) E.g.

U V
X W

Q3

	W	X	Y	Z
W	0	1	1	1
X	1	0	1	1
Y	1	1	0	1
Z	1	1	1	0

Q4 a)

	A	B	C	D	E	F
A	–	23	12	15	–	–
B	23	–	–	–	34	–
C	12	–	–	10	–	–
D	15	–	10	–	7	21
E	–	34	–	7	–	–
F	–	–	–	21	–	–

b)

	V	W	X	Y	Z
V	–	–	15	–	10
W	–	–	9	22	–
X	15	9	–	17	–
Y	–	22	17	15	12
Z	10	–	–	12	8

c)

	P	Q	R	S
P	–	10	12	15
Q	10	–	14	25
R	–	13	–	–
S	15	25	–	16

d)

	A	B	C	D	E	F
A	–	4	–	–	–	3
B	–	–	–	–	10	–
C	8	–	–	–	–	–
D	–	–	6	–	–	–
E	–	–	8	–	–	–
F	–	–	7	5	–	–

Q5 a) E.g.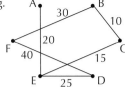

b) E.g.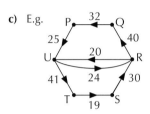

c) E.g.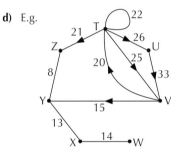

d) E.g.

e) (i) There's no route from W, X, Y or Z to T, U and V.

(ii) Reverse the direction of either edge TZ or edge VY (or make one of them undirected).

2. Minimum Spanning Trees

Exercise 2.1 — Kruskal's algorithm

Q1 a) BC (12), EG (13), BG (14), AB (14), CG (15), CE (16), AF (16), FG (17), CD (18), DG (20), AG (21), AC (23), EF (25), DE (26), BF (26)

Arcs with the same weight can be written in either order e.g. AB could come before BG in this list.

b) First choose arc BC (weight 12), then EG (weight 13). The parts of the graphs are not connected at this stage.

Now choose either BG or AB (weight 14). I'll choose BG as that was first in my list.

Next add the other arc of weight 14, AB, to get:

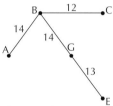

The next choice would be CG (weight 15), but that would create a cycle, so it can't be added.

For the same reason don't choose CE, so next choice is AF (weight 16). Note that you're always trying to add a vertex that is not already attached to the tree, or to join two bits of the tree together.

Finally choose CD (weight 18). All vertices are now connected so the minimum spanning tree is complete.

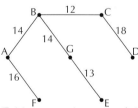

To join seven vertices you need six arcs in the spanning tree — this is a good way to check your answer. For n vertices you'd need (n − 1) arcs.

c) The arcs chosen were BC (12), EG (13), BG (14), AB (14), AF (16) and CD (18).

So the total weight of the spanning tree is 12 + 13 + 14 + 14 + 16 + 18 = 87

Q2 a) 13 **b)** 31 **c)** 97

Q3 a)

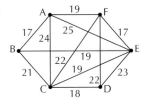

b) E.g. In ascending order, the arcs are: AB (17), EF (17), CD (18), AF (19), BE (19), CE (19), BC (21), CF (22), DF (22), DE (23), AC (24), AE (25).

Selecting the arcs for the tree, avoiding any cycles, gives the following list:
AB (17), EF (17), CD (18), AF (19), CE(19)

And the minimum spanning tree is:

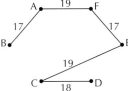

The total weight is 17 + 17 + 18 + 19 + 19 = 90.

The smallest distance needed to join the towns is 90 km.

You might have a slightly different MST that includes arc BE instead of AF.

Q4 Weighted network, e.g.:

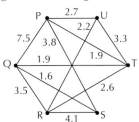

In ascending order, the arcs are:
QS (1.6), PT (1.9), QT (1.9), RU (2.2), RT (2.6), PU (2.7), TU (3.3), QR (3.5), PS (3.8), RS (4.1), PQ (7.5)

Selecting the arcs for the tree, avoiding any cycles, gives the following list:
QS (1.6), PT (1.9), QT (1.9), RU (2.2), RT (2.6)

And the minimum spanning tree is:

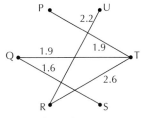

The total weight is 1.6 + 1.9 + 1.9 + 2.2 + 2.6 = 10.2

So 10.2 m of cabling is needed to form a minimum spanning tree for these computers.

You might have put the vertices of your graph in a different position, but the arcs joining them together should be the same as in the diagram above.

Q5 In ascending order, the arcs are:
CG (60), BT (80), CS (100), CR (100), EG (100), CV (130), EC (140), PT (150), SV (160), RS (170), GR (190), BV (200), CP (220)

Selecting arcs to form a minimum connector, avoiding cycles, gives the arcs:
CG (60), BT (80), CS (100), CR (100), EG (100), CV (130), PT (150), BV (200)

And the minimum connector would be:

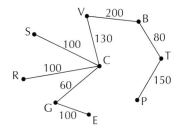

The total weight of the chosen arcs is
60 + 80 + 100 + 100 + 100 + 130 + 150 + 200
= 920 metres

Each metre of pathway costs £175 to lay, so the total cost would be 920 × £175 = £161 000

Q6 a) In ascending order, the arcs have lengths:
AB (90), DE (110), BC (120), AC (130), BD (130), BE (140), CE (160), CF (180), EF (180), BF (190)

Selecting arcs to form a minimum spanning tree, without creating cycles, gives:
AB (90), DE (110), BC (120), BD (130), CF (180)

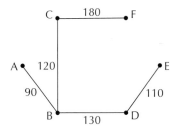

And the total weight of the minimum spanning tree is 90 + 110 + 120 + 130 + 180 = 630 m

b) BF must now be included in the tree. The three arcs BC, CF and BF now form a cycle, which is not allowed in a MST. The most efficient way to modify the tree is to remove arc CF, which has the greatest weight, to give:

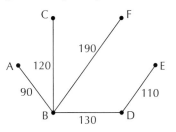

The total weight has therefore increased by 10 m to a total of 640 m.

Q7 In ascending order, the arcs are:
AI (35), BJ (45), EF (45), GH (50), AB (55), AH (65),
DJ (65), GJ (70), BI (75), DE (80), CJ (90), GI (90),
EJ (95), FG (100), CD (110), EG (120)

Selecting arcs to form a minimum spanning tree,
avoiding cycles, gives the arcs:
AI (35), BJ (45), EF (45), GH (50), AB (55), AH (65),
DJ (65), DE (80), CJ (90)

And the minimum spanning tree would be:

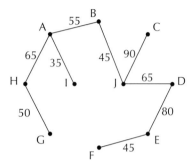

The total weight of the chosen arcs is
35 + 45 + 45 + 50 + 55 + 65 + 65 + 80 + 90
= 530 metres

Exercise 2.2 — Prim's algorithm on graphs

Q1 a) From vertex A there are three choices, AB (9),
AF (15) or AG (21). The arc of lowest weight is
AB (9) so this starts the tree.

Now look at all arcs joining either vertex A or
vertex B to a vertex not yet in the tree.
The list of choices is:
AF (15), AG (21), BC (16), BD (26), BF (20), BG (4)

The arc of lowest weight in this list is BG (4),
so add this arc to the tree.

Now look for any arc from A, B or G to a vertex
not yet in the tree. Choose from:
AF (15), BC (16), BD (26), BF (20), GC (4),
GD (18), GE (6), GF (9)

Add the next lowest arc, GC (4).
The tree so far looks like this:

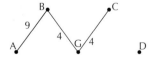

Now you can add any of the following edges:
AF (15), BD (26), BF (20), CD (11), CE (5),
GD (18), GE (6), GF (9)

The lowest weight is CE (5) so add this to the tree.

At this stage you only have nodes F and D left to
add to the tree. You can use any of:
AF (15), BD (26), BF (20), CD (11), ED (19),
EF (12), GD (18), GF (9)

So the next lowest weight arc is GF (9).

Finally, to attach D we can add BD (26), CD (11),
ED (19) or GD (18) — the lowest weight is
CD (11).

Hence the final minimum spanning tree is:

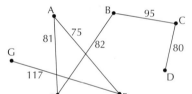

The order the arcs were added was:
AB (9), BG (4), GC (4), CE (5), GF (9), CD (11)

b) The weight of the minimum spanning tree is
9 + 4 + 4 + 5 + 9 + 11 = 42

Q2 Starting at node D, the order in which arcs must be
chosen is:
DC (80), CB (95), BF (82), FA (81), AE (75), EG (117)

And the minimum connector is:

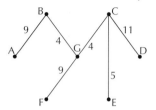

The total weight of the minimum connector is
80 + 95 + 82 + 81 + 75 + 117 = 530
so the total cost is 530 × £100 = £53 000

Q3 Starting at vertex J, the arcs are chosen in the order:
JN (9.5), NL (8), LP (5), PQ (10.5), QO (8.5),
QM (12), MK (15)

And the minimum spanning tree is:

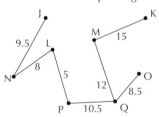

The total weight of the MST, and the total length of
power lines needed, is
9.5 + 8 + 5 + 10.5 + 8.5 + 12 + 15 = 68.5 km

Q4 Starting at vertex R, the arcs are chosen in the order:
RZ (130), ZW (120), ZS (160), SV (140), ST (180),
TU (150), WX(190), XY (190)

And the minimum spanning tree is:

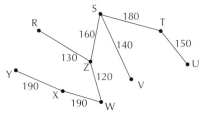

The total weight of the MST, and the total length of
cabling needed, is 130 + 120 + 160 + 140 + 180 +
150 + 190 + 190 = 1260 m
So the total cost of installing the cabling is
1260 × 1.25 = £1575

Q5 a) Starting at G, the arcs are chosen in the order:
GC (13), CB (15), GF (15), GD (18), FE (20),
BA (23)

And the minimum spanning tree is:

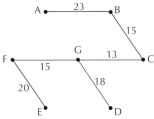

*You could have chosen GF first, then CB — remember,
if two arcs share the same lowest weight, choose one at
random.*

b) The total weight of the MST found in part a) is
13 + 15 + 15 + 18 + 20 + 23 = 104 minutes
Veronica's quickest route will take her along each
arc of the MST twice, so the least time it would
take her is 104 × 2 = 208 minutes (or 3 h 28 min)
*Veronica's route would end up being something like
GCBABCGFEFGDG — she travels from G to each of
A, D and E, then back to G each time.*

Q6 a) The minimum spanning tree would be:

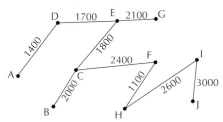

The order the arcs are chosen, starting at J, is:
JI (3000), IH (2600), HF (1100), FC (2400),
CE (1800), ED (1700), DA (1400), CB (2000),
EG (2100), which gives a total weight of 18 100,
which represents a cost of £18 100.

b) If bridge CF is destroyed it splits the minimum
spanning tree into two pieces as shown below:

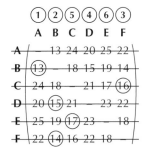

The two parts need to be joined together in the
most economical way possible. The only options
are to join G to F (£3100) or B to H (£4400).

The researchers should build a bridge between
sites F and G, which will cost £3100.

Exercise 2.3 — Prim's algorithm on matrices

Q1 Final labelled matrix:

	①	②	⑤	④	⑥	③
	A	**B**	**C**	**D**	**E**	**F**
A	—	13	24	20	25	22
B	⑬	—	18	15	19	14
C	24	18	—	21	17	⑯
D	20	⑮	21	—	23	22
E	25	19	⑰	23	—	18
F	22	⑭	16	22	18	—

The arcs of the minimum connector were added in
the order AB (13), BF (14), BD (15), FC (16), CE (17).
The weight of the minimum connector is
13 + 14 + 15 + 16 + 17 = 75

Q2 Final labelled matrix:

	⑥	②	①	⑦	③	⑤	④
	A	**B**	**C**	**D**	**E**	**F**	**G**
A	—	3.1	4.4	2.9	3.3	2.7	⑴.⑼
B	3.1	—	⑷.⑴	3.5	2.7	—	3.7
C	4.4	4.1	—	—	4.4	4.3	4.2
D	2.9	3.5	—	—	2.8	⑴.⑼	3.2
E	3.3	⑵.⑺	4.4	2.8	—	4.5	2.6
F	2.7	—	4.3	1.9	4.5	—	⑴.⑴
G	1.9	3.7	4.2	3.2	⑵.⑹	1.1	—

Minimum spanning tree:

E.g.

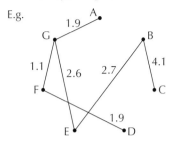

The arcs of the minimum spanning tree were added in the order CB (4.1), BE (2.7), EG (2.6), GF (1.1), GA (1.9), FD (1.9).
The total weight of the minimum spanning tree is
4.1 + 2.7 + 2.6 + 1.1 + 1.9 + 1.9 = 14.3 km
You could have added arc FD before arc GA, as they have the same weight. This would give slightly different labelling on the final matrix, but the same minimum spanning tree. Your minimum spanning trees in this exercise might not look exactly like the ones given here — it doesn't matter how you arrange the vertices, as long as the same arcs are chosen.

Q3 Final labelled matrix:

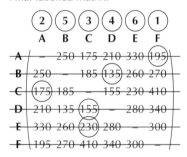

	②A	⑤B	③C	④D	⑥E	①F
A	–	250	175	210	330	⑲⑤
B	250	–	185	⑬⑤	260	270
C	⑰⑤	185	–	155	230	410
D	210	135	⑮⑤	–	280	340
E	330	260	②③⓪	280	–	300
F	195	270	410	340	300	–

The arcs of the minimum spanning tree were added in the order FA (195), AC (175), CD (155), DB (135), CE (230).
The total weight of the minimum spanning tree is
195 + 175 + 155 + 135 + 230 = 890 m
So the total cost of the cabling is 890 × 3 = £2670

Q4 Final labelled matrix:

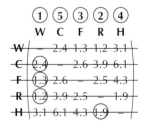

	①W	⑤C	③F	②R	④H
W	–	2.4	1.3	1.2	3.1
C	②.④	–	2.6	3.9	6.1
F	①.③	2.6	–	2.5	4.3
R	①.②	3.9	2.5	–	1.9
H	3.1	6.1	4.3	①.⑨	–

The arcs of the minimum spanning tree were added in the order WR (1.2), WF (1.3), RH (1.9), WC (2.4).
The total weight of the minimum spanning tree, and the minimum length of cabling needed, is
1.2 + 1.3 + 1.9 + 2.4 = 6.8 miles

Q5 Final labelled matrix:

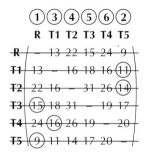

	①R	③T1	④T2	⑤T3	⑥T4	②T5
R	–	13	22	15	24	9
T1	13	–	16	18	16	⑪
T2	22	16	–	31	26	⑭
T3	⑮	18	31	–	19	17
T4	24	⑯	26	19	–	20
T5	⑨	11	14	17	20	–

Minimum spanning tree:

E.g.

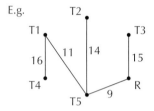

The arcs of the minimum spanning tree were added in the order R-T5 (9), T5-T1 (11), T5-T2 (14), R-T3 (15), T1-T4 (16).
The total weight of the minimum spanning tree, and the minimum length of piping needed, is
9 + 11 + 14 + 15 + 16 = 65 miles

3. Dijkstra's Algorithm
Exercise 3.1 — Dijkstra's algorithm

Q1 **a)** First give A a final value of 0. From A we can reach B in a distance of 4, or E in a distance of 3. Add these as working values.

The smallest working value available is the 3 at vertex E, so make this a final label.

From E we can reach F in a total distance of 5, or D in a total distance of 11, so add these working values.

The new lowest working value available to choose is 4 at B, so put this as a final label. From B we can reach C in a total distance of 9, or D in a total distance of 10. Put these as working values. At D, this means replacing the previous value of 11.

The next lowest working value is 5 at F, so put a final value of 5 at F. From F we can reach D in a new shortest distance of 8, so replace the current working value of 10 with 8. We can also reach G from F in a total distance of 7.

At this point we have a working label of 7 at our final destination of vertex G. None of the other working values are lower than this, so we cannot possibly find a route that would reach G in a distance less than 7. Label G with a final label of 7. Notice that vertices C and D have not been chosen.

This gives a completed diagram as follows:

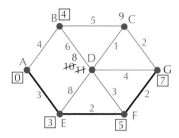

b) Working backwards from G, the distance FG = 2 and the difference between their final labels is 2, so this is on the shortest route.

From F, the distance EF = 2 and this is the difference between the final labels at E and F, so EF is on the shortest route.

Finally, the distance AE = 3 is the difference between the final labels at A and E, so AE is on the shortest route.

The shortest route is A E F G with total length 7. This is shown in bold on the diagram.

Q2 The final diagram, showing all the working values and final values, is:

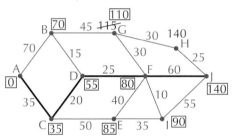

The optimal route is A C D F J with a total time of 140 minutes. This is shown above in bold.

Q3 The final diagram is:

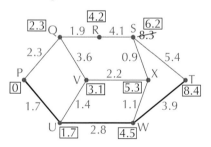

The optimal route for the newspaper boy (shown in bold) is P U W T with a total time of 8.4 mins, meaning he would reach house T at approximately 6.38 am. Therefore the owner of house T will get his newspaper before he leaves for work.

Q4 The final diagram is:

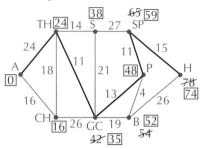

The optimal route is A TH GC P SP H, giving a total walking time for the pilot of 74 mins.
The optimal route is shown in bold on the diagram.

Q5 If we start from the warehouse and apply the algorithm working from right to left, the nearest depot can be identified without having to apply the algorithm twice.

Working right to left gives the diagram below:

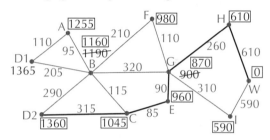

The first depot to be given a final label is D2. This means depot 2 is closest to the warehouse and we stop at this point. Working backwards through the diagram produces the route D2 C E G H W (shown in bold), with a total distance of 1360 m.
Be careful with this one — when you're working backwards, the distances need to be getting shorter. So CB is not on the route, even though it looks like it should be.

Q6 The final diagram is

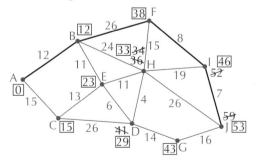

The optimal route is A B F I J which has a total duration of 53 mins. The latest time David could leave his Hall of Residence is 8:07 am if he is to be on time for the 9 am lecture.

Q7 a) The shortest route from A to I is indicated in the diagram below. The route is A B F E D I and has a total cost of 555 pence (i.e. £5.55).

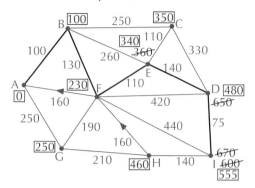

Beware of directed edges — if you missed those little arrows and treated AF and FH as two-way routes, you'd have got this question all wrong.

b) The new route means that C could be reached with a minimal cost of 200 pence.
Possible routes from A to I via C could be A C D I or A C E D I.
A C D I costs 200 + 330 + 75 = 605p
A C E D I costs 200 + 110 + 140 + 75 = 525p

So the new bus makes A C E D I the new cheapest route for Ammar.

Q8 Starting at node B, the optimal route to G is shown in the diagram below.

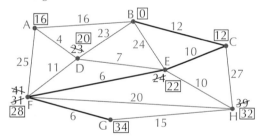

The optimal route is B C E F G, with a total length of 34.

Q9 The shortest route from B to K is 120 km, travelling along the route B C F G H K.

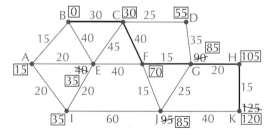

At a maximum speed of 20 km/h, the shortest possible time needed to transport the piece of equipment to the site is 120 ÷ 20 = 6 hours.
There are two points where there was a tie for the lowest working value — either of E and I could have been randomly chosen first, and either of G and J.

Q10 The optimal route from E to L is shown below. The route is E D J K L and has a total cost of £380.

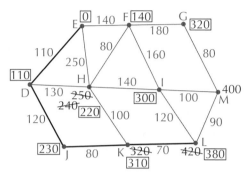

When booking the journey, Ambreen might also wish to take into account factors such as

- the number of flight changes;
- the flight times and availability;
- any booking fees;
- the airline operating on each route;
- baggage weight restrictions;
- other possible modes of transport, e.g. train

For example, flying E F I L costs £420 but involves only three flights, rather than the four flights needed on the optimal route. Ambreen might prefer this as it would be more convenient.

Q11 The final diagram is:

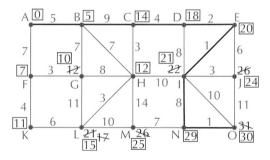

The optimal route is A B C D E I N O, giving a journey time of 30 minutes.

When carrying out these calculations, it's assumed that there are no delays on any of the sections of the journey and that there is a train waiting in the station at each changeover (i.e. there is no 'waiting time' to take into account).

It's also assumed that no time is required to walk between platforms at each station, and that the times given are precise and not rounded to the nearest minute.

Review Exercise — Chapter 2

Q1 a) A graph which has a number associated with each edge.

b) A graph in which one or more of the edges have a direction associated with them.

c) A connected graph with no cycles.

d) A subgraph which contains all the vertices of the original graph and is also a tree.

Q2 a) E.g.

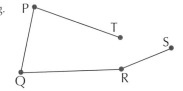

b) Remove vertex S as you can't find a cycle containing S which means no Hamiltonian cycles.

c) You'd have to remove one of the edges between Q and R because a simple graph can't have more than one edge connecting two vertices. You'd also have to remove the loop from T to T as simple graphs can't contain loops.

Q3 a) E.g.

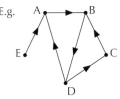

b) CBDA

c) There is no route to point E.

Q4 a)

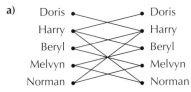

b) Harry

Q5 a) E.g. (i) (ii)

b) 5

c) E.g. ADBC

d) E.g. BCDB

e) E.g.

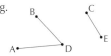

f) A = 1, B = 2, C = 3, D = 3, E = 1
Sum of degrees = double number of edges

Q6 a) E.g. PQRT or PSRT

b) E.g. QRSPQ or QPSRQ

c) 4 (add R row)

d) 9 (sum of degrees then divide by 2)

Q7 In ascending order the arcs are: AG (5), DH (5), EG (7.5), CH (8), BG (9.5), AB (10), CD (10), DE (10), AF (11), EF (11), FH (12), BC (13), CG (15)

Selecting arcs for the tree, avoiding any cycles, gives the following list: AG (5), DH (5), EG (7.5), CH (8), BG (9.5), DE (10), AF (11)

And the minimum spanning tree is:

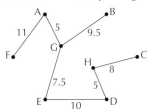

The total weight of the minimum spanning tree is
5 + 5 + 7.5 + 8 + 9.5 + 10 + 11 = 56

So the lowest cost of providing the sewerage system is 56 × £100 = £5600.
You might have chosen EF as your final arc instead of AF, as they have the same weight. You'd have ended up with a slightly different-looking MST to the one above, but with the same total weight.

Q8 a) E.g. Prim's algorithm forms a connected tree at each stage of the process, whereas Kruskal's algorithm can produce a non-connected graph as it is formed.

In Kruskal's algorithm, the shortest arc is added next, whereas in Prim's algorithm, the nearest unattached node is attached next at each stage.

You do not need to check for cycles using Prim's algorithm, but you do with Kruskal's algorithm.

b) (i) Starting at A, the order of adding arcs is AB (8), AF (9), BE (9), ED (9), BC (12).
AF and BE could have been selected in the opposite order, but one of them would always be the second choice if starting at A. If BE was selected second, you could then select ED third and AF fourth.

This produces the following minimum spanning tree, with total weight 47:

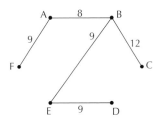

(ii) Starting at D, the order of adding arcs is DE (9), EB (9), BA (8), AF (9), BC (12) which produces the following minimum spanning tree, with total weight 47:

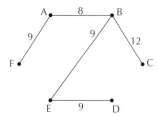

The trees are exactly the same in both cases. *In general, you might get a slightly different minimum spanning tree depending on which vertex you start from, but the overall weight of the tree will always be the same. In this question, whichever node we start at, the MST will have total weight 47.*

Q9 There are two possible answers to this question. Final labelled matrix:

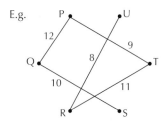

This gives the following minimum spanning tree:

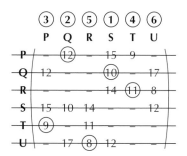

The order of choosing the arcs is SQ (10), QP (12), PT (9), TR (11), RU (8)

Alternatively, we can select SU instead of QP as the second arc. The matrix would then look like this:

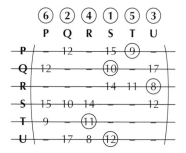

The minimum spanning tree would then be:

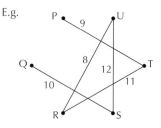

The order of choosing the arcs in this case is SQ (10), SU (12), UR (8), RT (11), TP (9)

Both MSTs have a total weight of 50.

Q10 Final labelled matrix:

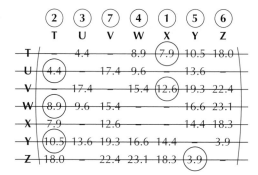

| | ② | ③ | ⑦ | ④ | ① | ⑤ | ⑥ |
	T	U	V	W	X	Y	Z
T	—	4.4		8.9	⑦.⑨	10.5	18.0
U	④.④	—	17.4	9.6		13.6	—
V		17.4	—	15.4	⑫.⑥	19.3	22.4
W	⑧.⑨	9.6	15.4	—		16.6	23.1
X	7.9		12.6		—	14.4	18.3
Y	⑩.⑤	13.6	19.3	16.6	14.4	—	3.9
Z	18.0		22.4	23.1	18.3	③.⑨	—

Minimum spanning tree:

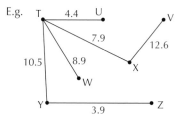

The order of choosing the arcs is XT (7.9), TU (4.4), TW (8.9), TY (10.5), YZ (3.9), XV (12.6) giving a total weight of 48.2 km.

Q11 a) The final diagram is:

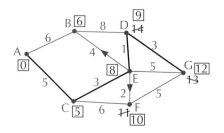

The optimal route is A C E D G, with a total weight of 12.

b) The final diagram is now:

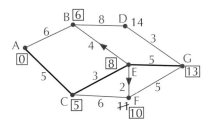

The optimal route is A C E G, with a total weight of 13.

Q12 The final diagram is:

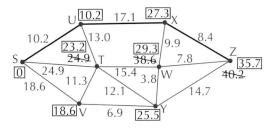

The optimal route for the cable is S U X Z, with a total length of 35.7 m. So the cost of cabling needed is 35.7 × 2.5 = £89.25.

Exam-Style Questions — Chapter 2

Q1 a) DG (22) – add; EF (24) – add; BE (25) – add;

DE (25) – add; EG (26) – don't add; AB (26) – add;

BD (27) – don't add; BF (28) – don't add;

FH (28) – add; CF (30) – add; AC (32) – don't add;

GH (33) – don't add. Edges of equal length can be considered in either order.

[3 marks available — 1 mark for edges in correct order, 2 marks for all added edges correct. Lose 1 mark for each error.]

b) 22 + 24 + 25 + 25 + 26 + 28 + 30 = £180
[1 mark]

c)

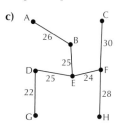

[2 marks for correct edges. Lose 1 mark for each error.]

d) FC / CF.
Order edges added: EF, EB, ED, DG (or ED, DG, EB), BA, FH, FC.

[2 marks available. 1 mark for correct edge, 1 mark for evidence that Prim's algorithm has been applied.]

e) E.g. Prim's algorithm can be applied to data in matrix form; you don't have to check for cycles using Prim's; the tree grows in a connected way using Prim's. *[2 marks — 1 mark for each.]*

Q2 a)

	①	②	④	⑤	③
	A	B	C	D	E
A	–	14	22	21	18
B	⑭	–	19	21	20
C	22	19	–	21	⑮
D	㉑	㉑	㉑	–	24
E	⑱	20	15	24	–

Order arcs added: AB, AE, EC, AD/BD/CD
(Arcs AD, BD and CD are interchangeable.)

[3 marks available — 2 marks for arcs in correct order (1 mark if one error). 1 mark for correct use of matrix.]

Each time you circle a number, write down which arc it represents by reading the row and column labels — don't leave it until the end.

b) E.g.

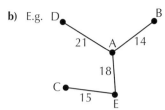

D may be connected to B or C instead of A
[1 mark]. weight = 68 *[1 mark]*.

c) 2 (using any of the alternatives AD, BD and CD)
[1 mark].

Q3 a) Bipartite graph *[1 mark]*

b) 3 (A2, B1, B3) *[1 mark]*

c) 1 (e.g. AD) *[1 mark]*

d) 8 (2 × number of edges) *[1 mark]*

e) The sum of the orders is double the number of
edges, so is always even *[1 mark]*. There are 5
vertices, and the sum of 5 odd numbers is always
odd *[1 mark]*.

Q4 a) 8 (no. of vertices − 1) *[1 mark]*

b)

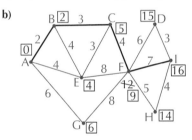

Fastest route = ABCFI, 16 minutes

*[6 marks available — 1 mark for route, 1 mark
for 16 minutes, 4 marks for all vertices correctly
completed in diagram, lose 1 mark for each
error.]*
*Find the fastest route by tracing back from the final
destination. You know an edge is on the route if its
weight is the difference between the final values at either
end of it.*

c) $6 + x + 4 < 16$, $x < 6$

Fastest route from A to G is 6. Fastest route from
H to I is 4.

Total route AGHI must be less than 16 minutes.

*[2 marks available — 1 mark for 6 + x + 4 as
new route length, 1 mark for solving inequality
for x.]*

Q5 a) $\dfrac{n(n-1)}{2}$ *[1 mark]*

b) m *[1 mark]*

c) $p - 1$ *[1 mark]*

Chapter 3: The Route Inspection Problem

1. Eulerian Graphs

Exercise 1.1 — Eulerian and semi-Eulerian graphs

Q1
a) Eulerian, 12 edges
b) Semi-Eulerian, 7 edges
c) Eulerian, 9 edges
d) Neither
e) Semi-Eulerian, 9 edges
f) Semi-Eulerian, 13 edges

Q2 e.g. A B C D A B C D A (once around the circle and once around the square).
This is just an example — there are lots of different routes.

Q3 e.g. A B E A C B D E D C

Q4 e.g. A B C D E F G D H I J K L I C M A

2. Route Inspection Problems

Exercise 2.1 — Eulerian graphs

Q1
a) e.g. C D F G H A B E D B C
Route length:
$2 + 3 + 6 + 5 + 4 + 4 + 2 + 3 + 2 + 1 = 32$
b) e.g. C D E B A H G F D B C
$2 + 3 + 2 + 4 + 4 + 5 + 6 + 3 + 2 + 1 = 32$

Q2 e.g. E F A B C D A D E
$3 + 4 + 4 + 3 + 4 + 7 + 12 + 4 = 41$

Q3 e.g. A B C D A E D F E A
$1 + 6 + 3 + 5 + 9 + 2 + 14 + 6 + 10 = 56$
So the length is 5600 m or 5.6 km.

Q4 e.g. A B I C D E F G D H I J A
$2 + 2 + 3 + 5 + 2 + 2 + 2 + 2 + 4 + 7 + 2 + 2 = 35$
So the length is 350 m.

Exercise 2.2 — Semi-Eulerian graphs

Q1
a) The two odd vertices are A and D, and the shortest route from A to D is A B C D (9)

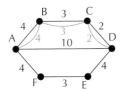

The repeated route is shown in grey.

b) e.g. A B C D <u>A B C D</u> E F A
The repeated route has been underlined.

c) Weight of network
$= 4 + 3 + 2 + 10 + 4 + 3 + 4 = 30$
Weight of route $= 30 + 4 + 3 + 2 = 39$

Q2
a) The two odd vertices are B and D, and the shortest route from B to D is B C D (4).
b) e.g. B C D B C D A B A <u>D C B</u>
c) Weight of network $= 2 + 2 + 7 + 5 + 6 + 2 + 3 + 4 + 5 = 36$; weight of route $= 36 + 2 + 2 = 40$

Q3
a) E and G
b) E B G and E F G, both have weight 6.
c) e.g. E B G A B C D E F <u>G F E</u>
d) Weight of network $= 3 + 3 + 5 + 4 + 3 + 5 + 4 + 2 + 4 = 33$
Weight of route $= 33 + 4 + 2 = 39$

Q4
a) Odd vertices are A and D, and the shortest route between them is A D ($4t$), so that should be the repeated section.
b) Length of complete circuit = total weight of network + weight of shortest path
$= 4t + 4t + 3t + 5t + t + t + (t + 3) + t + t + (t + 2) + (t + 1) + 4t = 27t + 6$
So for the race to last an hour,
$27t + 6 = 60 \Rightarrow 27t = 54 \Rightarrow t = 2$ minutes
c) e.g. A B C D A I E F G H E <u>D A</u>

Q5
a) B and D
b) B C D (3)
c) e.g. A B C D E <u>B A</u> H G F D
For this one, treat it like a normal semi-Eulerian question, where you start at one odd vertex and end at the other, and find a route from B to D — you won't have to repeat any edges. Then add on to the start the shortest route from A to the nearest odd vertex (B), so you end up repeating AB.
d) Weight of network $= 1 + 2 + 3 + 2 + 2 + 4 + 5 + 6 + 3 = 28$; weight of route $= 28 + 2 = 30$
So the length is 3000 m or 3 km.

Exercise 2.3 — Other graphs

Q1
a) The odd vertices are B, C, E and F.
b) BC + EF, weight $= 2 + 2 = 4$
BE + CF, weight $= 8 + 8 = 16$
BF + CE, weight $= 6 + 8 = 14$
The route B A F is shorter than the direct route BF.
c) BC and EF is the pairing with the smallest total path length, so repeat those paths.
e.g. A B C D E F <u>B C</u> E <u>F</u> A
Path length $= 37 + 4 = 41$

Q2
a) The odd vertices are A, B, C and E.
b) AB + CE, weight $= 4 + 4 = 8$
AC + BE, weight $= 6 + 8 = 14$
AE + BC, weight $= 4 + 4 = 8$
For AC the path taken was A F G D C.
c) Either AB and CE or AE and BC would work as the repeated paths (using AB and CE here).
e.g. G D F A B C D E F G <u>E D C</u> A B G
Path length $= 49 + 8 = 57$

Q3 a) The network is not Eulerian (there are 4 odd vertices), so it isn't traversable — she'll have to repeat paths and pass some stalls more than once.

b) The odd vertices are C, D, F and H.
Pairing up the odd vertices:
CD + FH, weight = 10 + 2 = 12
CF + DH, weight = 16 + 8 = 24
CH + DF, weight = 18 + 6 = 24

CD and FH is the pair that adds the least total weight if repeated, so she'd have to pass 12 stalls more than once.

c) e.g. A B C A D C F <u>D C</u> E B G E F H G I <u>H F</u> D A

Q4 Start by finding all the possible pairs of odd vertices and calculating the shortest total paths between them: A, B, C and D are the odd vertices.

AB + CD, weight = 250 + 210 = 460
AC + BD, weight = 100 + 250 = 350
AD + BC, weight = 180 + 350 = 530

The shortest total length of pairings is 350 m, so if he repeats those paths the distance he has to travel is 2890 + 350 = 3240 m.

Q5 The odd vertices are C, I, J, K
All possible pairs not involving K are:
CI, weight 6   CJ, weight 5   IJ, weight 5
The shortest of these are CJ and IJ, both with weight 5, so repeat either. The total length of the inspection route is therefore 71 + 5 = 76 km.

Q6 a) The odd vertices are B, C, E, J
All possible pairs are:
BC, weight 60   BE, weight 35   BJ, weight 125
CE, weight 70   CJ, weight 95   EJ, weight 90

The shortest of these is BE with weight 35, so that's the path to repeat. Start and end at either C or J.
e.g. C I C B E D A A B E H G J F D F G H I J
Total length = 765 + 35 = 800 m

b) The network would become Eulerian, so the length would be 765 × 2 = 1530 m.

Review Exercise — Chapter 3

Q1 a) Eulerian   **b)** semi-Eulerian
c) semi-Eulerian   **d)** neither

Q2 The odd vertices are A, B, F, J. The possible pairings are: AB and FJ, AF and BJ, AJ and BF

Q3 a) It's Eulerian, so length = weight of network = 36.

b) It's semi-Eulerian where the two odd vertices are A and B, so length = 31 (weight of network) + 4 (distance AB) = 35.

c) 4 odd vertices: A, B, D, F. Possible pairings:
AB + DF, weight = 7 + 8 = 15
AD + BF, weight = 5 + 3 = 8 (minimum)
AF + BD, weight = 4 + 7 = 11
Length = 42 (weight of network) + 8 = 50

Q4 a) 36, any vertex.

b) 31, start and end at A and B.

c) BF is shortest distance between odd vertices, so start and end at A and D. Length = 42 + 3 = 45.

Q5 a) Odd vertices are G and J, and the shortest route between them is G D C I J (4).

b) Length of route = weight of network + length of repeated path = 25 + 4 = 29.

Q6 a) B, C, F, J

b) BC + FJ, weight = 11 + 7 = 18
The route BC is B I J K C, not the direct one
BF + CJ, weight = 8 + 7 = 15
BJ + CF, weight = 4 + 14 = 18

c) Repeating BF and CJ:
Length of route = weight of network + length of repeated paths = 120 + 15 = 135.

Q7 a) The odd vertices are A, C, D and F.
AC + DF = 9 + 9 = 18 (= 180 m)
AD + CF = 10 + 10 = 20 (= 200 m)
AF + CD = 1 + 2 = 3 (= 30 m)
Repeating AF and CD, length = 56 + 2 + 1 = 59. So the shortest path is 590 m.

b) e.g. E B C D E G <u>D C</u> G B A G F <u>A F</u> E

c) Walking down each path twice makes the network Eulerian, so distance = 560 × 2 = 1120 m.

Exam-Style Questions — Chapter 3

Q1 **a)** Logo A = semi-Eulerian *[1 mark]*
Logo B = neither *[1 mark]*

b) **(i)** Logo A = 0 *[1 mark]*; Logo B = once *[1 mark]*

(ii) B or D *[1 mark]*

c) Logo A = 1 *[1 mark]*; Logo B = 2 *[1 mark]*

Q2 **a)** There are odd vertices so the network is not Eulerian, so some edges would have to be repeated. *[1 mark]*

I's not Eulerian. And there are four odd vertices, so it's not even semi-Eulerian.

b) Odd vertices are A, D, I, J
Possible pairings are AD + IJ, AI + DJ and AJ + ID *[1 mark]*

Weights: AD + IJ = 180 + 100 = 280 *[1 mark]*

AI + DJ = 440 + 310 = 750 *[1 mark]*

AJ + ID = 490 + 340 = 830 *[1 mark]*

minimum pairing = AD + IJ
route length = 2740 + 280 *[1 mark]*
= 3020 m *[1 mark]*

The question says that you must start and end at K — but as you've made the graph effectively Eulerian, it doesn't actually matter where you start and finish.

c) **(i)** IJ is minimum distance between odd vertices. *[1 mark]*

Length of route = 2740 + 100 = 2840 m *[1 mark]*

(ii) A or D *[1 mark]*

Q3 **a)** Odd vertices are B, G, M, L
Possible pairings are BL + GM, BG + LM and BM + GL *[1 mark]*

Weights: BL + GM = 41 + 26 = 67 *[1 mark]*

BG + LM = 30 + 29 = 59 *[1 mark]*

BM + GL = 30 + 28 = 58 *[1 mark]*

minimum pairing = BM + GL

route time = 336 + 58 *[1 mark]*
= 394 mins *[1 mark]*

b) **(i)** GM is minimum *[1 mark]* so end at L *[1 mark]*

(ii) 336 + 26 = 362 minutes *[1 mark]*

Q4 **a)** Odd vertices are A, D, E, F
Possible pairings are AD + EF, AE + DF and AF + DE *[1 mark]*

Weights: AD + EF = 12 + 15 = 27 *[1 mark]*
AE + DF = 12 + 21 = 33 *[1 mark]*
AF + DE = 18 + 6 = 24 *[1 mark]*

minimum pairing = AF + DE
route length = 106 + 24 *[1 mark]*
= 130 miles *[1 mark]*

b) Example route = ABFG<u>E</u>FBA<u>C</u>B<u>E</u>D<u>EC</u>DA
[1 mark] so 5 times *[1 mark]*.

Alternatively, you could say that C has four edges connected to it, so must be passed through twice.

E has six edges connected to it (including the extra pass along DE) so must be passed through three times *[1 mark]*, so 2 + 3 = 5 times past an ice-cream shop *[1 mark]*.

c) 106 × 2 *[1 mark]* = 212 miles *[1 mark]*

You've effectively doubled the edges and made the graph Eulerian. You have to traverse it twice, so the distance is just double the network's weight.

Chapter 4: Travelling Salesperson Problem
1. Hamiltonian Cycles

Exercise 1.1 — Finding Hamiltonian cycles

Q1 **a)** Add the edges C-E, D-F (shown in black), giving the cycle e.g. A B C D E F A.

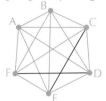

b) Add the edges A-C, B-C, B-D, C-E (shown in black), giving the cycle e.g. A B C D E A.

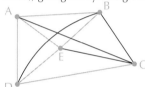

For all of these there's more than one solution so you might not get the one that's written here. If you don't just double check your cycle definitely works.

Q2 **a)** E.g. A B C E D A

b) E.g. A D E F B C A

Q3 **a)** E.g. C D E F A G B C
Length = 9 + 6 + 3 + 5 + 8 + 5 + 5 = 41
C D F E A G B C
Length = 9 + 7 + 3 + 5 + 8 + 5 + 5 = 42

b) E.g. A E B C D F A
Length = 6 + 5 + 4 + 4 + 2 + 4 = 25
A B E D C F A
Length = 8 + 5 + 3 + 4 + 5 + 4 = 29

Exercise 1.2 — TSP in non-Hamiltonian networks

Q1 **a)** **(i)** E.g. A E C E B D A
Length = 3 + 5 + 5 + 3 + 4 + 4 = 24

(ii) Vertex E is visited twice.

b) **(i)** A B C D E D C B A
Length = 4 + 3 + 7 + 6 + 6 + 7 + 3 + 4 = 40

(ii) Vertices B, C and D are visited twice.

Q2 **a)** **(i)** Add the edges AD (16), BD (10)

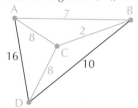

(ii) E.g. A B D C A
Length = 7 + 10 + 8 + 8 = 33

(iii) A B C D C A

b) **(i)** Add the edges AD (5), AE (7), BE (13), BD (11)

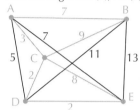

(ii) E.g. A C D E B A
Length = 3 + 2 + 2 + 13 + 7 = 27

(iii) A C D E D C B A

2. The Nearest Neighbour Algorithm

Exercise 2.1 — The nearest neighbour algorithm

Q1 **a)** The route is A B C D A
Upper bound = 5 + 9 + 10 + 10 = 34

b) The route is C A B D C
Upper bound = 8 + 5 + 10 + 10 = 33

c) Starting at C gives the better upper bound.

Q2 **a)** **(i)** Starting at the bank: bank newsagent greengrocer chemist library bank
Upper bound = 30 + 20 + 50 + 90 + 150 = 340 m

(ii) Starting at the library: library newsagent greengrocer chemist bank library
Upper bound = 50 + 20 + 50 + 50 + 150 = 320 m

b) Starting at the library gives the better upper bound.

Q3 **a)** **(i)** Starting at A: A E B C D A
Upper bound = 2 + 3 + 5 + 4 + 8 = 22

(ii) Starting at E: E A B C D E
Upper bound = 2 + 7 + 5 + 4 + 7 = 25

b) Part (i) gives the better upper bound.

c) C D B E A — there's no direct link back to C at this point. You need to add an edge to fix this — the shortest route from A to C is A E B C (weight = 10), so the route is C D B E A E B C.
So the upper bound starting from C is 4 + 6 + 3 + 2 + 2 + 3 + 5 = 25

Q4 **a)** Starting at D: D B E A C D
Upper bound = 5 + 3 + 10 + 11 + 7 = 36

b) Starting at A: A E B C D A — need to add an edge between D and A. The quickest path is D E A, so the route is A E B C D E A

There are other paths with the same length (18), so you could choose any of them.

Upper bound = 10 + 3 + 4 + 7 + 18 = 42

c) Starting at D gives the better upper bound.

Q5 **a)** Starting at the Marmosets: M L C P W M
Upper bound = 2 + 4 + 3 + 9 + 4 = 22 minutes

Starting at the Lemurs: L M W C P L
Upper bound = 2 + 4 + 7 + 3 + 5 = 21 minutes

Starting at the Porcupines: P C L M W P
Upper bound = 3 + 4 + 2 + 4 + 9 = 22 minutes

Starting at the Wallabies: W M L C P W
Upper bound = 4 + 2 + 4 + 3 + 9 = 22 minutes

Starting at the Coypus: C P L M W C
Upper bound = 3 + 5 + 2 + 4 + 7 = 21 minutes

b) The best upper bound for the route is 21 minutes (found by starting at the lemurs and coypus).

Exercise 2.2 — Nearest neighbour algorithm on a matrix

Q1

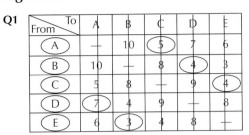

From \ To	A	B	C	D	E
A	—	10	(5)	7	6
B	10	—	8	(4)	3
C	5	8	—	9	(4)
D	(7)	4	9	—	8
E	6	(3)	4	8	—

The route is: A C E B D A
Upper bound = 7 + 3 + 5 + 4 + 4 = 23

Remember you just need to add up the circled numbers to find the upper bound.

Q2 **a)**

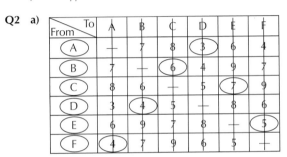

From \ To	A	B	C	D	E	F
A	—	7	8	(3)	6	4
B	7	—	(6)	4	9	7
C	8	6	—	5	(7)	9
D	3	(4)	5	—	8	6
E	6	9	7	8	—	(5)
F	(4)	7	9	6	5	—

The route is: A D B C E F A
Upper bound = 4 + 4 + 6 + 3 + 7 + 5 = 29

b)

From \ To	A	B	C	D	E	F
A	—	7	8	3	6	(4)
B	7	—	(6)	4	9	7
C	8	6	—	(5)	7	9
D	(3)	4	5	—	8	6
E	6	(9)	7	8	—	5
F	4	7	9	6	(5)	—

The route is: C D A F E B C
Upper bound = 5 + 3 + 4 + 5 + 9 + 6 = 32

c) Applying the nearest neighbour algorithm from A gives the better upper bound.

Q3 **a)** Starting at A:

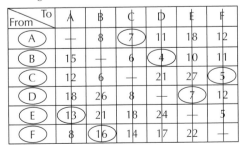

From \ To	A	B	C	D	E	F
A	—	8	(7)	11	18	12
B	15	—	6	(4)	10	11
C	12	6	—	21	27	(5)
D	18	26	8	—	(7)	12
E	(13)	21	18	24	—	5
F	8	(16)	14	17	22	—

The route is: A C F B D E A
Upper bound = 13 + 16 + 7 + 4 + 7 + 5 = 52

Starting at C:

To From	A	B	C	D	E	F
A	—	⑧	7	11	18	12
B	15	—	6	④	10	11
C	12	6	—	21	27	⑤
D	18	26	8	—	⑦	12
E	13	21	⑱	24	—	5
F	⑧	16	14	17	22	—

The route is: C F A B D E C
Upper bound = 8 + 8 + 18 + 4 + 7 + 5 = 50

b) Applying the nearest neighbour algorithm from C gives the better upper bound.

Q4 a)

To From	A	B	C	D	E	F
A	—	8	4	5	9	**11**
B	8	—	12	10	6	3
C	4	12	—	**9**	**13**	13
D	5	10	**9**	—	**14**	7
E	9	6	**13**	**14**	—	**9**
F	**11**	3	13	7	**9**	—

b) (i) Starting at A:

To From	A	B	C	D	E	F
A	—	8	④	5	9	11
B	8	—	12	10	⑥	3
C	4	12	—	⑨	13	13
D	5	10	9	—	14	⑦
E	⑨	6	13	14	—	9
F	11	③	13	7	9	—

The route is: A C D F B E A
Upper bound = 9 + 3 + 4 + 9 + 6 + 7 = 38

(ii) Starting at E:

To From	A	B	C	D	E	F
A	—	8	④	5	9	11
B	8	—	12	10	6	③
C	4	12	—	9	⑬	13
D	⑤	10	9	—	14	7
E	9	⑥	13	14	—	9
F	11	3	13	⑦	9	—

The route is: E B F D A C E
Upper bound = 6 + 3 + 7 + 5 + 4 + 13 = 38

c) Starting at E requires you to go from B to F, but starting from A doesn't, so the upper bound in part (ii) would increase (it becomes 43) but the upper bound in part (i) would stay the same.

3. The Lower Bound Algorithm

Exercise 3.1 — The lower bound algorithm

Q1 Weight of shortest edges incident to A = 3 + 4 = 7.

Then use Prim's algorithm to find a minimum spanning tree:
E.g.

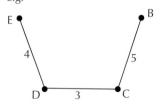

Weight of MST = 4 + 3 + 5 = 12.
So lower bound = 12 + 7 = 19.

For all the questions in this exercise, you might come up with an MST that looks a bit different to the ones given — but they should always have the same weight as the ones here.

Q2 Weight of shortest edges incident to A = 7 + 8 = 15.

Then use Kruskal's algorithm to find a minimum spanning tree:

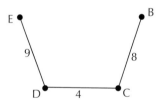

Weight of MST = 9 + 4 + 8 = 21.
So lower bound = 15 + 21 = 36.

Q3 Weight of shortest edges incident to C = 3 + 4 = 7

Then use Prim's algorithm to find a minimum spanning tree:
E.g.

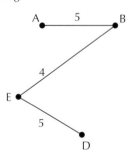

Weight of MST = 5 + 4 + 5 = 14.
So lower bound = 7 + 14 = 21.

Q4 Weight of shortest edges incident to A = 3 + 6 = 9

Then use Kruskal's algorithm to find a minimum spanning tree:

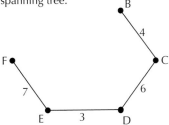

Weight of MST = 7 + 3 + 6 + 4 = 20.
So lower bound = 9 + 20 = 29.

Q5 Weight of shortest edges incident to C = 6 + 7 = 13.
Then use Prim's algorithm to find a minimum spanning tree:
E.g.

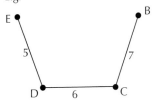

From \ To	A	B	C	D	E
A		8	7	11	18
B	⑧		6	4	10
C	7	6		21	27
D	11	④	21		7
E	18	10	27	⑦	

Weight of MST = 8 + 4 + 7 = 19.
So lower bound = 13 + 19 = 32 km.

Q6 a) By deleting A:
Weight of shortest edges incident to A
= 8 + 11 = 19.
Then use (e.g. Prim's) algorithm to find a minimum spanning tree:
E.g.

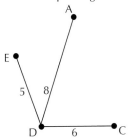

Weight of MST = 5 + 6 + 7 = 18.
So lower bound = 19 + 18 = 37.

By deleting B:
Weight of shortest edges incident to B
= 7 + 7 = 14.
Then use (e.g. Prim's) algorithm to find a minimum spanning tree:

Weight of MST = 5 + 8 + 6 = 19.
So lower bound = 14 + 19 = 33 m.

b) The higher the lower bound the better, so deleting A gives the better lower bound.

Q7 Weight of shortest edges incident to A = 5 + 7 = 12
Then use Prim's algorithm to find a MST:
E.g.

From \ To	A	B	C	D	E	F
	①	②	⑤	④	③	
A		9	5	7	10	12
B	9		8	11	15	8
C	5	⑧	—	13	5	4
D	7	11	13		16	⑧
E	10	15	⑤	16	—	6
F	12	8	④	8	6	

Weight of MST = 8 + 5 + 4 + 8 = 25.
So lower bound = 12 + 25 + 37.

Q8 a) Completed matrix:

From \ To	J	S	D	N	F	B
J	—	8	14	10	12	6
S	8	—	12	16	20	9
D	14	12	—	6	15	8
N	10	16	6	—	9	7
F	12	20	15	9	—	14
B	6	9	8	7	14	—

Weight of shortest edges incident to box
= 6 + 7 = 13.
Then use Prim's algorithm to find a MST:
E.g.

From \ To	J	S	D	N	F	B
	①	②	④	③	⑤	
J	—	8	14	10	12	6
S	⑧		12	16	20	9
D	14	12	—	⑥	15	8
N	⑩	16	6	—	9	7
F	12	20	15	⑨	—	14
B	6	9	8	7	14	—

Weight of MST = 8 + 10 + 6 + 9 = 33.
So lower bound = 13 + 33 = 46.

b) Find the upper bound with the nearest neighbour algorithm:

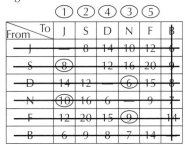

The route is B J S D N F B
Upper bound = 6 + 8 + 12 + 6 + 9 + 14 = 55

Review Exercise — Chapter 4

Q1 E.g. B G C F D A E B, B C F D A G E B

Q2 Add edges: AD (4), CD (5)
Cycles are e.g:
C B A E D C, length = 3 + 2 + 7 + 5 + 5 = 22
C A E B D C, length = 5 + 7 + 6 + 2 + 5 = 25
C E D B A C, length = 5 + 5 + 2 + 2 + 5 = 19

Q3 a) Starting at A:
The route is: A F E D C B A.
Upper bound = 3 + 6 + 3 + 5 + 6 + 5 = 28.

b) Starting at C:
The route is: C D E A F B C.
Upper bound = 5 + 3 + 5 + 3 + 7 + 6 = 29.

Q4 a) (i) Starting at B:

From\To	A	B	C	D	E	F
A	—	⑤	10	6	8	12
B	5	—	6	12	④	10
C	⑩	6	—	8	12	5
D	6	12	8	—	7	④
E	8	4	12	⑦	—	9
F	12	10	⑤	4	9	—

The route is: B E D F C A B
Upper bound = 4 + 7 + 4 + 5 + 10 + 5 = 35

(ii) Starting at F:

From\To	A	B	C	D	E	F
A	—	⑤	10	6	8	12
B	5	—	6	12	④	10
C	10	6	—	8	12	⑤
D	⑥	12	8	—	7	4
E	8	4	⑫	7	—	9
F	12	10	5	④	9	—

The route is: F D A B E C F.
Upper bound = 6 + 5 + 12 + 4 + 4 + 5 = 36.

b) Applying the nearest neighbour algorithm starting from B gives the better upper bound.

Q5 a)

From\To	A	B	C	D	E	F
A	—	6	11	10	9	5
B	6	—	5	12	13	9
C	11	5	—	7	10	13
D	10	12	7	—	5	7
E	9	13	10	5	—	4
F	5	9	13	7	4	—

b) Weight of shortest edges incident to C
= 5 + 7 = 12.

Then find a minimum spanning tree:
E.g.

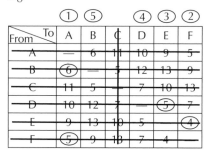

From\To	① A	⑤ B	C	④ D	③ E	② F
A	—	6	11	10	9	5
B	⑥	—	5	12	13	9
C	11	5	—	7	10	13
D	10	12	7	—	⑤	7
E	9	13	10	5	—	④
F	⑤	9	13	7	4	—

Weight of MST = 5 + 6 + 5 + 4 = 20.
So lower bound = 12 + 20 = 32.

Q6 a) E.g. A B C D E A, A C E B D A, A E B D C A

b) From A, the route is: A C E B D A.
Upper bound = 4 + 3 + 5 +12 + 7 = 31
From B, the route is: B E C A D B.
Upper bound = 5 + 3 + 4 + 7 + 12 = 31
From C, the route is: C E B A D C.
Upper bound = 3 + 5 + 9 + 7 + 6 = 30
From D, the route is: D C E B A D.
Upper bound = 6 + 3 + 5 + 9 + 7 = 30
From E, the route is: E C A D B E.
Upper bound = 3 + 4 + 7 + 12 + 5 = 31
The best upper bound is 30.

c) Deleting A:

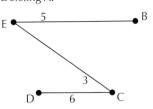

$x = 4$, $y = 7$, $W = 14$, Lower bound = 25.

Deleting B:

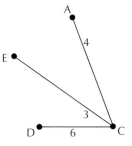

$x = 5$, $y = 7$, $W = 13$, Lower bound = 25.

Deleting C:

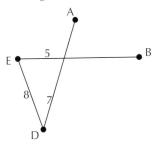

$x = 3$, $y = 4$, $W = 20$, Lower bound = 27

Deleting D:

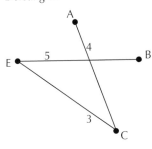

$x = 6$, $y = 7$, $W = 12$, Lower bound = 25

Deleting E:
E.g.

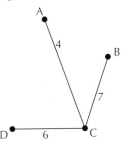

$x = 3$, $y = 5$, $W = 17$, Lower bound = 25

Best lower bound = 27.

d) $27 \leq$ optimum solution ≤ 30

Q7 **a)** The route is: F C E B A D F.
Upper bound = $5 + 3 + 6 + 4 + 5 + 15 = 38$.

b) Weight of shortest edges incident to B
$= 4 + 6 = 10$.
E.g.

From\To	A	B	C	D	E	F
A	—	4	6	5	8	12
B	4	—	14	22	6	11
C	⑥	14	—	18	3	5
D	⑤	22	18	—	13	15
E	8	6	③	13	—	20
F	12	11	⑤	15	20	—

(column headers marked ① ③ ② ④ ⑤)

Weight of MST = $6 + 5 + 3 + 5 = 19$.
So lower bound = $10 + 19 = 29$.

Exam-Style Questions — Chapter 4

Q1 **a)**

From\To	A	B	C	D	E	F
A	—	90	80	170	210	**220**
B	90	—	120	**220**	150	130
C	80	120	—	100	**270**	170
D	170	**220**	100	—	**240**	140
E	210	150	**270**	**240**	—	100
F	**220**	130	170	140	100	—

[2 marks available — 2 marks for all 4 distances correct, 1 mark for 2 or 3 distances correct.]

b) $90 + 120 + 100 + 240 + 100 + 220$ *[1 mark]*
$= 870$ m *[1 mark]*

c) The route is: A C D F E B A *[1 mark]*
$= 80 + 100 + 140 + 100 + 150 + 90$ *[1 mark]*
$= 660$ m *[1 mark]*

d) 660 m *[1 mark]*

e) Apply either Prim's or Kruskal's algorithm to get MST for reduced network. E.g:

From\To	A	B	C	D	E	F
A	—	90	80	170	210	220
B	⑨⓪	—	120	220	150	130
C	⑧⓪	120	—	100	270	170
D	170	220	100	—	240	140
E	210	150	270	240	—	①⓪⓪
F	220	①③⓪	170	140	100	—

(column headers marked ① ③ ② ⑤ ④)

$80 + 90 + 130 + 100 = 400$ m

[4 marks — 1 mark for attempting to apply appropriate algorithm or 2 marks for correct application, 1 mark for correct edges, 1 mark for MST.]

Shortest edges incident to D
$= 100 + 140 = 240$ m *[1 mark]*

Lower bound $= 400 + 240 = 640$ m *[1 mark]*

Q2 **a)** **(i)** To complete the graph, you need to add edges between A and C, A and D, C and F and D and F — so you need to add 4 edges *[1 mark]*.

(ii) The shortest distance between A and C is 43 (ABC).

The shortest distance between A and D is 41 (AED).

The shortest distance between C and F is 62 (CEF).

The shortest distance between D and F is 49 (DEF).

[2 marks for all distances correct, 1 mark for up to 3 distances correct].

Adding these edges to the diagram:

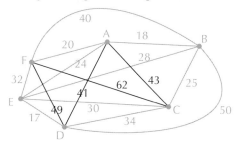

[1 mark]

b) Shortest edges incident to C are 25 and 30 *[1 mark]*. Then deleting vertex C and applying Prim's algorithm:

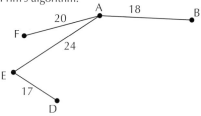

[2 marks for correct MST, using either Kruskal's or Prim's algorithm]
Weight of MST = 18 + 20 + 24 + 17 = 79 *[1 mark]*
Lower bound = 25 + 30 + 79 = 134 *[1 mark]*.

c)

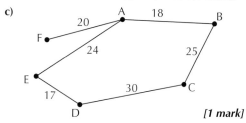

[1 mark]

d) The route is: A B C E D F A *[1 mark]*
Weight = 18 + 25 + 30 + 17 + 49 + 20 *[1 mark]*
= 159, so upper bound = 159 *[1 mark]*

Q3 a) E.g. A B C D E F G A

[2 marks available — 1 mark for including all vertices exactly once each, 1 mark for returning to start vertex.]

b) There are a few possible MSTs here. Only 1 is shown:

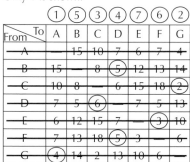

Order added: AG, GC, CD, DB, DF, FE.

[4 marks — 1 mark for attempting to apply appropriate algorithm or 2 marks for correct application, 1 mark for correct edges, 1 mark for order.]

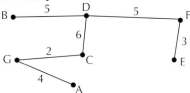

[1 mark]

Weight = 4 + 2 + 6 + 5 + 5 + 3 = 25 mins
[1 mark]

You could have included AE (6) or FG (6) instead of CD (6). It doesn't change the weight though. Also, your tree might look completely different, depending on how you arranged your vertices.

c) Weight = 25 − 5 = 20 *[1 mark]*
Shortest edges incident to B = 5 + 8 = 13
[1 mark]

Lower bound = 20 + 13 = 33 mins *[1 mark]*

Note — this method of finding the lower bound after finding an MST for the whole network won't always work, so you shouldn't do it this way unless you're told to.

d)

The route is: F E A G C D B F *[1 mark]*

Weight = 3 + 6 + 4 + 2 + 6 + 5 + 13 *[1 mark]*
= 39 mins, so upper bound = 39 mins *[1 mark]*

e) 33 mins ≤ optimum weight of tour *[1 mark]*
≤ 39 mins *[1 mark]*

Chapter 5: Linear Programming

1. Linear Programs

Exercise 1.1 — Definitions

Q1 a) The decision variables are x and y.
The objective function is $P = 5x + 7y$, which is to be maximised.
The constraints are the inequalities that x and y are subject to ($5x + 2y < 4$, $x + y \geq 1$, $x, y \geq 0$).

b) The decision variables are h and a.
The objective function is $C = 200h + 250a$, which is to be minimised.
The constraints are the inequalities that h and a are subject to ($50h + 20a \leq 1200$, $h + a \leq 30$, $h, a \geq 0$).

c) The decision variables are x, y and z.
The objective function is $W = 2x + 3y + 4z$, which is to be maximised.
The constraints are the inequalities that x, y and z are subject to ($x, y, z > 0$, $3x - y + z \leq 0$, $2x \geq y$).

Q2 Non-negativity constraints mean that a decision variable must be equal to or greater than zero, and are needed when it's impossible for one of the decision variables to be negative. For example, if you're producing toys, you can't have a negative number of stuffed monkeys.

Q3 a) The decision variables are x (number of home shirts) and y (number of away shirts).

b) The objective function is profit, £P (where $P = 2x + 1.5y$), which will be maximised.

c) The problem does need non-negativity constraints, as you can't produce a negative number of football shirts: $x, y \geq 0$.

d) The total number of shirts produced can't be more than 900 (i.e. $x + y \leq 900$).
They must make at least twice as many home shirts (x) as away shirts (y) (i.e. $x \geq 2y$).

Exercise 1.2 — Setting up linear programming problems

Q1 The objective function is £C (cost) which is to be minimised, where heating elements (x) cost £2 and frothing motors (y) cost £3. This is subject to the constraints:
They must buy at least 5 of each component (from $x, y \geq 5$).
The total number of components they buy can't be more than 20 (from $x + y \leq 20$).
The number of heating elements added to twice the number of motors they buy can't exceed 30 (from $x + 2y \leq 30$).
They cannot buy more than 5 motors for every 3 heating elements (from $3y \leq 5x$) OR they must buy at least 3 heating elements for every 5 motors.

Q2 a)

MP3 Player Size	Software	Q–control	Profit (£)
16GB	5	2	40
32GB	3	3	30
Total minutes	180	150	

b) £$P = 40x + 30y$
You want the profit, so you need to look at how much money each makes to form the objective function, not how long they take to make.

c) $5x + 3y \leq 180$
$2x + 3y \leq 150$
$x, y \geq 0$

Remember to include non-negativity constraints even if they're not mentioned in the question (as long as it makes sense to have them).

Q3 The shop will want to spend as little as possible on buying fireworks, so the objective function is cost: £$C = 3x + 6y$, which is to be minimised.

Minimise   £$C = 3x + 6y$
Subject to $x + y \geq 90$
             $x \geq 2y$
             $0 < x \leq 120$
             $0 < y \leq 80$

The $x \geq 2y$ comes from the fact that they'll sell at least twice as many small boxes (x) as big boxes (y). This means if you double the number of big boxes (i.e. $2y$) it will still be smaller than or equal to the number of big boxes (x).
$0 < x \leq 120$ means x is between 0 and 120, but be careful with the signs — the shop will sell some of each box and so x can't be 0, so use $<$ instead of $\leq$.

2. Solving Linear Programming Problems

Exercise 2.1 — Feasible regions

Q1 a), b)

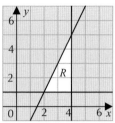

Q2 a), b)

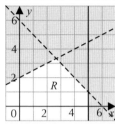

Q3 $x \leq 4$ $y \leq x + 2$ $y > 4 - x$ $(x, y \geq 0)$

Q4 $y < 4$ $2y \leq 12 - x$ (or $y \leq 6 - \frac{x}{2}$) $(x, y \geq 0)$

Q5 a), b)

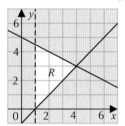

Q6 a) $2d \geq 3c$ $3c + 2d \leq 120$ $c, d \geq 0$
In $y = mx + c$ form, the inequalities become
$d \geq 1.5c$ and $d \leq -1.5c + 60$

b)

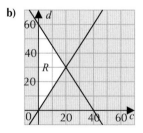

Q7 a) $y \leq x + 40$ $2y + x < 170$ (gradient $= -\frac{1}{2}$, y-intercept $= 85$)

b)

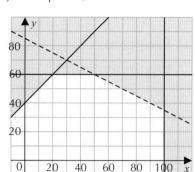

c) The two non-negativity constraints: $x, y \geq 0$

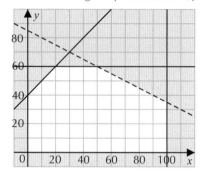

Q8 $x, y \geq 0$; $y \leq 100$; $5y + 4x \leq 800$
(gradient $= \frac{160}{-200} = -\frac{4}{5}$, y-intercept $= 160$);
$2y + 5x < 700$ (gradient $= \frac{0 - 100}{140 - 100} = -\frac{5}{2}$; using
$y = mx + c$ to find c: $0 = -2.5(140) + c \Rightarrow c = 350$);
$y < 2x - 20$ (gradient $= \frac{100 - 20}{60 - 20} = 2$,
y-intercept $= -20$)

*Even though you can't see that $x \geq 0$ from the graph, the
context shows you need non-negativity constraints.*
*You could also write some of the inequalities in different forms
— e.g. $5x + 4x \leq 800$ could be $y \leq 160 - \frac{4}{5}x$.*

Exercise 2.2 — Optimal solutions — the objective line method

Q1 a)

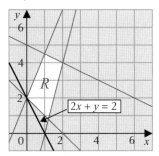

b)

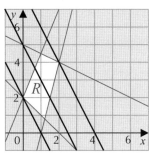

Q2 a) Starting with objective line $6 = 2x + 3y$

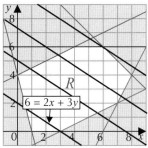

The last point within the feasible region that the lines touch is (6, 6), so the highest value Z can take is $(2 \times 6) + (3 \times 6) = 30$.

b) Starting with objective line $6 = 3x + 2y$

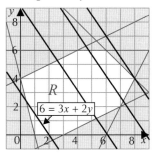

The last point within the feasible region that the lines touch is (8, 4), so the highest value Z can take is $(3 \times 8) + (2 \times 4) = 32$.

c) Starting with objective line $0 = 3x - 2y$

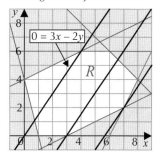

The last point within the feasible region that the lines touch is (7, 2), so the highest value Z can take is $(3 \times 7) - (2 \times 2) = 17$.

Q3 a) Starting with objective line $24 = 4x + 3y$

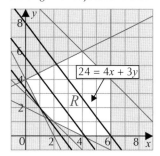

The last point within the feasible region that the lines touch is (1, 2), so the lowest value Z can take is $(4 \times 1) + (3 \times 2) = 10$.

b) Starting with objective line $20 = 2x + 5y$

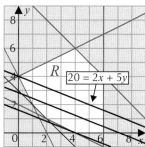

The last point within the feasible region that the lines touch is (4, 0), so the lowest value Z can take is $(2 \times 4) + (5 \times 0) = 8$.

c) Starting with the objective line $6 = 3x + y$

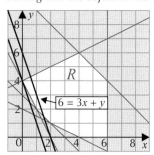

The last point within the feasible region that the lines touch is (0, 4), so the lowest value Z can take is $(3 \times 0) + 4 = 4$.

Q4 **a)**

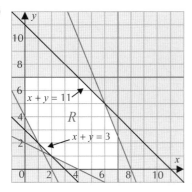

b) Starting with the objective line $6 = 3x + 2y$

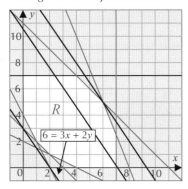

The last point within the feasible region that the lines touch is (6, 5), so the highest value T can take is $(3 \times 6) + (2 \times 5) = 28$. So the maximum takings are £28, when $x = 6$ and $y = 5$.

c) Starting with the objective line $12 = x + 4y$

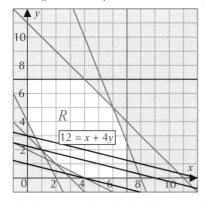

The last point within the feasible region that the lines touch is (4, 0), so the lowest value C can take is $4 + (4 \times 0) = 4$. So the minimum cost is £4, when $x = 4$ and $y = 0$.

Q5 **a)**

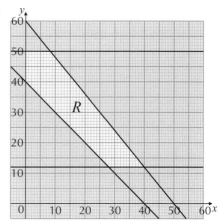

b) Starting with the objective line $60 = 0.8x + 1.2y$

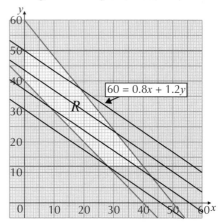

The last point within the feasible region that the lines touch is (28, 12), so the lowest value C can take is $(0.8 \times 28) + (1.2 \times 12) = 36.8$

Q6 **a)** The objective function is £$P = 2x + 5y$, which is to be maximised.

b) The insecticide constraint is $2x + 8y \leq 1000$. Simplifying, this becomes $x + 4y \leq 500$.

c) $4x + 5y \leq 1000$ (water constraint)
$x + 2y \leq 300$ (land constraint)
$x, y \geq 0$ (non-negativity constraint)

d)

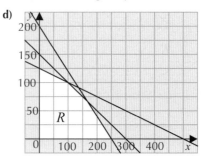

e) Starting with the objective line $500 = 2x + 5y$

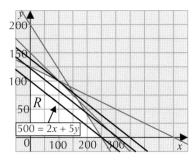

The last point within the feasible region that the lines touch is (100, 100), so the highest value $£P$ can take is $(2 \times 100) + (5 \times 100) = £700$.

This can be achieved by planting 100 indoor trees and 100 outdoor trees.

Exercise 2.3 — Optimal solutions — the vertex method

Q1 **a)** $y = 2x - 3$ (1) and $y = 6 - x$ (2)

Sub (2) into (1): $6 - x = 2x - 3 \Rightarrow x = 3$

Sub into (2): $y = 6 - 3 \Rightarrow y = 3$

b) $x + 4y = 14$ (1) and $9x - 2y + 26 = 0$ (2)

Rearrange (1): $x = 14 - 4y$

Sub into (2): $9(14 - 4y) - 2y + 26 = 0 \Rightarrow y = 4$

Sub into (1): $x + 16 = 14 \Rightarrow x = -2$

c) $2y = 4x - 19$ (1) and $6x + 2y - 23 = 0$ (2)

Sub (1) into (2): $6x + 4x - 19 - 23 = 0 \Rightarrow x = 4.2$

Sub into (1) $2y = 16.8 - 19 \Rightarrow y = -1.1$

Q2 At vertex A (0, 4), $P = (2 \times 0) + (3 \times 4) = 12$

At vertex B (5, 2), $P = (2 \times 5) + (3 \times 2) = 16$

At vertex C (3, 1), $P = (2 \times 3) + (3 \times 1) = 9$

So B would maximise P and C would minimise P.

Q3 **a)**

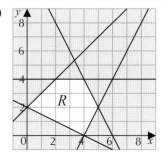

b) At (0, 2), $Z = 0 + (5 \times 2) = 10$

At (2, 4), $Z = 2 + (5 \times 4) = 22$

At (4, 4), $Z = 4 + (5 \times 4) = 24$

At (5, 2), $Z = 5 + (5 \times 2) = 15$

At (4, 0), $Z = 4 + 0 = 4$

So the maximum value of Z is 24 at (4, 4).

Q4 **a)**

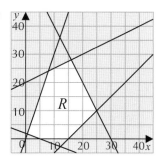

b) The (25, 10) coordinate is at the intersection between $x - y = 15$ (1) and $2x + y = 60$ (2)

Rearrange (1): $x = 15 + y$

Sub into (2): $30 + 2y + y = 60 \Rightarrow y = 10$

Sub into (1): $x - 10 = 15 \Rightarrow x = 25$

So the coordinates of the vertex are (25, 10)

The (16, 28) coordinate is at the intersection between $x - 2y + 40 = 0$ (1) and $2x + y = 60$ (2)

Rearrange (1): $x = 2y - 40$

Sub into (2): $4y - 80 + y = 60 \Rightarrow y = 28$

Sub into (1): $x - 56 + 40 = 0 \Rightarrow x = 16$

So the coordinates of the vertex are (16, 28)

c) At (25, 10), $P = (3 \times 25) + (7 \times 10) = 145$

At (16, 28), $P = (3 \times 16) + (7 \times 28) = 244$

So (16, 28) gives the optimal solution.

Q5 **a)**

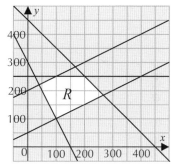

b) At (100, 250), $C = (3 \times 100) + 250 = 550$

At (200, 250), $C = (3 \times 200) + 250 = 850$

Use simultaneous equations to find the coordinates of the other vertices:

At (40, 220), $C = (3 \times 40) + 220 = 340$

At (100, 100), $C = (3 \times 100) + 100 = 400$

At $(\frac{800}{3}, \frac{550}{3})$, $C = (3 \times \frac{800}{3}) + \frac{550}{3} = 983\frac{1}{3}$

So the optimal solution is at (40, 220), where $C = 340$.

Q6 **a)** Let x be the number of steam trains and y be the number of electric trains:

Maximise $£P = 32x + 20y$

Subject to $x, y \geq 0$

$x + y \leq 60$

$2x + y \leq 100$

$x + 4y \leq 180$

b) First plot the constraints on a graph:

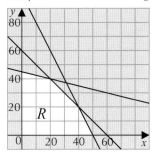

At (0, 0), $P = 0$

At (0, 45), £$P = 0 + (20 \times 45) = £900$

At (20, 40), £$P = (32 \times 20) + (20 \times 40) = £1440$

At (40, 20), £$P = (32 \times 40) + (20 \times 20) = £1680$

At (50, 0), £$P = (32 \times 50) + 0 = £1600$

So 40 steam trains and 20 electric trains should be made, making £1680 profit.

Q7 a) Minimise   £$C = 2x + 4y$
Subject to $x, y \geq 0$
$x + y \geq 30$
$x + y \leq 70$
$5y \geq 2x$
$y \leq 2x - 20$

b)

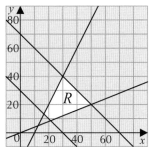

At (30, 40), £$C = (2 \times 30) + (4 \times 40) = £220$

At (50, 20), £$C = (2 \times 50) + (4 \times 20) = £180$
Use simultaneous equations to find the coordinates of the other two vertices.

At $(\frac{50}{3}, \frac{40}{3})$, £$C = £86.67$

At $(\frac{150}{7}, \frac{60}{7})$, £$C = £77.14$

So the optimal solution is at $(\frac{150}{7}, \frac{60}{7})$, costing a total of £77.14.

c) This solution isn't very realistic as the company would not be able to make a fraction of an ornament.

If the optimal solution is a decimal or fraction and you need a whole number, you need to find the optimal integer solution — there's more on this in the next section.

Exercise 2.4 — Optimal integer solutions

Q1 a) $2y + 3x \leq 12$ and $6y + 5x \leq 30$

b) Find the coordinates by solving simultaneous equations $2y + 3x = 12$ (1) and $6y + 5x = 30$ (2).
Rearrange (1): $2y = 12 - 3x \Rightarrow 6y = 36 - 9x$

Sub into (2): $36 - 9x + 5x = 30 \Rightarrow x = \frac{3}{2}$

Sub into (1): $2y + \frac{9}{2} = 12 \Rightarrow y = \frac{15}{4}$

so the coordinates of the vertex are $(\frac{3}{2}, \frac{15}{4})$
= (1.5, 3.75)

c) $Z = (4 \times \frac{3}{2}) + (3 \times \frac{15}{4}) = \frac{69}{4}$

d) At (1, 3), $Z = (4 \times 1) + (3 \times 3) = 13$

At (1, 4), $Z = (4 \times 1) + (3 \times 4) = 16$

(2, 4) is outside the feasible region.

At (2, 3), $Z = (4 \times 2) + (3 \times 3) = 17$

e) The optimal integer solution is at (2, 3), where $Z = 17$.

Q2 a) The constraints are: $3y + x \leq 15$
$6y + 5x \leq 36$
$y + 5x \leq 26$

Use simultaneous equations to find coordinates of
A: $3y + x = 15$ (1) and $6y + 5x = 36$ (2)

Rearrange (1): $x = 15 - 3y$

Sub into (2): $6y + 75 - 15y = 36 \Rightarrow y = \frac{13}{3}$

Sub into (1): $13 + x = 15 \Rightarrow x = 2$

So the coordinates of A are $(2, \frac{13}{3})$ (= (2, 4.33)).

For B use $6y + 5x = 36$ (1) and $y + 5x = 26$ (2)

Subtract (2) from (1): $5y = 10 \Rightarrow y = 2$

Sub into (2): $2 + 5x = 26 \Rightarrow x = \frac{24}{5} = (4.8)$

So the coordinates of B are $(\frac{24}{5}, 2)$.

b) At A, $Z = (3 \times 2) + (5 \times \frac{13}{3}) = \frac{83}{3}$ (= 27.6...)

At B, $Z = (3 \times \frac{24}{5}) + (5 \times 2) = \frac{122}{5}$ (= 24.4)

So the optimal solution is at A.

c) So to find the optimal integer solution, look at the integer solutions around A.

At (2, 4), $Z = (3 \times 2) + (5 \times 4) = 26$
(2, 5) isn't within the feasible region

So the optimal integer solution is at (2, 4), where $Z = 26$.

Q3 a)

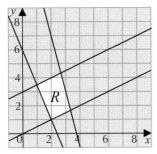

b) First find the coordinates of the points of intersection using simultaneous equations.

At $(2, 1)$, $Z = 2 + (5 \times 1) = 7$

At $(1, \frac{7}{2})$, $Z = 1 + (5 \times \frac{7}{2}) = \frac{37}{2}$ $(= 18.5)$

At $(\frac{8}{3}, \frac{13}{3})$, $Z = \frac{8}{3} + (5 \times \frac{13}{3}) = \frac{73}{3}$ $(24.3...)$

At $(\frac{10}{3}, \frac{5}{3})$, $Z = \frac{10}{3} + (5 \times \frac{5}{3}) = \frac{35}{3}$ $(= 11.6...)$

So the optimal solution is at $(\frac{8}{3}, \frac{13}{3})$

$(= (2.67, 4.33))$, where $Z = \frac{73}{3}$

You could have used the objective line method here — it would actually have been quicker, as you'd only have to solve one pair of simultaneous equations.

c) At $(2, 4)$, $Z = 2 + (5 \times 4) = 22$

$(2, 5)$ isn't within the feasible region.
$(3, 4)$ isn't within the feasible region.
$(3, 5)$ isn't within the feasible region.
So the optimal integer solution is at $(2, 4)$.

Q4 a)

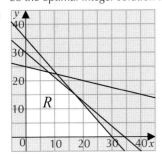

b) At $(0, 0)$, $Z = 0$

At $(0, 25)$, $Z = 0 + (8 \times 25) = 200$

At $(30, 0)$, $Z = (9 \times 30) + 0 = 270$

Use simultaneous equations to find the coordinates of the other two vertices $((8, 23)$ and $(\frac{120}{7}, 15))$.

At $(8, 23)$, $Z = (9 \times 8) + (8 \times 23) = 256$

At $(\frac{120}{7}, 15)$, $Z = (9 \times \frac{120}{7}) + (8 \times 15) = 274.2...$

So the optimal solution is at $(\frac{120}{7}, 15)$.

To find the optimal integer solution, look at points around this vertex with integer values:

At $(17, 15)$, $Z = (9 \times 17) + (8 \times 15) = 273$
$(18, 15)$ is not within the feasible region

So the optimal integer solution is at $(17, 15)$, where $Z = 273$.

Q5 a)

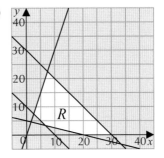

b) Using the objective line method, with starting line $75 = 3x + 5y$

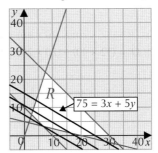

The optimal solution is at the intersection point between the lines $x + 4y = 20$ and $10 = x + y$ $(\frac{20}{3}, \frac{10}{3})$. To find the optimal integer solution, look at points around the vertex with integer values.

$(6, 3)$ isn't inside the feasible region.

At $(6, 4)$, $C = (3 \times 6) + (5 \times 4) = 38$

$(7, 3)$ isn't inside the feasible region.

At $(7, 4)$, $C = (3 \times 7) + (5 \times 4) = 41$

So the optimal integer solution is at $(6, 4)$.

You could have used the vertex method instead here — but the objective line method meant you had to solve fewer simultaneous equations.

Q6 a) Let x be the number of basic calculators and y be the number of scientific calculators.

Maximise $£P = 2.8x + 4.6y$
Subject to $x + y \leq 70$
$x + 3y \leq 135$
$4x + y \leq 240$
$x, y \geq 0$

b)

c) At (0, 0), £P = £0

At (60, 0), £P = (2.8 × 60) + 0 = £168

At (0, 45), £P = 0 + (4.6 × 45) = £207

Use simultaneous equations to find the coordinates of the other vertices.

At $(\frac{75}{2}, \frac{65}{2})$, £P = $(2.8 \times \frac{75}{2}) + (4.6 \times \frac{65}{2})$
= £254.50

At $(\frac{170}{3}, \frac{40}{3})$, £P = $(2.8 \times \frac{170}{3}) + (4.6 \times \frac{40}{3})$
= £220

So the optimal solution is at $(\frac{75}{2}, \frac{65}{2})$
(= (37.5, 32.5))

To find the optimal integer solution, look at points around the vertex with integer values.

At (37, 32), £P = £250.80
(37, 33) is not in the feasible region

At (38, 32), £P = £253.60
(38, 33) is not in the feasible region

So the optimal integer solution is at (38, 32).

The maximum profit of £253.60 is achieved by manufacturing 38 basic and 32 scientific calculators.

Q7 a) Minimise £C = 6000x + 3000y

Subject to $4 \leq x + y \leq 14$
$3y \leq 5x$
$x, y \geq 0$

b)

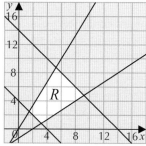

Use simultaneous equations to find the coordinates of the vertices.

At $(\frac{3}{2}, \frac{5}{2})$, £C = $(6000 \times \frac{3}{2}) + (3000 \times \frac{5}{2})$ = £16 500

At $(\frac{21}{4}, \frac{35}{4})$, £C = $(6000 \times \frac{21}{4}) + (3000 \times \frac{35}{4})$
= £57 750

At $(\frac{16}{5}, \frac{4}{5})$, £C = $(6000 \times \frac{16}{5}) + (3000 \times \frac{4}{5})$
= £21 600

At $(\frac{46}{5}, \frac{24}{5})$, £C = $(6000 \times \frac{46}{5}) + (3000 \times \frac{24}{5})$
= £69 600

So the optimal solution is at $(\frac{3}{2}, \frac{5}{2})$ (= (1.5, 2.5)).

To find the optimal integer solution, look at points around the vertex with integer values.

(1, 2) is not in the feasible region.

(1, 3) is not in the feasible region.

At (2, 2), £C = (6000 × 2) + (3000 × 2) = £18 000.

At (2, 3), £C = (6000 × 2) + (3000 × 3) = £21 000.

So the optimal integer solution is to manufacture 2 offroaders and 2 hatchbacks per production run.

Review Exercise — Chapter 5

Q1
Minimise $£C = 300x + 200y$
Subject to the constraints
$x \geq 5$
$y \geq 10$
$x + y \geq 20$
$5x + 2y > 60$

Q2 $x, y \geq 0$
$y \leq 4$
$x + 2y \leq 14$
$3y - 2x < 2$

Q3 **a)** They must produce at least 100 packs of each variety every day.

They can't produce more than 500 packs in total. For every 2 jumbo packs they want to make at least 1 standard pack.

They don't want to make more than 3 standard packs for every jumbo pack.

b)
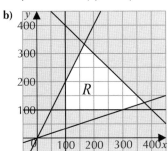

Q4 **a)** Starting with the objective line $1 = x + y$

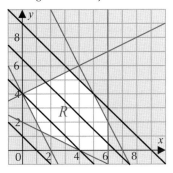

The last point within the feasible region that the lines touch is a line segment, so the optimal solution can be any point along this line segment — e.g $(4, 5)$ or $(5, 4)$.
So the largest value Z can take is $4 + 5 = 9$.

b) Starting with the objective line $10 = 2x + 5y$

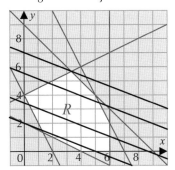

The last point within the feasible region that the lines touch is the crossing point between the lines $x + y = 9$ (1) and $2y - x = 8$ (2), so use simultaneous equations to find its coordinates:
Rearrange (1): $x = 9 - y$
Sub into (2): $2y - 9 + y = 8 \Rightarrow y = \frac{17}{3}$
Sub into (1): $x + \frac{17}{3} = 9 \Rightarrow x = \frac{10}{3}$
So the coordinates of the optimal solution are $(\frac{10}{3}, \frac{17}{3})$, and the highest value Z can take is $(2 \times \frac{10}{3}) + (5 \times \frac{17}{3}) = 35$.

c) Starting with the objective line $4 = 4x + y$

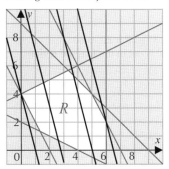

The last point within the feasible region that the objective lines touch is $(6, 2)$, so the highest value Z can take is $(4 \times 6) + 2 = 26$.

Q5 **a)**
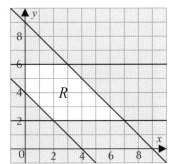

b) Starting with the objective line $6 = 3x + 2y$

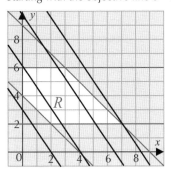

The last point within the feasible region that the lines touch is $(7, 2)$, so the largest value Z can take is $(3 \times 7) + (2 \times 2) = 25$

Q6 a) Let x be the number of square screen models and y be the number of widescreen models produced.

Maximise $£P = 40x + 32y$
Subject to $x + y \leq 25$
$0 \leq y \leq 10; \ x \geq 0$
$x + 2y \leq 30$

b)

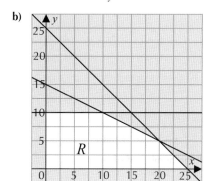

At $(0, 0)$, $£P = £0$
At $(0, 10)$, $£P = 0 + (32 \times 10) = £320$
At $(10, 10)$, $£P = (40 \times 10) + (32 \times 10) = £720$
At $(20, 5)$, $£P = (40 \times 20) + (32 \times 5) = £960$
At $(25, 0)$, $£P = (40 \times 25) + 0 = £1000$

So the optimal solution is at $(25, 0)$ — the company should make only square screen models.

Here you can see that linear programming doesn't always give a realistic solution — the company would probably still want to make some widescreen models. We'd need more constraints to get a more realistic model.

Q7 a)

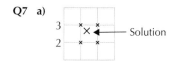

Solution

b) Not all points would necessarily need to be tested as some may not lie inside the feasible region.

Q8 a) Let x = number of large posters and y = number of small posters.

Maximise profit, $P = 6x + 3.5y$, subject to the constraints:

$10x + 5y \leq 250 \Rightarrow 2x + y \leq 50$
$6x + 4y \leq 200 \Rightarrow 3x + 2y \leq 100$
$x \geq y, \ y \geq 10$ and $x, y \geq 0$.

You could use x for the number of small posters and y for the number of large posters instead — so x and y in each inequality would just swap round.

b)

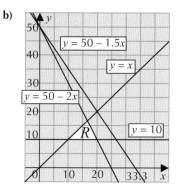

c) E.g. starting with the objective line for $P = 42$ (which goes through $(0, 12)$ and $(7, 0)$) and moving it towards R gives:

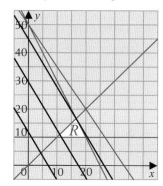

So the final point in the feasible region touched by the objective line is the point of intersection of the lines $y = x$ and $y = 50 - 2x$. Solving these simultaneous equations gives the point of intersection as $(\frac{50}{3}, \frac{50}{3})$. Putting these values into the objective function gives a maximum profit of £158.33.

You can choose any value of P as a starting value — 42 makes it easy to draw the line. This answer uses the objective line method, but you could have used the vertex method instead.

d) From part c) above, the maximum profit is found at $(\frac{50}{3}, \frac{50}{3})$. However, you can't have fractions of a poster, so an integer solution is required. The points with integer coordinates nearby are $(16, 16)$, $(16, 17)$, $(17, 17)$ and $(17, 16)$. $(16, 17)$ doesn't satisfy the constraint $x \geq y$ and $(17, 17)$ doesn't satisfy the constraint $y \leq 50 - 2x$. The value of the objective function at $(16, 16)$ is £152 and at $(17, 16)$ it's £158, so $(17, 16)$ gives the maximum solution.

Exam-Style Questions — Chapter 5

Q1 The objective function is cost, $C = 0.75x + 0.6y$ in £ (or $C = 75x + 60y$ in pence) *[1 mark]* which is to be minimised *[1 mark]* (where x is the number of red roses and y is the number of white roses), subject to the constraints:

$x, y > 0$ *[1 mark]* (from the statement that she will sell both red and white roses — x and y can't be 0).

$x > y$ *[1 mark]* (from the statement that she will sell more red roses than white roses).

$x + y \geq 100$ *[1 mark]* (from the statement that she will sell a total of at least 100 flowers).

$x \leq 300$ *[1 mark]* and $y \leq 200$ *[1 mark]* (from the statement that the wholesaler has 300 red roses and 200 white roses).

Don't waste time trying to solve these inequalities — the question doesn't ask for a solution. Just write them down.

Q2 a) The solid line that passes through (0, 6) and (3, 0) has equation $y = 6 - 2x$, and as the area below the line is shaded, the inequality is $2x + y \geq 6$.

The dotted line that passes through (2, 0) has equation $y = x - 2$, and as the area below the line is shaded, the inequality is $x - y < 2$.

The horizontal solid line that passes through (0, 4) has the equation $y = 4$, and as the area above the line is shaded, the inequality is $y \leq 4$.

[4 marks available — 1 mark for each line equation and 1 mark for all inequality signs correct]

b) The coordinates of the vertices of R are (1, 4) (the intersection of the lines $y = 4$ and $y = 6 - 2x$) *[1 mark]*, (6, 4) (the intersection of the lines $y = 4$ and $y = x - 2$) *[1 mark]* and $(\frac{8}{3}, \frac{2}{3})$ *[1 mark]* (the intersection of the lines $y = 6 - 2x$ and $y = x - 2$)

[1 mark for solving the simultaneous equations].

c) The value of C at (1, 4) is 8, the value of C at (6, 4) is 28 and the value of C at $(\frac{8}{3}, \frac{2}{3})$ is $\frac{34}{3} = 11\frac{1}{3}$ *[1 mark for use of a correct method].*

Hence the minimum value of C is 8 *[1 mark]*, which occurs at the point (1, 4) *[1 mark]*.

This answer uses the vertex method, but you could also have used the objective line method to answer this question — pick whichever method you prefer.

Q3 a) There are 6 sheets of foil in a gold pack, so in x gold packs there will be $6x$ sheets of foil. There are 2 sheets of foil in a silver pack, so in y silver packs there will be $2y$ sheets of foil. There is 1 sheet of foil in a bronze pack, so in z bronze packs there will be z sheets of foil. There are 30 sheets of foil available, so the inequality is $6x + 2y + z \leq 30$

[2 marks — 1 mark for LHS, 1 mark for correct inequality sign and RHS].

Using the same method for sugar paper produces the inequality $15x + 9y + 6z \leq 120$ *[1 mark]*, which simplifies to give $5x + 3y + 2z \leq 40$ *[1 mark]*.

For tissue paper, the inequality is $15x + 4y + z \leq 60$ *[2 marks — 1 mark for LHS, 1 mark for correct inequality sign and RHS].*

Finally, the amount of foil used is $6x + 2y + z$, and the amount of sugar paper used is $15x + 9y + 6z$. The amount of sugar paper used needs to be at least three times the amount of foil, so the inequality for this constraint is

$15x + 9y + 6z \geq 3(6x + 2y + z)$ *[1 mark]*
$15x + 9y + 6z \geq 18x + 6y + 3z$
$\quad\quad 3y + 3z \geq 3x$
$\quad\quad\quad y + z \geq x$ *[1 mark]*

b) (i) If the number of silver packs sold is equal to the number of bronze packs, then $y = z$. Substituting this into the inequalities from part **a)** gives:

$6x + 2y + y \leq 30 \Rightarrow 6x + 3y \leq 30 \Rightarrow 2x + y \leq 10$
$5x + 3y + 2y \leq 40 \Rightarrow 5x + 5y \leq 40 \Rightarrow x + y \leq 8$
$15x + 4y + y \leq 60 \Rightarrow 15x + 5y \leq 60$
$\quad\quad\quad\quad\quad\quad\quad\quad\quad \Rightarrow 3x + y \leq 12$
$y + y \geq x \Rightarrow 2y \geq x$

[3 marks available — 1 mark for making the correct substitution, 1 mark for correctly forming the inequalities and 1 mark for simplifying the inequalities.]

(ii)

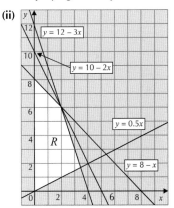

[5 marks available — 1 mark for each of the four inequality lines (with equations as shown on the graph) and 1 mark for correct feasible region]

(iii) Using the vertex method, the feasible region has vertices (0, 0) (the origin), (0, 8) (intersection of the y-axis and $y = 8 - x$), (2, 6) (intersection of $y = 8 - x$ and $y = 10 - 2x$) and $(\frac{24}{7}, \frac{12}{7})$ (intersection of $y = \frac{1}{2}x$ and $y = 12 - 3x$) *[1 mark]*.

The number of packs made on Monday is $x + y + z = x + 2y$ *[1 mark]*, so the numbers made at each vertex are 0, 16, 14 and $\frac{48}{7} = 6.857$, so the maximum number of packs made that day is 16 = 8 silver and 8 bronze *[1 mark]*.

You could have used the objective line method instead, using the line $Z = x + y + z = x + 2y$ to find the maximum.

(iv) The objective function is
$P = 3.5x + 2y + z = 3.5x + 2y + y = 3.5x + 3y$, which needs to be maximised.

The value of P for each of the vertices found in part (iii) is £0, £24, £25 and £17.14 *[1 mark]*.

The maximum value is £25 *[1 mark]*, which occurs at (2, 6), so the company needs to sell 2 gold packs, 6 silver packs and 6 bronze packs (as the number of bronze packs is equal to the number of silver packs) *[1 mark]*.

Chapter 6: Matchings

1. Matchings

Exercise 1.1 — Bipartite graphs

For all these questions, you can put the nodes in each set in any order, as long as the arcs still link the right ones.

Q1

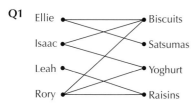

Q2

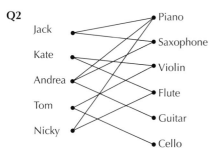

Q3

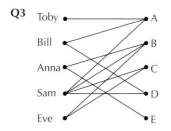

Q4
  a) Cleaning the car and feeding the dog
  b) Dad, David and Karen
  c) Karen

Exercise 1.2 — Matchings

Q1 **a)**

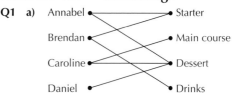

  b) Annabel = starter, Brendan = drinks, Caroline = main course, Daniel = dessert.

    Remember — you don't always have to draw the matching. Here, it's just been written out.

Q2 E.g.

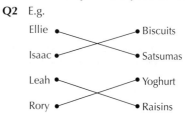

You might end up with a slightly different matching — Ellie = satsumas, Isaac = yoghurt, Leah = raisins, Rory = biscuits.

Q3 **a)**

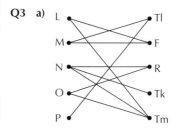

  b) Lamarr = team member, Marcus = facilitator, Nadia = timekeeper, Oliver = recorder, Pippa = team leader

Q4

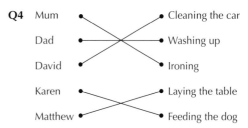

So the complete matching is Mum = ironing, Dad = washing up, David = cleaning the car, Karen = feeding the dog, Matthew = laying the table

Q5 **a)**

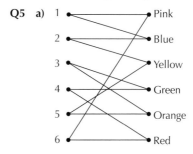

b) 1 = pink, 2 = blue, 3 = orange, 4 = green, 5 = yellow, 6 = red

Q6 Yes — e.g.

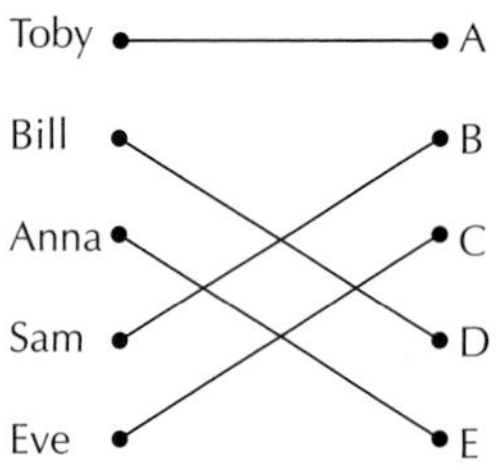

Sam and Eve could swap round and still produce a complete matching.

Q7 a)

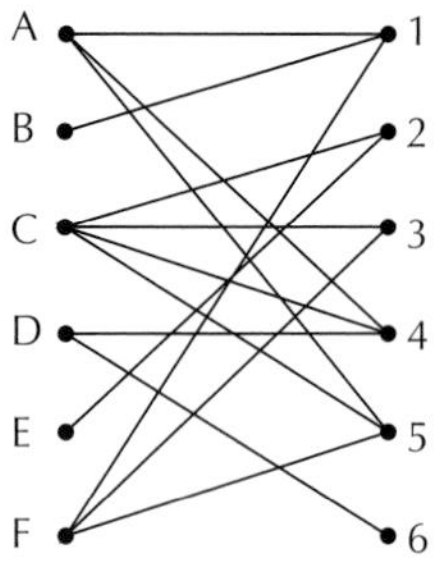

b) e.g. A = 4, B = 1, C = 3, D = 6, E = 2, F = 5

There are a few different complete matchings you could make here — but B, D and E can't change.

Q8 a)

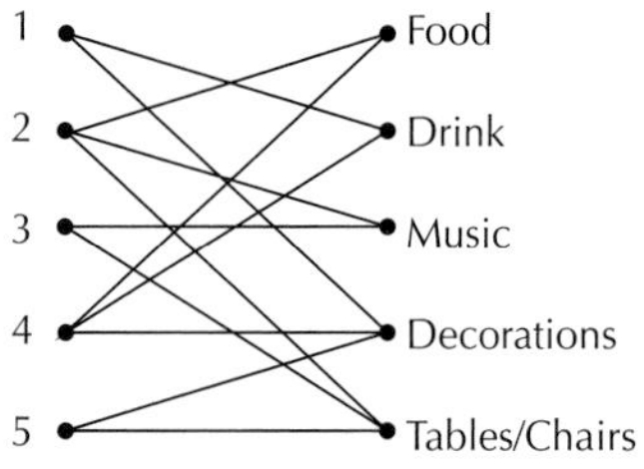

b) E.g. 1 = drink, 2 = food, 3 = music, 4 = decorations, 5 = tables/chairs

Again, there's more than one complete matching for this one.

2. Maximum Matchings

Exercise 2.1 — Alternating paths

Q1 a)

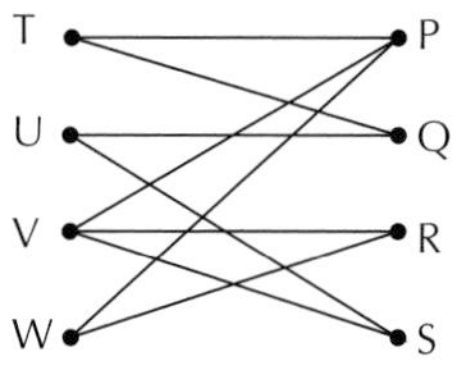

b) Initial matching: T — P, U — Q, V — R.
E.g. Alternating path: W - - R — V - - S (where — = in and - - = not in). Changing the status of the arcs: W — R - - V — S.
So the new matching is
T = P, U = Q, W = R, V = S.

If you'd started off with W - - P, you'd have ended up with a different alternating path and new matching.

Q2 Alternating path: E - - 1 — B - - 4. Changing the status of the arcs: E — 1 - - B — 4. So the improved matching is A = 2, B = 4, C = 3, D = 5, E = 1.

Q3 a)

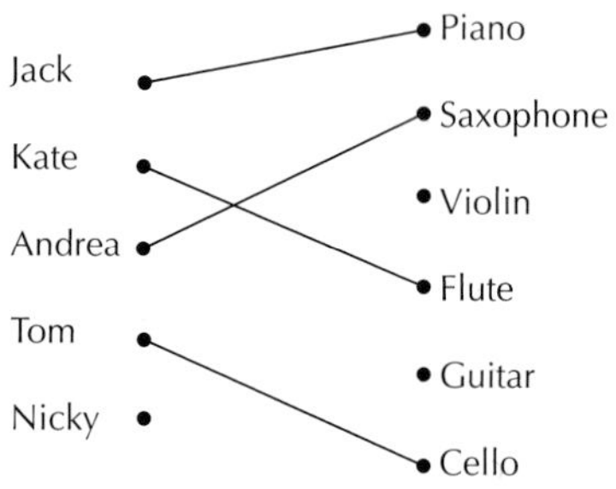

b) Alternating path: Nicky - - flute — Kate - - violin. Changing the status of the arcs: Nicky — flute - - Kate — violin. Improved matching: Jack = piano, Kate = violin, Andrea = saxophone, Tom = cello, Nicky = flute.

Q4 a)

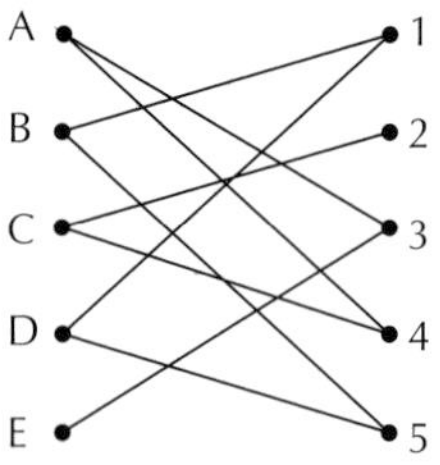

b)

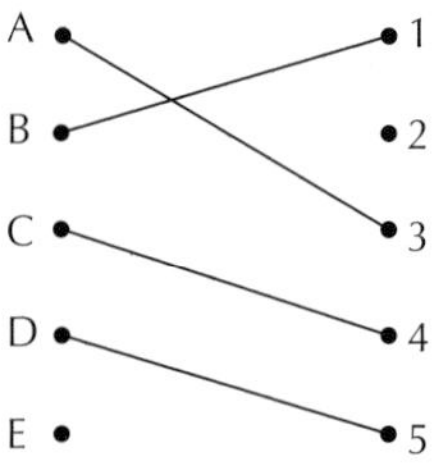

c) Alternating path: E - - 3 — A - - 4 — C - - 2.
Changing the status of the arcs:
E —3 - - A — 4 - - C — 2.
So the improved matching is Alan = 4, Bobby = 1, Charlotte = 2, Dylan = 5 and Emily = 3.

Exercise 2.2 — Maximum matchings

Q1 a)

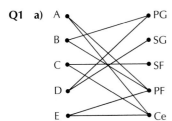

Initial matching: A = PF, B = PG, C = Ce, D = SG.

b) Alternating path: E - - Ce — C - - SF. Changing the status of the arcs: E — Ce - - C — SF. So the improved matching is A = PF, B = PG, C = SF, D = SG, E = Ce. There are no more unmatched nodes so this is a maximum (and complete) matching.

This alternating path reaches a breakthrough the quickest — the other one takes longer, as you'll see below.

c) Alternating path: E - - PF — A - - Ce — C - - SF. Changing the status of the arcs: E — PF - - A — Ce - - C — SF. So the improved matching is A = Ce, B = PG, C = SF, D = SG, E = PF. There are no more unmatched nodes so this is a maximum (and complete) matching.

Q2 Initial matching 1 = pink, 2 = yellow, 3 = orange, 4 = red. Alternating path: 5 - - yellow — 2 - - blue. Changing the status of the arcs: 5 — yellow - - 2 — blue. So the new matching is 1 = pink, 2 = blue, 3 = orange, 4 = red, 5 = yellow. There are still 2 unmatched nodes (6 and green) so you need another alternating path:

       ↗ pink — 1 - - blue

6 ⟨

       ↘ red — 4 - - green   Breakthrough

Changing the status of the arcs: 6 — red - - 4 — green. So the improved matching is 1 = pink, 2 = blue, 3 = orange, 4 = green, 5 = yellow, 6 = red. There are no more unmatched nodes, so this is a maximum (and complete) matching.

You could have found the alternating path from 6 first, then the one from 5. If you'd followed through the alternating path starting 6 - - pink, you'd have found that it failed when it got to 5, as 5 can only be yellow.

Q3 a)

Lian	Joe
Eva	Raj
Sophie	Troy
Kim	Akil
Betty	Chris
Maria	George

The initial matching is shown by the bold arcs on the bipartite graph.

b) E.g. Alternating path: Eva - - Raj — Lian - - Troy — Kim - - Chris — Betty - - Joe. Changing the status of the arcs: Eva — Raj - - Lian — Troy - - Kim — Chris - - Betty — Joe. So the improved matching is Lian = Troy, Eva = Raj, Kim = Chris, Betty = Joe, Maria = Akil.

There are still two unmatched nodes, so find another alternating path: Sophie - - Akil — Maria - - George. Changing the status of the arcs: Sophie — Akil - - Maria — George.

So the improved matching is Lian = Troy, Eva = Raj, Sophie = Akil, Kim = Chris, Betty = Joe, Maria = George. There are no more unmatched nodes, so this is a maximum (and complete) matching.

Q4 E.g. Alternating path: B - - 1 — A - - 4 — D - - 6.

Changing the status of the arcs: B — 1 - - A — 4 - - D — 6. So the improved matching is A = 4, B = 1, C = 2, D = 6, F = 5.

There are still two unmatched nodes, so find another alternating path from E: E - - 2 — C - - 3. Changing the status of the arcs: E — 2 - - C — 3.

The improved matching is A = 4, B = 1, C = 3, D = 6, E = 2, F = 5. There are no more unmatched nodes, so this is a maximum (and complete) matching.

Review Exercise — Chapter 6

Q1 **a)** Anya, Elodie and Alex

b) Anya

c) German and Italian

Q2 **a)**

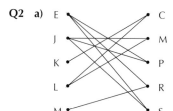

b)

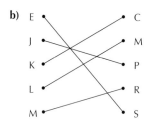

So E = S, J = P, K = C, L = M, M = R.

An alternative complete matching would start with E = P and J = S. Kitty, Lydia and Mary can't change.

These are both complete matchings — it shows that you can have more than one.

Q3 **a)**

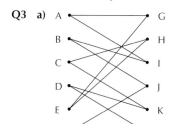

b)

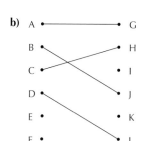

c) Find an alternating path starting from E:
E - - G — A - - I (where - - = not in, — = in).
(You could have done E - - H — C - - K instead — it reaches a breakthrough just as quickly.)

Changing the status of the arcs gives:
E — G - - A — I

Construct the improved matching:
A = I, B = J, C = H, D = L, E = G

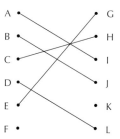

Now try and find an alternating path from F to K:

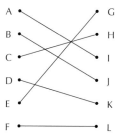

    ·L — D - - K   Breakthrough
F
    ·J — B - - I

The path F - - L — D - - K reaches a breakthrough first, so use this one (if you found a path from E to K in your first alternating path, the second path would be F - - J — B - - I).

Changing the status of the arcs: F — L - - D — K
Construct the improved matching:
A = I, B = J, C = H, D = K, E = G, F = L

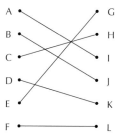

There are no more unmatched nodes, so this is a complete matching.

An alternative complete matching would be A = G, B = I, C = K, D = L, E = H, F = J if you'd used the alternating paths in brackets.

Q4 **a)** There are more people than languages so a complete matching is not possible.

b) e.g.

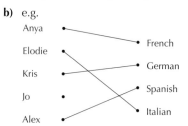

Q5 a) The alternating path Satomi - - Marrakech — Hannah - - Barcelona — Tariq gets stuck at Tariq, as he has only visited Barcelona.

b) E.g. alternating path: Satomi - - Las Vegas — Damon - - Florence — Lisa - - Sydney.

Changing the status of the arcs: Satomi — Las Vegas - - Damon — Florence - - Lisa — Sydney.

So the improved matching is: Damon = Florence, Hannah = Marrakech, Lisa = Sydney, Satomi = Las Vegas, Tariq = Barcelona.

There are still two unmatched nodes, so look for another alternating path: William - - Marrakech — Hannah - - Barcelona — Tariq.

This path fails, and there is no alternating path that matches William to an unmatched node.

This means that a complete matching is not possible, so the improved matching above is a maximum matching.

c) Lisa is the only person to have visited Sydney and Tokyo, so a complete matching is not possible.

d) e.g. alternating path:

Las Vegas — Damon - - Florence
Satomi ⟨
Marrakech — Hannah - - Sydney Breakthrough

Changing the status of the arcs: Satomi — Marrakech - - Hannah — Sydney, so the improved matching is: Damon = Las Vegas, Hannah = Sydney, Lisa = Florence, Satomi = Marrakech, Tariq = Barcelona.

There are still two unmatched nodes, so find another alternating path: William - - Marrakech — Satomi - - Las Vegas — Damon - - Florence — Lisa - - Tokyo. Changing the status of the arcs: William — Marrakech - - Satomi — Las Vegas - - Damon — Florence - - Lisa — Tokyo.

The improved matching is now: Damon = Florence, Hannah = Sydney, Lisa = Tokyo, Satomi = Las Vegas, Tariq = Barcelona, William = Marrakech. There are no more unmatched nodes, so this is a complete matching.

Q6 a)

Isabel
Sophie
Charlie
James
Fairy
Fireman
Doctor
Princess
Monster

b) E.g.

Isabel
Sophie
Charlie
James
Fairy
Fireman
Doctor
Princess
Monster

This isn't the only possible matching.
You weren't actually asked to draw the matching here (you could have just written it out), but it'll come in handy for the rest of this question.

c) There are more costumes than children so a complete matching isn't possible.

d) There are now the same number of children as costumes, and a complete matching is now possible: E.g. Harvey = fireman, Isabel = fairy, Sophie = monster, Charlie = doctor, James = princess.

e)

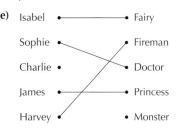

Isabel ● ———————— ● Fairy
Sophie ●   ● Fireman
Charlie ●   ● Doctor
James ●   ● Princess
Harvey ●   ● Monster

f) Alternating path:

        ⟋Doctor — Sophie - - Monster Breakthrough
Charlie⟨
        ⟍Fairy — Isabel - - Fireman

Changing the status of the arcs: Charlie — doctor - - Sophie — monster. So the improved matching is: Isabel = fairy, Sophie = monster, Charlie = doctor, James = princess, Harvey = fireman.

There are no more unmatched nodes, so this is a complete matching.

Exam-Style Question — Chapter 6

Q1 a)

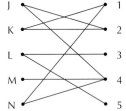

[2 marks —1 mark lost for each incorrect or missing line]

b) Alternating path is M - - 4 — J - - 2 (where - - = not in, — = in) *[1 mark]*.
Change the status of the arcs: M — 4 - - J — 2 *[1 mark]*

So in the new matching, Mia will teach class 4 and Jamal will teach class 2. Lee and Kelly are unchanged.
Construct the improved matching:
J = 2, K = 1, L = 3, M = 4 *[1 mark]*

c) Lee is the only person who can teach class 3 and the only person who can teach class 5, so both classes cannot be taught at the same time *[1 mark]*.

d) The improved matching from part b) is:

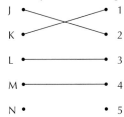

Finding a new alternating path from N:

4 — M - - 3 — L - - 5   Breakthrough
N
1 — K - - 2 — J - - 4

The path N - - 4 — M - - 3 — L - - 5 reaches a breakthrough quicker, so use this one *[1 mark]*.
Change the status of the arcs: N — 4 - - M — 3 - - L — 5 *[1 mark]*.
Construct the improved matching:
Jamal = 2, Kelly = 1, Lee = 5, Mia = 3 and Nick = 4 *[1 mark]*

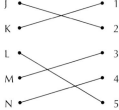

There are no more unmatched nodes, so this is a complete matching.

Glossary

A

Adjacency matrix
A matrix (number grid) that shows the number of links between each pair of **vertices** in a **graph**.

Algorithm
A set of instructions for solving a problem.

Alternating path
A way of improving an **initial matching**.

Arc
The line connecting two **vertices** of a **graph**. Also called an **edge**.

B

Bipartite graph
A graph with two sets of **nodes**, joined by **arcs**. The arcs only join nodes from one set to nodes in the other.

Breakthrough
Reaching an unmatched **node** using the **alternating path** method.

Bubble sort
An **algorithm** that sorts a list into order by systematically swapping terms. Similar to the **shuttle sort** but less efficient as it requires more comparisons.

C

Chinese postman problem
Another name for the **route inspection problem**.

Complete graph
A **graph** where every **vertex** has a direct connection to every other vertex.

Complete matching
A **matching** with the same number of **arcs** as there are **nodes** in each set.

Connected graph
A graph where every **vertex** is connected to every other vertex by a **path** (not necessarily a direct edge).

Constraint
A limiting factor in a **linear programming** problem.
Usually written as an inequality in terms of the **decision variables**.

Cycle
A closed **path** through a **graph** that brings you back to your starting point. Also called a circuit.

D

Decision variable
An item being made, bought, sold etc. in a **linear programming** problem.

Degree
The number of **edges** connected to a **vertex**.

Digraph
A **graph** in which some **edges** have a direction (known as directed edges).

Dijkstra's algorithm
A method for finding the shortest **path** between two **vertices** of a **network**.

Distance matrix
A matrix (number grid) that shows the distance (or **weight**) between each pair of **vertices** in a **graph**.

E

Edge
The line connecting two **vertices** of a **graph**. Also called an **arc**.

Eulerian cycle
A **cycle** through a **graph** which goes along every **edge** exactly once and ends up back at the starting point.

Eulerian graph
A **graph** in which every **vertex** is even.

Eulerian trail
A route through a **graph** which goes along every **edge** exactly once but doesn't end up at the starting point.

Even vertex
A **vertex** with an even **degree**.

F

Feasible region
An area on a graph in which all points are **feasible solutions** to a **linear programming** problem.

Feasible solution
A set of values that satisfies all the **constraints** in a **linear programming** problem.

Flow chart
A way of visually representing an **algorithm**.

G

Graph
A diagram made up of points (called **vertices** or **nodes**) joined by lines (called **edges** or **arcs**).

H

Hamiltonian cycle
A **cycle** through a **graph** that goes through every **vertex** exactly once.

Hamiltonian graph
A **graph** that contains a **Hamiltonian cycle**.

I

Improved matching
A **matching** with more **arcs** than the **initial matching**.

Initial matching
Any **matching** on a **bipartite graph**.

Inspection route
The shortest possible route through a **network** that crosses each **edge** at least once.

K

Kruskal's algorithm
A way of finding **minimum spanning trees** by adding **arcs** in order of **weight**.

L

Linear programming
A way of finding an **optimal solution** to a problem subject to **constraints**.

Loop
An **edge** connecting a **vertex** to itself. Adds 2 to the **degree** of the vertex.

Lower bound
A minimum **weight** for a **Hamiltonian cycle** in a **travelling salesperson problem** that the optimum tour must be greater than or equal to.

M

Matching
A solution that assigns **nodes** on one side of a **bipartite graph** to nodes on the other side. Each node can have at most one **arc** coming from it.

Maximum matching
A **matching** that uses the greatest number of **arcs** possible.

Minimum spanning tree
A **spanning tree** of a graph with the smallest possible total **weight**. Also called a minimum connector.

N

Nearest neighbour algorithm
An **algorithm** for finding an **upper bound** for the **travelling salesperson problem** in a **network**.

Network
Another name for a weighted **graph**.

Node
The name given to the points on a **graph** (also called **vertices**).

O

Objective function
A function in terms of the **decision variables** in a **linear programming** problem that you're trying to minimise or maximise, usually profit or cost.

Objective line method
A way of finding **optimal solutions** in **linear programming** problems by drawing lines on a graph.

Odd vertex
A **vertex** with an odd **degree**.

Optimal solution
A solution to a **linear programming** problem that maximises or minimises the **objective function**.

P

Path
A route in a **graph** that doesn't go through a **vertex** more than once.

Pivot
An item chosen in the **quick sort** algorithm, usually the first in the list.

Prim's algorithm
A way to find **minimum spanning trees** by adding the smallest adjacent **arcs**.

Pseudo-code
A way of writing an **algorithm** in short precise instructions, similar to computer programming language.

Q

Quick sort
An **algorithm** that sorts a list into order by arranging the items around **pivots**.

R

Route inspection problem
Finding the shortest route through a **graph** that crosses every **edge** at least once.

S

Semi-Eulerian graph
A **graph** with exactly 2 odd **vertices**.

Shell sort
An **algorithm** that sorts a list into order by breaking it into smaller lists called subsets, which are then sorted and put back together.

Shuttle sort
An **algorithm** that sorts a list into order by systematically swapping terms. Similar to the **bubble sort** but more efficient as it requires fewer comparisons.

Simple graph
A **graph** that has no **loops** or multiple **edges** between **vertices**.

Spanning tree
A **subgraph** that includes all the **vertices** of the original **graph** and is a **tree**.

Subgraph
A **graph** where all the **vertices** and **edges** are from a larger **graph**.

T

Trace table
A table used to keep track of an **algorithm**.

Travelling salesperson problem
Finding the shortest route through a **graph** that visits every **vertex** at least once.

Tree
A **connected graph** with no **cycles**.

U

Upper bound
The weight of a path in a **travelling salesperson problem** that an optimum tour must be less than or equal to.

V

Vertex/Vertices
The name given to the points on a **graph** (also called **nodes**).

Vertex method
A way of finding **optimal solutions** in a **linear programming** problem by testing every **vertex** of the **feasible region**.

W

Weight
The number associated with an **edge** of a weighted graph (or **network**), often relating to a distance.

Index

P

passes 12-19
paths 27, 31
pivots 21, 22
Prim's algorithm 44-49, 89-91
  on graphs 44, 45
  on matrices 48, 49, 90, 91
pseudo-code 5, 6

Q

quick sort 21, 22

R

route inspection problems 65-71
ruler method 107
Russian Peasant Algorithm 3, 7

S

semi-Eulerian graphs 61-63, 67
Shell sort 18, 19
shuttle sort 15, 16, 18, 19
simple graphs 30
sorting algorithms 12-22
spanning trees 32, 41-49
stopping conditions 1, 3, 9
subgraphs 29, 32
subsets 18, 19

T

trace tables 2, 3, 6, 8, 9
travelling salesperson problems
    78-91
traversable graphs 61
tree diagrams 130, 131
trees 32
  spanning trees 32, 41-49
triangle numbers 5

U

upper bounds 78, 81-87

V

vertex method 111-115
vertices (or nodes) 26-53, 61-71,
    78-90, 122-131

W

weighted graphs — see 'networks'
working values 51-53

MAD1T51